PRM

DISCOV.

SPIRITUAL EXERCISES

OF SAINT IGNATIUS

Text copyright © Larry Warner 2011
The author asserts the moral right
to be identified as the author of this work

Published by
The Bible Reading Fellowship
15 The Chambers, Vineyard
Abingdon OX14 3FE
United Kingdom
Tel: +44 (0)1865 319700
Email: enquiries@brf.org.uk
Website: www.brf.org.uk
BRF is a Registered Charity

ISBN 978 1 84101 883 6

First published 2011 by InterVarsity Press USA, under the title *Journeying with Jesus*.
InterVarsity Press
P.O. Box 1400, Downers Grove, IL 60515–1426
World Wide Web: www.ivpress.com
E-mail: email@ivpress.com
First UK edition published 2011
10 9 8 7 6 5 4 3 2 1 0

Acknowledgments
Unless otherwise stated, scripture quotations are taken from the Holy Bible, New International
Version, copyright © 1973, 1978, 1984 by International Bible Society, used by permission of
Hodder & Stoughton Publishers, a division of Hodder Headline Ltd. All rights reserved. 'NIV'
is a registered trademark of International Bible Society. UK trademark number 1448790.

Scripture taken from the New American Standard Bible Copyright © 1960, 1962, 1963, 1968,
1971, 1972, 1973, 1975, 1977, 1995 by The Lockman Foundation. Used by permission.

The poem 'The Cross' by Lois A. Cheney is taken from *God Is No Fool* (Abingdon, 1969),
p. 105. It is reprinted here by permission of the author.

A catalogue record for this book is available from the British Library

Printed in Singapore by Craft Print International Ltd

The paper used in the production of this publication was supplied by mills that source their
raw materials from sustainably managed forests. Soy-based inks were used in its printing and
the laminate film is biodegradable.

DISCOVERING THE

SPIRITUAL EXERCISES

OF SAINT IGNATIUS

LARRY WARNER

This book is dedicated to the students, faculty and staff of the Institute of Spiritual Formation at Biola University from 2007 to 2010 who allowed me to journey with them through the Spiritual Exercises of St Ignatius of Loyola. This book is an outflow of our times together in class and spiritual direction. Thank you for permitting me to be a part of your journey with Jesus. I count it an honour and privilege to have been able to journey with you through the Exercises and to be given a front-row seat from which to watch what God was doing in and through you during that season of your life.

ACKNOWLEDGMENTS

There is much that went into writing this book and many who played small and large roles in its development. It is a delight to be able to name a few of those who helped the idea of this book to become a reality.

My first words of thanks go to my lovely wife, Donna. I often referred to this as her book, especially as I struggled to write it, for she believed in the value of this project long before I did. She has been a support and encouragement during the long hours that went into writing *Discovering the Spiritual Exercises of Saint Ignatius*, and she willingly helped me to create the space and time needed for its completion, even as we were in the process of moving to a new city.

I am also indebted to Jan Johnson, who recommended me for this writing project after reading through the materials I had put together on the Exercises. Her belief in this project and in my ability to write it helped to convince me to say yes and move forward.

Celia Bradley was a godsend. She graciously agreed to edit the rough draft, offering her wisdom and insight along the way. Her hard work in the initial editing stages helped me to feel much better about all I submitted to InterVarsity Press and saved me much work in the rewrite stages.

Rich and Katy Murray, true friends in the richest sense of the term, allowed me to use their cabin at a critical time in the writing of this book. I was able to work uninterrupted for hours and days on end. This was a huge gift.

Cindy Bunch, my editor at InterVarsity Press, who believed in the value of this project, expanded the reach of the material and gently guided me each step of the way. Her efforts helped the manuscript to take shape and form in ways that would be beneficial for all those who choose to journey through the Exercises. She was a much-needed support to my writing process.

I am thankful to Father Albert Haase and Marilyn Stewart who each read my original manuscript and whose comments and insights were encouraging and extremely helpful. I listened to your wisdom and incorporated much that you suggested. I believe the book is much better because of the input you shared with me.

Finally, I thank Mick and Carol Berberian. God used this couple to bring me into the kingdom more than 30 years ago. I learned and witnessed grace and freedom at their feet and in their home. God has used them greatly to help me to become who I am today by embracing me and freeing me to be me. They spent much time journeying with me and helping me better to partner with God's Spirit in order to become the one-of-a-kind creation God created me to be.

CONTENTS

Part 4: Resources

INTRODUCTION

This book, an adaptation of the Spiritual Exercises of St Ignatius, was written to help you to enter into a holistic, life-transforming journey toward Christlikeness. This is not another book about the methods or techniques of Christian formation but a vehicle that enables you to come before God through the Gospel narratives in order to meet Jesus again for the first time. If you have grown weary of hearing and reading about spiritual formation and are ready to dive heartfirst into a spiritual formation experience, this book may be the right book for you. In fact, near the end of this introduction, you will find a list of statements under the heading 'Is this book for you?' that will help you determine just that.

If you are continuing to read through this introduction, then you are feeling a pull toward, or at least an interest in, the journey set down in the pages of this book. *Discovering the Spiritual Exercises of Saint Ignatius* is not for spectators but for those with a hunger for something deeper, a yearning to walk with Jesus (not just read about Jesus), a desire to embrace more of what God has for them, a longing to be equipped to partner with what God is doing in and through them, and a willingness to be brutally honest with God, Jesus and yourself. These desires will serve you well as you embark on the adventure of faith contained within these pages. But I am getting ahead of myself. Let us continue with the introduction.

MY EXPERIENCE WITH THE SPIRITUAL EXERCISES

This book is an outgrowth of two worlds colliding: my 21st-century world of Protestant Christianity and a set of writings from the Counter-Reformation period of the 16th century: the Spiritual Exercises of St Ignatius of Loyola. The catalyst for this collision of worlds were the words of Dallas Willard in his book *The Divine Conspiracy*. While reading it, I ran across a sentence that momentarily caught my attention and was then forgotten. Yet, unbeknown to me, that sentence would be used by God to fuel my exploration of the 16th-century writings that form the foundation and essence for what will be found, entered into and experienced in the pages of this book. Willard suggested that the Spiritual Exercises of Ignatius would be a good template for creating a curriculum for Christlikeness.

If you... make necessary adjustments to the content... you will see [the Spiritual Exercises of Ignatius] offer in substance... a curriculum, a course for training, for life on the rock. And that is why, century after century, they have exercised incredible power over all who open themselves up to them as disciples of Jesus.[1]

Though at the time I had no idea what the Spiritual Exercises of Ignatius were, these words of Willard would be used by God to open me up to the richness and value contained in these writings of Ignatius at the appropriate time.

It turned out that the 'appropriate time' came about five years later, when I felt God's prompting to pursue training in the art of spiritual direction. I hesitantly moved forward and eventually enrolled in a training course at a Catholic university. As I began the course, I discovered that the Exercises would serve as the foundation for my training. It was at this point that my Protestant world and the 16th-century writings of Ignatius began to collide.

Over the next two years, as I worked my way through the Exercises, I began to fall in love with the various types of prayer that comprise them. The prayer styles enabled me to come before God with a new openness and honesty, to be with God and to hear from God in ways I never had before. I was also delighted by the emphasis on the person of Jesus. He was presented in the Exercises not as a subject to be studied, but as a person to dialogue with, learn from and walk alongside. I began to see and experience first-hand what Willard had alluded to in his book regarding the use of the Exercises as a curriculum for Christlikeness. As I spent time with Jesus in the Exercises, my spirit was enlivened and my heart transformed. The wisdom and insight contained in them, as well as the holistic emphasis on body, mind and spirit, made so much sense to me.

In the years following the spiritual direction course, I began introducing people to the Exercises and experimenting with many of the prayer styles incorporated throughout them. I watched and observed how the Exercises helped people to reconnect with Jesus and with themselves in life-giving ways. After a couple of years of doing this, I was asked to co-author a book entitled *Imaginative Prayer for Youth Ministry*, which was drawn from material found in the Exercises.

A little more than four years ago, a professor and administrator of an evangelical theological college asked me, 'If you could teach anything you wanted to in the area of spiritual formation, what would you like to teach?' I heard myself saying, 'I would love to lead an interactive class based on the Exercises, because I have come to appreciate them as a powerful tool for spiritual formation.' Now, as they say, 'the rest is history'. I am finishing my fourth year at that college, leading deans, professors, administrative staff and students through the Exercises and, again, seeing lives touched and transformed by God using them. The material that comprises much of this book flows out of my experience in leading people through the Exercises at that college.

ABOUT THE EXERCISES

For nearly 500 years, the Spiritual Exercises of Ignatius have been a tool for spiritual formation into Christlikeness. During those years, their popularity has ebbed and flowed, but they are now experiencing a revival of sorts within both Protestant and Catholic circles. I believe this is due, in large part, to the renewed emphasis on spiritual formation, as well as the desire many Christians have to experience the person of Jesus in meaningful ways, thus making the Exercises the perfect choice.

My attraction to the Exercises flows from the fact that they were not written by a theologian or scholar but by Ignatius long before he received any formal religious education. These writings are an outpouring from Ignatius' own conversion and subsequent experience of walking with God (see biography, pages 306–310). Ignatius took notes on what happened as he walked with God, on what he read and on what others taught him along the way, and he eventually compiled all that into a manual of sorts that became known as the Spiritual Exercises of St Ignatius of Loyola.

The Exercises were crafted by Ignatius to help people, all people, to encounter Jesus. So strong was his passion for giving the Exercises to others, so they might know Jesus, that he willingly went to jail on a number of occasions for leading people through them. The emphasis of the Exercises is growth and development into internal conformity to Christ, freedom in Christ and greater intimacy and union with God. These Exercises are built on a twofold foundation of scripture and Jesus, with the vast majority of the material being drawn from the Gospels. The trajectory of the Exercises follows Jesus' life—birth, early ministry, passion and resurrection—using the relevant biblical narratives to guide retreatants through the life of Christ.

More and more Protestants are discovering the treasure chest of spiritual formation tools contained in these ancient writings, once the sole property of Catholics, and are beginning to make use of them as never before. Rather than seeking to make use of these tools independently from the Exercises, this book keeps the tools firmly situated within the intended structure of the Exercises. This will enable you to get a sense of their original intention and use as you journey through them, and will also familiarise you with them so you can wisely continue to make use of them once you have completed your time in the Exercises.

The sections of the Spiritual Exercises of St Ignatius of Loyola used in this book are paraphrases based on the literal translation of the Spanish autograph by Father Elder Mullan (1909) and the translation of David Fleming, both of which were published in Fleming's *Draw Me into Your Friendship*[2] and the translation of George Ganss found in his book, *The Spiritual Exercises of Saint Ignatius*.[3] For the most part, the text of the Exercises is not quoted here in this book, but functional equivalents have been chosen. References in the notes referring to these paraphrases and quotes are from Fleming's book.

ADAPTABILITY

Jesus had radically changed Ignatius' life, and he wanted others to have the opportunity to experience that change for themselves. Thus Ignatius designed the Exercises so they would be accessible to all people who desired to walk more closely with Jesus, no matter what their station or vocation in life.

Traditionally, when people speak of the Spiritual Exercises of Ignatius, they are referring to a format of a 30-day experience in which a retreatant would remove himself from his ordinary responsibilities and withdraw to a retreat centre or monastery. During this time, the retreatant would spend five one-hour periods in prayer each day, beginning at midnight. He would also meet daily with a spiritual director.

But this was not the only method Ignatius made available to those desiring to journey through the Exercises. He was well aware that the 30-day method would make it nearly impossible for many to take advantage of this remarkable means of spiritual formation, so he provided two other methods for people to journey through the Exercises. One of these is known as the '19th Annotation', which allows those involved in 'public affairs or pressing occupations' to journey through the Exercises. This type of experience in the Exercises is also referred to as 'the Spiritual Exercises made in everyday life'. It is this form of the Exercises that is found in this book.

I want to assure you that this book is not a watered-down version of the Spiritual Exercises of Ignatius. Its form is in harmony with Ignatius' original intention, and there is ample evidence that he made use of this mode of giving the Exercises to others. Although it is seemingly less intense and demanding than the 30-day retreat, do not think that using the 19th Annotation is easy or is used by God in less significant or transforming ways.

I have journeyed with a few people who had experienced the 30-day retreat and then went through the nine-month journey as well. As I spoke with them, there were aspects of the 19th Annotation journey that were far more difficult in their own way than some aspects of the 30-day retreat. These individuals also commented on the value of journeying through the Exercises in the midst of life and how that experience naturally led to their making many of the practices an ongoing part of the rhythm of their life long after the Exercises were over. The question of how to take the practices back into the 'real' world was not one they had to deal with in the abstract, but rather one that was lived out naturally each and every day.

Although this book has sought to retain the spirit of the Exercises, it also differs from the original Exercises in a number of ways. First, the fact that you—the one who may soon be journeying through the Exercises—are holding this book containing them is a major deviation from tradition. Traditionally, the only person in possession of the Exercises was the person who was journeying with you through them as your spiritual director. This is because the written Exercises were really a manual to be used to guide someone else. The director would speak about the part of the Exercises you needed to know, but you would not be given the manual.

The Exercises were not to be journeyed through alone, and this is the danger inherent in producing a book like this. As with the original version, this adaptation is not to be journeyed through without the help of a spiritual director. A spiritual director plays an extremely important role in helping you to get the most out of the Exercises, while also assisting you so you do not fall into the snares that are common to many who take this journey, including Ignatius. So, when the time comes for you to enter into the Exercises, I strongly urge you to seek out a director who will make this journey with you. If I could make it a criminal offence to go through the Exercises without a spiritual director, I would.

Another difference in this adaptation is the inclusion of some quotes, optional exercises and prayers to bring greater variety to your time in the Exercises and to create a little extra space and freedom for you from time to time. Also added are questions that follow the scripture passages for each day and were not part of the original Exercises. These are provided to help you explore and interact with the text. All these additions to the Exercises are a result of my journey through them with others and are provided to enhance your experience in them.

Finally, in the body of the Exercises is a voice in the form of text boxes sprinkled throughout. This voice serves as a guide. These were not part of the original Exercises but were added as I discovered some of the difficulties that those going through the Exercises often have. They are provided to help you deal with these common struggles. They are not there to replace the need for a spiritual director but to augment the director's role.

These adaptations to the Exercises as found in this book have sought to keep intact the essence and genesis of the Spiritual Exercises of Ignatius while also providing ongoing guidance and direction as you journey through them. These additional pieces are in harmony with the spirit with which Ignatius penned the original Exercises.

BENEFITS OF THE EXERCISES

WALKING WITH JESUS

It was my desire to walk with Jesus that helped me to engage fully in the Exercises and journey through them. This has also been true for those with whom I have journeyed through the Exercises. They each have had a deep yearning to walk with Jesus, to know and experience Jesus in an interactive and personal way. That is exactly what the Exercises help to facilitate.

The goal of the prayer practices found in the Exercises is not to learn more about Jesus but rather to walk personally with Jesus, meet Jesus and interact with Jesus. The daily prayer practices and the use of the Gospel narratives are intended to engender encounter with Jesus so that you will begin to know Jesus more clearly, love Jesus more dearly and follow Jesus more nearly. In fact, to know Jesus more clearly, love Jesus more dearly and follow Jesus more nearly is the stated purpose of Week 2 of the Exercises. The sections that follow Week 2 continue the journey with Jesus, walking with Jesus to the cross (Week 3) and journeying with the resurrected Christ (Week 4). The thrust of the Exercises is encountering the person of Jesus, fostering a deeper relational knowledge of him and a greater desire and the freedom to say 'yes' to him. This daily walking with, encountering and fixing your eyes on Jesus is one of the great benefits for those who journey through the Exercises. If you have this same desire to be with Jesus, this book will help you do just that.

FINDING GOD IN ALL THINGS

Another result of the days, weeks and months spent in the Exercises is a greater awareness of God in the ordinary stuff of everyday life. In fact, those who study Ignatius' Exercises use the phrase 'finding God in all things' as the quintessential summary of them.[4] The daily prayer practices each morning, afternoon and evening, when truly entered into, bring to birth a growing awareness of God within you and around you. Your spirit becomes sensitised to the movements of God in and through the circumstances and relationships of your life. You gradually begin to develop the spiritual eyesight needed to see 'the invisible which is eternal rather than merely the visible which is temporal' (to paraphrase the apostle Paul's words). You will see your times in the word—at work, at college, at home and with others—through new eyes. And you will begin to realise that it is through these various realities that you are provided with the opportunity to experience God and partner with God's Spirit in being more and more conformed to the image of Jesus.

This 'finding God in all things' is another of the benefits that gradually become internalised over the course of your time in the Exercises and will continue to be a part of internal awareness long after you have finished your journey through the Exercises. You are equipped to live life with the ongoing awareness that in God you live, move and have your being, come what may.

DEVELOPING PRAYER PRACTICES

Finally, as you journey through the Exercises, you will participate in a wide variety of prayer practices. These practices may initially feel cumbersome but will eventually become part of the fabric of your experience in the Exercises and in your life. Although these prayer practices are tied to Ignatius' Exercises, their value extends beyond the Exercises, and they can be spiritual formation tools that will continue to be a part of your life, shaping and moulding you into Christlikeness long after the Exercises are over. Many of those who have made use of these prayer practices after finishing the formal Exercises have also introduced some of these practices to family and friends.

IS THIS BOOK FOR YOU?

Prayerfully and honestly work through the statements below, asking God to reveal to you if this book is the right spiritual formation vehicle for you at this time.

1. You have a strong desire to know Jesus more intimately, love Jesus more fully and follow Jesus more wholeheartedly.
2. You have a longing for a deeper, richer and more expansive relationship with God.
3. You desire to live with an internalised awareness that in God you live, move and have your being, and to find God in all things.
4. You have the desire, time (50–75 minutes a day, seven days a week for about nine months) and space in your life to engage fully in the Exercises.
5. You are willing to be open and honest with God, your spiritual director and yourself as you journey through these Exercises.
6. You are willing to follow Jesus during good times and difficult times.
7. You are open to having your theology and image of Jesus challenged and expanded.

8. You yearn to walk with Jesus through the Gospel narratives in a holistic and interactive way rather than merely read about Jesus.
9. You are willing to say 'no' to whatever holds you back from spiritual freedom.
10. You desire to enter into a spiritual practice that will help you better partner with what God is doing in you to conform you to the image of Christ.
11. You long for a vehicle that will help you to be more consistent and intentional in spending time with Jesus and connecting with God throughout the day.
12. You sense the gentle invitation of God to enter into the Spiritual Exercises of St Ignatius of Loyola.

If there is a 'yes' that rises from deep within you as you read through the above list, or if you sense the quivering of excitement beginning to grow in your spirit as you consider the possibility of walking with Jesus through the Gospels, or if it is not so dramatic but simply a gentle knowing that this is for you, I strongly encourage you to embark on this journey.

If none of the above is the case, this may not be the right vehicle for you at this time. God works uniquely with each person, and the important thing is not that you are doing this or that, but that you are where God wants you. If this is not the right timing for you, please do not forget about the Spiritual Exercises of Ignatius of Loyola, for there may very well be a time when these Exercises will be the exact vehicle for spiritual formation that God desires you to embrace.

FOLLOWING THE RHYTHM

As you read through this introduction, you may be getting eager to embark on your journey through the Exercises. Please resist this temptation and slowly make your way through Part 1, which offers an overview of what your daily time with God will look like, important tips on getting the most out of the Exercises, an explanation of the methods you will use to interact with God through the scriptures, an expanded daily rhythm template and some down-to-earth explanations of prayer practices, journalling, the importance of a spiritual director and tips on how to find a spiritual director.

Skipping over Part 1 could very well rob you of many of the benefits associated with going through the Exercises and open you up, to a greater degree, to the struggles that can be experienced. Part 1 will help you be prepared for what is likely to arise during your journey through the Exercises, while also providing excellent tips so you can maximise your experience. You will find that once you are familiar with it, Part 1 will be a place you will revisit throughout your journey through the Exercises, a place filled with wisdom and insight to be drawn upon and used time and time again.

The Spiritual Exercises of St Ignatius of Loyola have been a valuable spiritual formation tool for almost 500 years, and, in this book, great care has been taken to remain true to the original form and spirit of the Exercises, while also making them readily accessible for those in our day and age who are hungering for more from their Christian life. These exercises will bring you face to face with Jesus, helping you to love Jesus more dearly, follow Jesus more closely and love God and others as never before. Do not grow weary or lose heart as you journey, but keep your eyes on Jesus, the author and perfecter of your faith, who journeys with you, guiding, directing, enlightening and empowering you.

Please note that Week (with a capital W) does not refer to a seven-day period but rather to a section or movement with the Exercises. Each Week has its own focus.

PART 1

GETTING THE MOST OUT OF THE EXERCISES

—— 1 ——

THE DAILY ELEMENTS
OF THE EXERCISES

This section provides an overview of what a normal day in the Exercises will look like, while also explaining the components involved. If you desire further elaboration on a specific component, you will be directed where to find this information at the end of the component's summary. The format below will appear at the beginning of each week. As your journey continues, you will naturally flow through your time in the daily prayer practices, but at first it can seem overwhelming.

You are expected to spend 50–75 minutes in the Exercises each day. This period is comprised of the parts delineated below, including the General Examen of Conscience, which is done at noontime and in the evening. There are no individual periods listed for the components (except for the examen: 5–15 minutes). You proceed as God guides and directs. Some days it may take you a long time to slow down; other days you may spend a long time journalling or sitting in silence with God. There is flexibility within this structure so that you may be free to connect with God as God leads and directs you. The structure keeps you on track and provides you ample opportunity to linger along the way.

If possible, begin each new section of the Exercises on Mondays. This way, Sunday, which can be a very busy and demanding day, is a review or repetition day—something easier to enter into on a busy day than a new meditation. But by all means, feel free to choose any day to be your beginning day.

DAILY ELEMENTS

OPENING

Your time each day begins with the opening,[1] which is designed to prepare you to enter into the presence of God and ready you for the assigned meditation for the day. This opening format is made of several components and will remain unchanged in structure for the most part throughout your time in the Exercises.

Prayer: The opening begins with you coming into God's presence, remembering who you are and who God is. Seek to foster an attitude of respect and also ask God for help throughout your day. This opening is referred to as preparatory prayer and involves a conscious effort to present yourself before God 'as living sacrifices, holy and pleasing to God' (Romans 12:1) and readying yourself to be present to God.

This is also the time to practise the prayer of recollection. Recollection involves a profound turning of the self at its root toward God, in order to allow God to mark, mould and shape you.

The prayer of recollection involves orienting all that you are, just as you are, to God. This means remembering and reflecting on who you are, on your struggles and difficulties with yourself and with God, and on who this God is into whose presence you are entering. The preparatory prayer and the prayer of recollection provide the foundation on which your daily prayer time is built. It is not to be hurried through. This is all part of offering yourself to God as a living and holy sacrifice, which is pleasing to God.

Slowing down: The next step will be the slowdown. The goal of the slowdown is to settle down and settle into this time with God. (There are a number of suggestions regarding how to conduct a slowdown under 'Slowing down' below.)

Ask for desired grace:[2] The desired grace is what you will be asking God for—not demanding from God, but asking God for.

The grace will change from time to time but, as a rule, each section has one or two graces you will be asking God for each time you enter the day's meditation. The graces asked for are the very things that the daily meditations in each section are meant to foster within you. The specific grace you will ask for will be noted at the beginning of each new week.

Ask God to guide and direct you: Finally, you will close this opening segment by asking God to guide and direct you through your time.

As you can see, throughout this opening you will be continuing to present yourself before God and to convey your need for God and your desires to God. This opening should be fully entered into and not rushed through. Some days you may want to linger as you initially come before God, while other days you may need to take a few minutes to begin to slow yourself down internally. God may very well meet you during the beginning, so seek to be truly present to God and yourself as you make your way through the opening each day.

DAILY EXERCISE

Each day, you will be provided with the subject matter of the meditation and the suggested way to interact with that subject matter. Often questions will be furnished to help you interact with material for your prayer time. The questions are not a part of the original Exercises and are given as an aid, a prompt, a suggestion, not as an assignment to complete.

Sometimes there will be prayers to pray during this time in addition to the meditation—prayers such as the Lord's Prayer or the Soul of Christ.[3] Often you will be invited to pray to God and/or Jesus in what is called a colloquy, a 'little conversation'. These will all be outlined in your daily exercise material.

JOURNALLING

Some people also find it helpful to journal during this time. After your meditation time (or during it), take time to journal. (For additional information and tips, see 'Journalling' below.)

CLOSING

When you have finished the prayer time and journalling, you will take a few moments to be with God, seeking to be present to the One who is always present to you, taking time to soak in God's love for you, God's presence within you. The time here often lengthens as you journey through the Exercises. When you are ready, you will conclude your time with prayer. This concludes your prayer time in the Exercises.

NOONTIME AND EVENING EXAMEN[4]

This brings you to the General Examen of Conscience, or what is commonly referred to as the prayer of examen. You will be given questions at the beginning of each section to use during Step 3 of the examen. These questions apply to the material you spent time with during the morning prayer time. The examen takes 5–15 minutes and is prayed twice a day. Please make sure you read the section on the prayer of examen (see 'Prayer of examen' below).

WEEKLY REVIEW/REPETITION DAYS

One or two days each week are review days. If you start going through the exercises for the week beginning on Monday (called Day 1), your review/repetition day will usually be every Thursday

(Day 4) and will definitely be every Sunday (Day 7). Feel free to switch the midweek review/repetition day around a little. It is best to have it on Day 3, 4 or 5 of the week. These days afford you the opportunity to go back and explore passages you felt strongly drawn to or resistant toward. These can be very powerful and insightful days that lead to new personal as well as divine discoveries.

The outline above is the daily rhythm you will be following throughout your time in the Exercises. There will be minor changes made from time to time: the grace will change, and the questions for the examen will change with each section. There will also be new additions, which will be highlighted and explained at the beginning of the section in which they appear. It is helpful to read the grace and the examen every time you move into a new section of the Exercises.

SLOWING DOWN

How you enter into the Exercises is very important. It sets the tenor of your time with God. The slowdown is a time of personal preparation before entering into your daily time with God. It is a time to ready your heart, mind and spirit to come before God, be open to God and listen for the still small voice of God. Although the methods below are not a part of Ignatius' Exercises, they emphasise the need for preparation when you come into God's presence.

Below are three methods to help you slow down and be present to God and yourself. Each method contains common elements of breathing (focus on body), letting go of thoughts, worries and pressures (focus on mind/heart), and prayer (focus moves from self to God). These elements will help prepare you to be open to what God has for you. Remember to go slowly. Intentionally making this step a part of your daily experience will make a huge difference as you continue your journey through the Exercises.

1. Start by getting into a comfortable position. Once you are comfortable, begin to take slow, deep breaths. Breathe in enough air to expand your chest. Breathe in through your nose and out through your mouth. As you continue taking slow, deep breaths, allow your mind to slow down, letting go of thoughts and worries. Release the tension of your body. Let the stress flow from your muscles. Allow your body to relax.

Continue taking slow, deep breaths in through your nose and out through your mouth as you imagine that God is breathing life, love and peace into you with each breath you take. As you breathe out, imagine stress, anxiety, fear and any feelings that weigh you down leaving you. Feel yourself sinking deeper and deeper into the presence of God.

Conclude this time with a silent prayer, offering yourself to God, asking that God would guide and direct you through the Exercise and requesting the desired grace for the day. (Allow at least three to five minutes for this method.)

2. (This slowdown step is similar to the previous, but it adds hand movements combined with deep breathing.) Start by getting into a comfortable position, then begin to take slow, deep breaths. Breathe in enough air to expand your chest. Breathe in through your nose and out through your mouth. As you continue taking slow, deep breaths, allow your mind to slow down, letting go of thoughts and worries. Release the tension of your body. Let the stress flow from your muscles. Continue taking slow, deep breaths in through your nose and out through your mouth.

As you continue to breathe slowly and deeply, turn your hands over, palms down. Imagine yourself dropping those things that are weighing you down: your worries, concerns and frustrations, the things that bring you emotional discomfort or pain. When you feel you've been able to let these things go, turn your hands over, palms up. This represents your readiness to enter into imaginative prayer and to receive what God has for you.

Conclude this time with a silent prayer, offering yourself to God, asking that God would guide and direct you and requesting the desired grace for the day. (Allow at least three to five minutes for this method.)

3. This method may or may not be combined with the breathing techniques of the above slowdown methods. The difference here is that instead of imagining you are breathing out your worries and concerns or dropping them to the ground, you write them on a piece of paper and then put the paper somewhere out of sight until you are done with the Exercises. This way, you have told yourself, 'I am not going to think about all this now, but I will be able to, if I so choose to, after I am finished with my time with God in the Exercises.' When you have finished writing out your worries and concerns, come to God, asking God to guide you through the Exercise and also requesting the desired grace for the day.

Don't be afraid to explore different ways of doing the slowdown, and put into practice what is most helpful to you. The slowdown's purpose is to help you to let go of those things in your mind and heart that would hinder your ability to be present to God. Whatever means you use to help you to do this is great.

Caution: At some points in your journey, you may be convinced that those things that surface during the slowdown are the things you should be spending your prayer time pondering. Resist this temptation, because it will take you away from the rhythm and flow of what God is doing through your journey, away from what God called you to be present to.

Also, do not get stuck in trying to get the slowdown right. Slow down your inner being the best you can and move on, trusting that God will honour the intention of your heart.

PRAYER OF EXAMEN

As you journey through the Exercises, you will be asked to do a prayer of examen at noontime and in the evening. The noontime examen helps you to reconnect with God after your initial morning time in the Exercises, while the evening examen is designed to help you bookend your day with time spent with God. You will follow the traditional format for the examen outlined below and use the assigned examen questions from the daily Exercises during Step 3. The examen should take no longer than 15 minutes and can be completed within a much shorter timeframe.

The prayer of examen, over time, will enable you to become more aware and sensitive to the reality of living, moving and being in God's presence (Acts 17:28) and alert to the invitations that flow from God to you throughout your day. Make sure you become familiar with the prayer of examen and endeavour to quickly make it a part of your daily experience in the Exercises. This prayer practice will have an extraordinary impact on your experience and will assist you in 'finding God in all things', which is a desired outcome of your time in the Exercises.

The examen was the central element of Ignatian spirituality. Ignatius would give permission to his followers to refrain from various types of prayers for a season, but not from the prayer of examen. This prayer is steeped in biblical tradition. The essence of the examen is not external change but internal transformation. It is not another avenue of self-scrutiny but rather an opening to divine awareness. The goal of the examen is gradually to develop an internalised openness and sensitivity to the promptings and invitations of God throughout the course of your day. It is an aid to finding God in all things and becoming aware of the disordered attachments within you that hinder your freedom to say 'yes' to God.

The origins for the prayer of examen are traced back to the Psalms, in particular Psalm 139:23–24, in which David asked God to 'Search me, O God, and know my heart; test me and know my anxious thoughts. See if there is any offensive way in me, and lead me in the way everlasting.' The prayer of examen was born out of this passage.

There are two examens in Ignatius' Exercises: the Daily Particular Examen of Conscience and the General Examen of Conscience/Consciousness. As indicated by the name, the Particular Examen of Conscience is highly focused, while the General Examen of Conscience involves an overall sense of an entire day or other period.

GENERAL EXAMEN OF CONSCIENCE

Listed below are the steps for the General Examen of Conscience,[5] which captures the essence of Psalm 139:23–24. It is a five-step form of the examen you will be using as you proceed through the Exercises.

1. Give thanks to God for what you have received. This causes you to focus on God and God's goodness and grace, and on the greatness of God.
2. Ask God to reveal your sins to you. This may seem moralistic and externally driven, but that is not the case. According to Ignatius' rules for discernment, the focus is not on the external sin but on the roots from which that weed sprouted. It also affirms that you cannot do this alone but only as God gives insight and illumination.
3. Examine how you lived this day, looking at your thoughts, words and deeds. During this step you will use the examen questions given in the daily/weekly exercises. This step helps you to discover how you might have missed God today, so that tomorrow you will have a better chance of connecting with God and with what God is up to.

4. Ask forgiveness, expressing sorrow for your sins while recalling to mind God's love and grace. This provides the opportunity to soak in God's grace, forgiveness, mercy and love.

5. Ask God for the grace to amend your ways and live more fully out of a sense of connection with God. In this step you are once again affirming your need for God and dependence on God. You begin to internalise that it is not up to you and your effort, for 'apart from [Jesus] you can do nothing' (John 15:5).

When the General Examen of Conscience is regularly practised, it generates an internal spiritual sensitivity to the movements and invitations of God, while fostering a greater awareness of God's love, grace and forgiveness and your dependency on God. (This prayer can be done in 5–15 minutes. The key is being totally open and honest with God and yourself.)

As you go through the Exercises, you will be making use of the General Examen of Conscience. The questions you will use for Step 3 of this examen are provided to you weekly and are designed to help you explore your day in light of the grace you have asked God for and the focus of the meditation time for that particular day. As you go through the Exercises, you will make use of a modified General Examen of Conscience.

PARTICULAR EXAMEN OF CONSCIENCE

The second type of examen prayer, the Particular Examen of Conscience,[6] is highly focused and is meant to be prayed three times throughout the day. You will practise this prayer style in the morning shortly after rising, again right after lunch and the third time after dinner. This prayer's focus is on a fault or sin over which you desire to gain victory.

In the first prayer time, you ask God for the grace to deal with the fault or sin in the coming day. At the examen time following lunch, you ask God for the grace to reveal your shortcomings in the previous period, ask for forgiveness of that fault or sin, and then ask God for the grace to amend your ways. (This follows the structure of the General Examen of Conscience, Steps 1–5). You then write down your failures and repeat this process during the examen time after dinner, again writing down your failures.

This entire prayer process is repeated the next day and the next, with charting to compare periods, days and weeks with each other. The charting aspect of this prayer can be overwhelming but, when practised, it is a helpful aid in discovering trends and formulating plans to partner better with God at times of great difficulty. The Particular Examen of Conscience might be a tool you will find helpful if God brings something to your mind and heart to work on as you journey through the Exercises. However, remember— and this is essential—it is not the outward action that is the real concern, but the internal roots (thoughts, desires and so on) that need to be your focus.

As I have journeyed with individuals through the Exercises, I have found that the examen is the single most important factor in deepening the experience of the Exercises. I have also noticed that this practice, although it takes only a few minutes, is the hardest for those going through the Exercises to do regularly. This is not because it is difficult, but because people tend to forget it.

JOURNALLING

Journalling is part of the DNA of the Exercises, for the Exercises themselves are a byproduct of Ignatius' discipline of journalling. Journalling is strongly encouraged and considered an important component of the Exercises, even though it was not an original element of them. A journal helps preserve the unique journey you are embarking on and may become a treasured possession, a spiritual snapshot of a significant piece of your spiritual journey. Journalling is yet another way to open yourself up to God as you journey through the Exercises.

Morton Kelsey writes, 'Without a journal... we remain out of touch with large parts of ourselves.'[7] Journalling is an excellent tool for becoming honest with God and yourself. The discipline of journalling helps you:

- pay attention to God. It is a way of hearing and responding to God.
- process what is going on inside. It slows you down enough to notice what is happening within.
- listen to and learn about yourself and God, giving direction and insight to live a more authentic life.
- understand your unfolding story and discover where God is in that story.
- put feelings into words.
- develop your thinking and lead to the generation of new thoughts, extending your knowledge in new ways.
- record your growth into Christlikeness.
- put marks on your spiritual wall, recording and denoting growth.
- gain perspective, encouragement and hope, and combat desolation.

JOURNALLING TIPS

Choosing a journal: There are many styles of journals: bound, loose-leaf, spiral, lined, blank, small, large, leather, cardboard, recycled paper—and the list goes on. The important thing is to choose a journal that works for you. I have used many types, but I now use an 8½ by 11-inch spiral notebook with no lines. The spiral design allows me to fold my journal over; the blank page gives me freedom and plenty of room for artistry; and the size allows me to get into a flow and keep writing without constantly turning pages. There are many people who journal on computers, which I find limiting because I can take my hardcopy journal anywhere and can even glue notes and other things into it. But the choice is yours.

Incorporating creativity: Journal as you can, not as you think you should. Journalling needs to flow out of your creative, free self without restraint, fear or performance anxiety. Seek to approach journalling as a child entering into a time of mystery, a time when you are not sure what will happen yet you are excited about the possibilities. It is best to approach journalling as a dynamic adventure, seeing where it leads you, rather than as a prescribed, static act.

Write as little or as much as you like, but also feel free to draw, paint or make collages. Do not worry about spelling, sentence structure, grammar and the like. Experiment with different ways of journalling: write in crayon with your nondominant hand, write prayers, paraphrase a passage, write a letter to God, write a letter from God, paint, use clay. The possibilities are endless, so give yourself permission to explore and experiment as you journal.

I suggest that, as you journal, you have on hand a box containing coloured markers, pencils, crayons, construction paper, a glue stick, a pair of scissors or even watercolours. Sometimes images and colours communicate what words cannot. Also, the use of art can release emotions that are hard for you to get in touch with or communicate. Do not use the excuse that you are not good at art. Instead give it a go, focusing on God's grace and love rather than on your perceived weakness. See God as your heavenly Parent, who receives your art project with great joy and delight, not because of your skill but because of God's great love of you and delight in you.

From time to time, experiment with colours. Even something as simple as writing a word or phrase that God has brought to mind in big, coloured letters can become a powerful expression of what is going on within you. Step out and have fun, not trying to be a great artist but entering into and enjoying the creative process, knowing that whatever you end up with is received by God as a precious expression of your heart and thus cherished by God and firmly affixed on the gigantic refrigerator of heaven.

Addressing emotion: Use journalling as a time to become aware of your feelings. Are you in the midst of consolation or desolation? Expressing your feelings will provide something to share with your spiritual director or listener when you get together, and it will help you know what might be a good focus. Ignatius tells us that prior consolations are a great resource during times of desolation, and journalling can help you to recall previous consolations. As you journal through times of desolation, God can bring insight that can enable you to escape the despair and discouragement that desolation can bring and will help stir the embers of faith, hope and love that remain in your heart.

In the Exercises, Ignatius attaches great importance to the emotional affect of the retreatant. If you struggle with articulating your feelings, do not give up; instead, give grace to yourself and continue. This is a long journey, so do not expect to do everything well, especially at the beginning. Please continue to unpack what you are feeling, because in your journey through the Exercises, time is on your side and so is God. As you continue, you will become more self-aware and God-aware, and you will have ample material to process with your spiritual director or listener.

Please give yourself the freedom to journal as you are able and not to seek to live up to an idealised sense of what journalling should be. Embrace freedom and grace, choosing to journal as you can and not as you cannot. Continue to remind yourself that it is the process of journalling and not the finished product that is important. And finally, take a day off from journalling every so often.

EXPLORING THE BIBLICAL TEXT

There will be a number of ways you will interact with God during your prayer times each day, but there are two main methods you will be using to interact with God through the scriptures: *lectio divina* and imaginative prayer.

LECTIO DIVINA

The *lectio divina* (sacred reading) method has been around for centuries and actually incorporates a variety of ways to interact with God as you enter into the scriptures. This style of interacting with the word flowed from a Benedictine insight that reading, if it is to be authentic and nourishing, cannot be undertaken simply with the eyes and the mind. It must involve the whole person: mind, heart, body and spirit. It is reading for formation, not information, and for encounter with the living God in such a way that the heart and life are transformed.

Eugene Peterson, author of THE MESSAGE, writes, '*Lectio divina* is not a methodical technique for reading the Bible. It is a cultivated, developed habit of living the text in Jesus' name. This is the way, the only way that the Holy Scripture becomes formative in the Christian Church and becomes salt and leaven in the world.'[8]

Lectio divina has four steps:

1. **Lectio:** This involves slowly and gently reading and rereading the assigned passage or passages of scripture until a word or phrase draws your attention through either attraction or resistance.

2. **Meditatio:** Once you have landed on a word or phrase, gently repeat that word or phrase to yourself. Receive and reflect on the thoughts, hopes, images and feelings that come to you through this word or words. Strong feelings (positive or

negative) are signs of deep inner movements in your heart. Permit the words, which are 'living and active' (Hebrews 4:12), to probe your attitudes, emotions and aspirations. What is being offered to you?

3. **Oratio:** Allow your whole being to become prayer. Honestly express your deepest thoughts, feelings and desires in dialogue with God. Pray yourself empty.

4. **Contemplatio:** Gently let go of all thoughts and feelings. Drop into God's presence beneath thought, beneath emotion. Rest completely in God, grateful for what has been given.

Lectio divina takes you out of the place of being in control as you read the scripture and turns you into a listener waiting to hear the still small voice of God guide and direct you during your time in the word. This method will be employed from time to time but will not be the primary method when reading the Gospel narratives. If you are new to this method, it may seem mechanical at first. But stick with it, because once you begin to learn the steps and settle into *lectio divina*, it will become a seamless experience between you and God, devoid of the initial steps that felt cumbersome or awkward.

During the Exercises, you will conclude your times in *lectio divina* with journalling and prayer.

IMAGINATIVE PRAYER

As you journey through the Exercises, you will be asked to make use of your imagination as you reflect on various Bible passages. One of the hallmarks of the Spiritual Exercises of Ignatius is this use of the imagination, which is not surprising, since Ignatius was brought to faith in Christ through his imagination. The turning point in his life came while he was recovering from a broken leg he suffered when hit by a cannon ball during a battle.

During the long hours of recovery, Ignatius spent lots of time imagining the future exploits he would have as a soldier once he fully recovered, but after a while he got bored with his daydreams and asked for something to read. The only two books available to him were one on the lives of the saints and the other on the life of Jesus. As he read these two books, Ignatius began to imagine what it would be like to live like the saints and to walk with Jesus. As he did this, he noticed the excitement and inner transformation that took place within his heart and soul, leaving him at peace and satisfied. God used Ignatius' imagination to get hold of him and transform him from a soldier into a follower of Christ.

So, in his writings, Ignatius instructed people to enter the Gospel stories imaginatively, to be present to see, smell, taste, touch and hear what was unfolding around them. He saw imagination as the place where we can experience, embrace and internalise spiritual truth. We do not just read about the manger, the garden and the cross. Instead we are present to hear the cries of the newborn king, to feel a Son's pain as he pleads with his Father and struggles within himself, and to see the nails driven into the tender flesh of our Saviour.

For Ignatius, imagination unites past with present and brings us face to face with the living God. For him, the use of imagination is essential to prayer and transformation.

Now, that is all well and good for Ignatius, but you may have concerns about the use of your imagination with scripture. First, know this: when I speak of the imagination I am referring to what C.S. Lewis called the baptised imagination and what Bruce Demarest refers to as the 'sanctified' use of imagination. The imagination is a God-given gift that is not frivolous, evil or childish.

When I refer to imaginative prayer, I am speaking of a Spirit-infused, God-directed use of your imagination that gives you the ability to enter experientially into the stories, symbolism and images of the Bible. It empowers you to hold the now with both the past and future, and to see and embrace the seen (physical) and the unseen (eternal). The Spirit-infused imagination moves you from sterile head knowledge to life-transforming, heart-healing, biblically informed ways of being and of doing life. It is as we embrace and employ the use of our God-given, Spirit-infused imagination that we can enter the wonder and mystery of God and God's word. As we use this method, we are trusting in God and will be evaluating the images that arise based on God's revealed truths found in the Bible.

Speaking of the imagination: Richard Foster, author of numerous books on spiritual formation, including *Celebration of Discipline*, talks about the benefits of using our imagination when we interact with scripture: 'We begin to enter the story and make it our own. We move from detached observation to active participation. Using the imagination also brings the emotions into the equation so that we can come to God with both mind and heart.'[9]

Eugene Peterson writes:

For Christians whose largest investment is in the invisible (eternal), the imagination is indispensable… Right now one of the essential Christian ministries in our ruined world is the recovery and exercise of the imagination… Imagination is the mental tool we have for connecting material and spiritual, visible and invisible, earth and heaven… Imagination catapults us into mystery.[10]

The greatest validation for using imagination as a tool for interacting with the scriptures is the Bible. In the opening chapters of Genesis, the earth is formless and void, and the Spirit of God moves across its surface. Out of nothing but God's own imagination, light, sky, mountains, valleys and all of life are created. The final book of Revelation is bursting with dramatic images and descriptions of Jesus, heaven, the turmoil of the world and the birth of a new heaven and new earth. From the first page of scripture to the last, our fully engaged imagination is needed to enter into and embrace this amazing story of creation and redemption, of good versus evil, of power, love, grace and hope.

The Bible is written imaginatively because we are imaginative. Dramatic biblical imagery exists to help us enter into the living word of God, to gaze upon the Lord, to look beyond the seen to the unseen (2 Corinthians 4:18) and to fully embrace the truth that in God we live, move and have our being. Imagination gives us wings to soar into the wonder, mystery and truth of God and God's word.

Imaginative prayer helps us experience the story and personally hear, see and touch Jesus. In imaginative prayer, God speaks personally and powerfully. It involves using our God-given imagination to hear from and experience God and truth in a deeply forming way. It helps us move from external head knowledge of God to an internalised, deeper knowing of God.

Try these five steps of imaginative prayer:

- **Step 1**: Choose a story from the Bible. It is probably best to begin with an account from the Gospels when you are first learning this way of prayer. Gospel stories are familiar to many of us, they connect with our issues, and they are brief. As such, they are easy to grasp and easy to imagine.
- **Step 2**: Read the story several times. As you do, pay attention to the details of the passage. Notice the setting, the characters and the situation. Who is the central figure? What is the problem? What is the outcome? What is unusual about this story? How does it connect with your life situation? Read the account enough times to understand its main point and to be familiar with its details.
- **Step 3**: Get quiet in yourself and focus on openness to God. Find a place and a posture that will allow you to meditate. Relax your body. Slow your breathing. At the same time, be in prayer, asking God for guidance.
- **Step 4**: Imagine yourself as a participant in the story. You may be an onlooker or you may be involved in the action, but put yourself in that place and time. Begin by noticing the details in the story. What do you see? Smell? Feel? Hear? Taste? Think? Watch the situation as it unfolds. Listen to what is said. What

is said to you? If Jesus is in the story, go to him. Tell him about your concerns. Listen to his response. Reply to him.

- **Step 5:** Let your mind move slowly from the past to the present. Take with you the 'feel' of the whole experience. Present that to God. Be open to God. Thank God. Listen to God.

Use your imagination to picture a scene or event from scripture. Let your senses come into play: sight, hearing, smell, touch and taste. Place yourself in the scene as an onlooker or as a participant in the action, allowing the drama of the story to make its impact on you. Be open to what the Lord wants to show you or say to you. Be open to any revelation or insight that may come through your imaginative contemplation.

Some people are especially adept at such use of the imagination (a right-brain activity) and can see a biblical story clearly, even in vivid colours. If you are not that way, do not get discouraged because of what you may perceive to be a deficiency in your ability to make use of imagination. Just do it to the degree you are able to, and trust that God will honour your efforts. The use of the imagination is a powerful tool of illumination and formation that Ignatius has incorporated into the Exercises.

If this type of prayer is new to you, be patient and gracious with yourself. This is a long journey, and you will have plenty of time to hone this skill. For now, have fun with it. Enter into the Gospel narratives with abandon and the playfulness of a child.

As you journey through the Exercises, you will be encouraged to use *lectio divina* or imaginative prayer to enter into that day's material. Once you are fully comfortable with each of these methods, do not be afraid to tweak them or design your own hybrid, combining what you find helpful in each. Remember, these are tools to be used as God leads. Experiment with each method and see if you find one more helpful than another. The goal is to encounter God through his living word rather than merely to learn about God.

2

THE BENEFITS OF A SPIRITUAL DIRECTOR OR LISTENER

Ignatius created the Spiritual Exercises with the intention that a spiritual director would be involved in the process. As stated earlier, the Spiritual Exercises of Ignatius were designed to be a manual that was never actually given to the retreatant, but was used as a tool by a spiritual director accompanying that individual. The first 20 paragraphs that Ignatius included in the Exercises, known as the 'Annotations', are not truly a part of the Exercises but are notes written for the benefit of those who would take someone through the Exercises. Thus, for Ignatius, it would be unthinkable for someone to journey through the Exercises alone. He would see this as unwise. Yet there will be the temptation not to find a listener or spiritual director and to travel this journey through the Exercises alone.

A spiritual director or listener gives you an extra set of ears, to help you better hear the still small voice of God. He gives you an extra set of eyes to help you see what God may be up to and to help you recognise traps you may be falling into and themes that may be emerging. She gives you another brain to think through how you might be able to enter more deeply into your experience through the Exercises. A spiritual director or listener is a critical component for your journey through the Exercises, bringing a depth and breadth to your experience that is not possible without one.

Most spiritual direction sessions are approximately one hour. Some of your times with your spiritual director or listener can be in a group setting (see 'Using the Exercises with a Group', pages 336–337). It is best to meet with a director at least twice a month (once a week is ideal) for about an hour each time when you are going through the Exercises.

FINDING A SPIRITUAL DIRECTOR

A spiritual director is someone trained in the art of spiritual direction. These individuals do not usually charge a fee for meeting with them. There is a list of questions on www.metamorpha.com that are good to ask a spiritual director when you first meet with her or him. The bottom line is that you need a spiritual director with whom you are able to be open and honest, someone you trust, who is safe for you and who may be a little ahead of you on the journey. Not all spiritual directors are familiar with the Exercises, so in this book is a special section designed as a resource for spiritual directors or listeners (see 'For Spiritual Directors and Listeners', pages 326–335). It is vitally important to make sure your spiritual director is willing to do the extra work needed to journey adequately with you through the Exercises.

Two websites that can help you find a spiritual director who can walk you through the Exercises are www.b-ing.org and Spiritual Directors International (www.sdiworld.org). There will also be a portion of the b-ing site dedicated to those going through the Exercises using this book.

Most retreat houses have someone on site trained in the art of spiritual direction. My first director was a nun, whom I went to for about eight years; I was truly blessed by her wisdom and insight. The important thing when choosing a spiritual director is not gender or denominational affiliation, but that you feel safe, at ease and understood by your director. Take time to interview potential directors, asking them questions that will help you discover if you could trust them, if they would understand you and if you would be able to be open and honest with them in your times together.

CHOOSING A LISTENER

Please resist the temptation to choose a listener rather than seeking first to find a spiritual director. Spiritual directors have gone through extensive training to accompany people who are seeking a deeper relationship with God, so it is worth the time and effort to find a spiritual director.

But if you are not able to find a spiritual director, search for a listener. Do not choose a close friend as your listener, because your friend is not detached from you and may tend to protect you, rescue you or even discount your experience. I have encountered this first-hand: when I first started giving spiritual direction to those I knew, it did not work well.

The listener needs to be a person you trust and with whom you will feel comfortable sharing, a person who is spiritually mature, has a growing relationship with God and knowledge of the scriptures, and is caring, gracious and loving. Consider asking your minister for a couple of recommendations for a listener. This person must also be willing to prepare ahead of your meeting time by going to www.b-ing.org and/or 'For Spiritual Directors and Listeners' to read the questions for the section through which you are currently journeying. Or you can purchase an additional copy of this book for the listener who has agreed to journey with you.

———— 3 ————

TIPS ON HOW TO APPROACH THE EXERCISES

Below are a number of tips that will help make your experience with the Exercises fuller and richer. These tips have emerged through the experiences of others I have taken through the Exercises. Do not expect that you will have all these in place by the end of the first week or even the first month.

PREPARATORY EXERCISES

You may be tempted not to enter into Part 2, 'Preparatory Exercises', thinking that you are a mature Christian who knows God and follows Jesus pretty consistently, so you do not need special preparation for entering the Exercises. Fight against such thinking. The Preparatory Exercises will help you to form a foundation on which the rest of the Exercises are built; they were added because so many who journeyed through the Exercises were having difficult struggles. The time you spend in the Preparatory Exercises will pay dividends as you continue your journey. So, begin at the beginning.

COMMITMENT

You may need to recommit yourself to your journey through the Exercises more than once over the next several months. This is not surprising, but normal. You are beginning a long journey, a journey that will have its ups and downs. There may be times when you will feel like giving up or as if you are just going through the motions. During these times, remember why you began the Exercises and how God has used them in so many lives over the centuries. Do not get discouraged by these feelings or pretend they are not there. Take time to acknowledge them and bring them to God, as well as to your spiritual director or listener, and to recommit yourself to this process of spiritual formation. It is also helpful to journal about these feelings.

EXPECTATIONS

Beware of your expectations. The expectations you bring to the Exercises can blind you to what God is actually doing, cause you to get discouraged or make you feel like giving up. Your expectations can become an inner voice of judgment of you, your experiences, God and the Exercises—a loud, demanding and cruel voice. It is not the voice of God and needs to be silenced or, at the very least, ignored.

Your expectations may be based on the experience of others. I ran up against this many times as I led people through the Exercises in a theological college setting. The first year was great; everyone entered them without expectations. However, every year after that, a new group of people came with a whole variety of expectations based on what they had heard about the experience of others who had gone through the Exercises. These expectations became a hurdle that individuals had to get over, a hindrance hampering their ability to be fully present to what was really happening. They were looking for something in particular, and the narrowness of their focus blinded them to all else. The beauty of the Exercises is that each person's experience is different. God will meet you as you need to be met.

Another source of expectations is your own desires—desires that are good and God-honouring. Your desire might be to become more like Christ or to do the Exercises well or not to miss a day. These desires then get subtly turned into self-imposed expectations: I will become like Christ (and you will have your own unique definition of what it means to become like Christ). I will do the Exercises perfectly. I will do the morning time, the afternoon examen, the evening examen, the journalling—I will do it all; I will not miss a day. Expectations soon become a master who evaluates you. This will drain the life out of you and your experience as you journey through the Exercises.

So, you will come to the Exercises with expectations. That is not the issue. The issue is when these expectations become the voice to which you listen. Each day, as you come before God, name your expectations and let them go. Then seek to be open to God, prepared to enter into whatever God has for you that day.

SPIRITUAL DIRECTOR OR LISTENER

The true benefit of having a spiritual director or listener is proportionate to the level of your honesty and openness with that person. Do not try to look spiritual or good, but determine to be real and truthful with your spiritual director or listener. It is when you are authentic in these encounters that you will reap the value that they are able to bring to you and your journey.

NOONTIME AND EVENING EXAMEN

Because the prayer of examen is such an important component and because so many people find it difficult to make the examen a part of their daily journey through the Exercises, find creative ways to remind yourself to do the prayer of examen. It may be easy to remember at lunchtime, but evening can be more difficult. I have found it helpful to write examen in big letters with a bright marker on the front of an index card and to write the examen questions on the back. I then place the card on my pillow or bedside table each day, so I remember my evening prayer of examen.

One suggestion that has been helpful to many is to put a sticky note on the mirror where you brush your teeth. Or set the alarm on your mobile phone before you go to bed, or put a reminder on the refrigerator or on your computer screensaver. Another way is to pick an activity you do most nights and link the examen to the beginning or completion of that activity. For example, plan to do examen after you change out of your work clothes, finish dinner or clear the table, or before you watch television in the evening.

BABY STEPS

When a baby begins to walk, we celebrate each step and overlook each fall. With small children, we understand that beginnings are difficult and seek to encourage rather than condemn. This is the attitude I suggest you bring to the Exercises: start small and build on those initial small successes. I am a big fan of 'something is better than nothing'. For example, doing the noontime and evening examen once a week is better than doing it no times a week. One of my favorite G.K. Chesterton quotes is, 'If a thing is worth doing, it is worth doing badly.'

Give yourself grace; be patient with yourself as you journey through the Exercises. Celebrate the baby steps of improvement. The journey on which you are embarking is not easy, so do not expect yourself to do it perfectly. Give yourself permission to start small and grow. This baby-step mindset helps you to enter into the Exercises freely and lightly, and helps you escape the stress to perform and do it right (whatever 'do it right' means). The stress to do it right works against you, while the baby-step attitude promotes ongoing excitement, joy and desire.

RESISTANCE

Pay attention to the resistance that arises within as you journey through the Exercises. It can be experienced as a feeling of not wanting to do the Exercises, as not liking the passage that will be the focus for that day, as a fear that surfaces around a theme or even as a sense that you are not able to believe or enter into a component of the Exercises. This resistance may arise within you for a variety of reasons. When it does, your tendency may be to want to run from it or ignore it, which is the way most people deal with resistance. The tip is this: when you sense resistance during the Exercises, pay attention to it and explore where it is coming from or what is giving birth to it. Resistance is not something to run from or ignore.

Your resistance will probably generate feelings of inadequacy ('I can't do this right') or insecurity ('I am not ready to do these Exercises'). These feelings are not helpful, so when you notice resistance, welcome it as a friend and sit down with it, exploring it rather than getting sucked into your negative and unhelpful feelings. Ask yourself questions such as, What am I feeling? Where is this coming from? What does this tell me about my belief and feelings about God and myself? You see, resistance is the doorway that will lead you to greater freedom and to new discoveries of yourself and the divine.

Resistance is a gift from God, a gift to embrace, be open to and explore. Resistance is a friend to welcome in, sit and talk with and learn from. Do not fear resistance. Do not let resistance get you down. Resistance is a good and powerful tool used by God for your transformation, so please choose to embrace it and explore it.

DISCIPLINE

Many people who are attracted to the Spiritual Exercises of Ignatius believe it will help bring discipline to their time with God, a discipline that they have not had before or had in some form at one time and wish to regain. If that is you, beware. You see, there is a reason you do not have a disciplined time with God, and, although the Exercises will provide structure, they will also be a struggle for you and possibly even a source of frustration. Just know this and be ready to extend grace to yourself and resist the temptation to condemn yourself or give up.

UPS AND DOWNS

Here's another tip—a heads-up, really: your experience in the Exercises will be an up-and-down affair. You will have good and wonderful times; God's presence at times will seem close and intimate, and the hour will pass in what seems like a moment. And you will have times when God will feel distant; the clock will seem as if it is not moving at all, and you will wonder how you will make it through the exercise for that day. This is normal. In fact, if these ups and downs are not happening, something is wrong.

EMOTIONS

Be aware of what you are feeling about God, yourself and the exercise of the day. We are often taught to ignore our emotions, but Ignatius found that our emotions are an aid to us in our spiritual formation. As you pay attention to your emotions and unpack them, you will learn more about yourself and your image of God in the process. Your emotions will prove to be an excellent source of material for journalling.

PROCESS, NOT EVENT

I liken the Spiritual Exercises experience to the gestation process. Something is always happening in the womb; growth and transformation are taking place; the baby is, and yet is also becoming. During the Exercises, God is deeply at work within the depths of your being. There may be times when you experience the movement of life within or the discomfort of internal growth as it develops and takes shape, but, for the most part, it will be hard to gauge or ascertain what is actually taking place until the process has reached completion. And that will take some time. My tip: do not be tempted to evaluate the value of the Exercises based on your daily experience, good or bad. Your daily experience in the Exercises is not an accurate picture of the work God is doing within you and the transformation that is taking place.

DAILY JOURNEY, NOT DESTINATION

This emphasis on the daily journey may seem to conflict with the above tip but, I assure you, it does not. The focus is not on evaluation but on the journey itself. This journey you are on is a long and, at times, arduous one. It is a marathon, not a sprint. Because of this, it can be discouraging, even overwhelming. When I rode my bicycle across the United States, I found that after a hard day it was easy to get discouraged and be tempted to give up, especially when I focused on how much farther I had to go. But when I could be thankful for the completion of another day of riding, no matter whether it had been easy or hard, it put me into a better mindset for the next day. It helped me to enter each day into the 'now' of the journey and to enjoy the beauty and meet the challenges of that day.

The words of Jesus, 'Therefore do not worry about tomorrow… Each day has enough trouble of its own' (Matthew 6:34), are apt for our topic. Do not get ahead of yourself and do not focus on how much further you still need to travel on this spiritual journey through the Exercises. Instead, enter fully into each day of the Exercises, paying special attention to the invitations and challenges God may bring your way. A focus on the finish line can cause you to become blind to the reality of the now, the presence of God, and what God may be inviting you into or challenging you with in this moment.

JOURNALLING

Journalling is a powerful tool for helping you to capture, explore and deepen your experience with God through the Exercises. Your journalling does not have to be confined to words and sentences. (Please take a look at pages 32–35, where you will find journalling discussed in depth.)

BE PREPARED

This is a good motto not just for Scouts but also for you as you begin and continue your journey through the Exercises. There are a number of ways to 'be prepared'.

1. Gather your materials (Bible, journal, pens, book) beforehand. Keeping all this together in a box or on a table can be helpful. This may seem unnecessary, but it will help you to jump in and get started if you don't have to gather your things.
2. Have the space in which you are going to do the Exercises free from things that tend to distract you, such as letters, bills, books, music or people. Also remove and silence all phones. This will help you to focus throughout your time in the Exercises.
3. As you arrive in your 'space', prepare yourself spiritually, mentally and emotionally to enter into the Exercises. Prayerfully quieten yourself before God.
4. Read tomorrow's passages the night before, as you are getting ready to go to sleep. This puts the passages in your mind and gives God a chance to stir up thoughts and feelings as you sleep. This is an especially good practice to employ if you are choosing to do the Exercises in the morning.
5. If you are seeking to get up early to do the Exercises each morning, be intentional about getting to bed early. For me, staying up late makes it extra difficult to get up early and do the Exercises, especially when the air is chilly.

BIBLE TRANSLATION

This can be a sensitive issue: do not use your regular Bible for your time in the Exercises. Your regular Bible tends to be full of you: your underlining, your handwritten notes in the margin, and your papers—old church notice sheets, sermon outlines, notes—stuffed throughout its pages. These can distract you from the daily focus or offer you a way of escape when you encounter difficulties during your time in the Exercises.

Now I will take this one step further: consider using a different translation from the one you are accustomed to. Some people know the words and vocabulary of their translation so well and are so familiar with the wording of the narratives, especially the narratives of Jesus' life, that they no longer read the words but go through the passage in autopilot. When you use a translation you are not familiar with, you may be surprised, caught off-guard and even made uncomfortable by the new wording you come across. These are all good things.

If you really like your current translation and are not willing to give it up, I suggest that you get a second Bible of a different translation. Each time you read a passage, do so in both your preferred and the new translation. The bottom line is this: I urge you not to use your current Bible exclusively.

FAITHFULNESS AND TIME

Each day you are asked to spend 50–75 minutes in the Exercises. Please be determined to spend that entire time. Some days will be easy while others may be extremely difficult, but, either way, put in the time. If you are having trouble, do things differently: take a walk as you spend your time in the morning, or put your head down and even allow yourself to doze off. By your presence, you are saying to God, 'I am here. I desire to be with you and to hear from you.' What you are doing each day as you enter the Exercises is exactly what Paul encouraged believers to do: present ourselves as a living and holy sacrifice, or gift, to God (Romans 12:1). That is always a good thing.

I have been writing a lot about putting in the time even when it is difficult to do so, but here is another tip: stop at the end of the allotted time. Without this time limit, the Exercises can be twisted to work against your other commitments. Ignatius suffered through this experience when his times with God began to take time from the very things God had called him to do. So be aware that this could happen, and stop after the allotted 50–75 minutes.

When you faithfully present yourself to God as a gift, each of your times with God will be 'successful'. You will have honoured God and, by your presence, will have declared to God, 'I want to know you, hear from you and be with you.' When you come into God's presence that way, day after day after day, you will be transformed. Put in the time and be faithful, and the God who is faithful will work within you in ways beyond anything you could ever think, ask or imagine.

REPETITION OR REVIEW DAYS

These days are not days off. Rather, these days, which will occur once or twice each week, afford you the opportunity to revisit and go deeper with God in an area of your choosing. These can be powerful times of revelation and discovery.

OPTIONAL EXERCISES

The optional exercises are just that—optional. It is entirely up to you to choose if you will do them or not. They are usually a bit different from the regular exercises and are designed to stretch and challenge you in terms of your definition of prayer and what it means to spend time with God. I encourage you to give one a try from time to time. You may be surprised how God will use these optional times, especially when they take you outside your comfort zone. If you do choose to do an optional exercise, have fun with it. Do not get stressed over doing it right; simply enter into it with an attitude of openness and playfulness.

WEBSITE

You may want to make use of the website www.b-ing.org, which has an area set aside to assist those journeying through the Spiritual Exercises using this book.

FINAL TIP

These tips are provided to aid you rather than to act as a bag of clubs with which to beat yourself. This is a list you can return to from time to time as you internalise the rhythm of the Exercises. You may even reach the end of your journey and realise you have not incorporated a number of these tips. That's OK! God will still have used the Exercises to mould, shape and transform you into the image of Jesus.

PART 2

PREPARATORY EXERCISES

—— 1 ——

THE HISTORY OF PREPARATORY EXERCISES

The Preparatory Exercises are designed to prepare you to enter into the formal Exercises from a place of greater spiritual health and wholeness. Because Ignatius experienced how arduous this journey can be and witnessed the same in many of those he led through the Exercises, he felt strongly that individuals must be adequately prepared to enter into the Exercises. Ignatius did not allow one of his earliest followers, Pierre Favre, to enter the Exercises until four years after Pierre first requested to do so, because he did not feel Pierre was ready.

These Preparatory Exercises are a time for your own personal and spiritual preparation, a time for making sure you can enter into the formal Exercises in a way that will lead to health and wholeness. If this groundwork is not laid, your practice of the Exercises can become a time of morbid introspection that can stir up a whirlpool of self-doubt and condemnation. This can lead to shame and self-condemnation rather than spiritual health, wholeness and freedom, which are hallmarks of the Ignatian experience. These Preparatory Exercises are extremely important for those who struggle with shame, self-doubt, self-condemnation and perfectionism, which we all do to some degree. As you begin your journey through the Exercises, you must have a positive sense of who God is, especially before beginning what is commonly referred to as Week 1.

I cannot state emphatically enough that the Preparatory Exercises are not an added hoop to jump through to earn the right to enter into the Exercises. The Preparatory Exercises are a critical component, grounding you in the essential, heartfelt understanding and experience needed. Do not skip these or skirt over them.

There are two pieces that together form the Preparatory Exercises. The first piece, 'God's love', focuses on the internalisation of God's love by transforming it from a theological construct that you mentally assent to into a heartfelt reality that pulsates through the veins of your being. The second piece of the Preparatory Exercises, the 'Principle and Foundation',[1] exposes you to the theological realities that form the foundation of the Exercises.

This first part of the Preparatory Exercises, focusing on God's love, arose out of a desire to prepare you better for entry into the entirety of the Exercises in general, but specifically into the rigours of Week 1. In Week 1, you will be invited to come face to face with your own sin and brokenness, which can be devastating apart from an internalised sense of God's unconditional, one-of-a-kind love for you. This section on God's love is also a result of Ignatius' emphasis on the need for those who enter into the Exercises to have great courage and generosity toward their Creator and Lord.[2] These attitudes of courage and generosity naturally arise from an internalised belief in the never-ending, unconditional love of God; therefore it is important that you have truly internalised this belief.

Finally, these first exercises were included because, as I have taken individuals through the Exercises, I have found that many people truly believe God loves everyone, but in their heart of hearts they doubt that God could truly love them just as they are. Though prevalent, this inability to internally embrace God's love while journeying through the Exercises multiplies the likelihood of shipwreck on the rocks of shame, guilt and self-condemnation. The goal of these next few weeks is to help you to know internally in a deeper and more profound way—heart-know not just head-know—the height, depth, width and breadth of God's love for you.

Spending a few weeks sitting in God's love may seem like a wonderfully desirable opportunity, but I forewarn you that this may not be your experience. I have found that, for many, these daily prayer sessions can be very trying. You see, it is one thing to believe 'God loves me' and quite another to spend 21 days pondering, reflecting on and exploring this truth. When some individuals journey through this time, anger begins to arise within them as they recall critical times when they did not experience God's love or caring presence. These individuals begin to wrestle with questions: Does God really love me? If God loves me, why don't I feel God's love? If God loves me, why did _____ happen to me?

If you are one of those who feels these questions arising within you, along with emotions that often accompany these kinds of questions, such as anger, sadness and frustration, do not be afraid to bring all this before God. In fact, read the verses and/or quotes for each day, and then share your feelings and questions with God. Do not try to force yourself to feel a certain way, but instead allow yourself to feel what you are feeling and bring that to God, because that will be the place where God meets you. God is not afraid of your questions or emotions. God wants to meet you in the midst of them. Remember, God desires honesty, so be honest and be real with God.

The following daily prayer sessions on God's love are very important, not only as you continue through the Exercises but also as you seek to know and follow God all the days of your life. During the next couple of weeks, you will be sitting in, soaking in and pondering God's love so that you will know it, rely on it and live in it (1 John 4:16). Before moving on to the second instalment of the Exercises ('Principle and Foundation'), make sure you have come to an internalised sense of God's love for you. There is nothing wrong with going through this preparatory section more than once before moving on. It is also not a problem to return to this section later as you continue through the Exercises.

This section on God's love will help to bring to the surface issues you may have with God concerning your ability to trust God and internally embrace God's love for you. It will also help develop some of the disciplines necessary to make the Exercises the life-shaping and life-transforming experience they were designed to be and have been for almost 500 years.

You are about to begin an incredible journey with God, with Jesus and with the Holy Spirit. The goal is not to get through the Exercises but to enter into the Exercises, to be open and honest with God and yourself, to be willing to embrace the good times and the difficult times, to determine to explore the times of inner harmony and internal resistance, welcoming both as friends and as doorways to personal and divine discovery. Let the journey begin.

'RULES OF DISCERNMENT' INSIGHTS

Before you begin your time in the Exercises, familiarise yourself with the Rules of Discernment for Week 1 (pages 122–126). Ignatius provided these rules to help people deal with the inner movements that arise as they journey through the Exercises. The first set of Rules of Discernment was designed by Ignatius for those who are just beginning the Exercises. He refers to this section as 'Rules for perceiving and knowing in some manner the different movements which are caused in the soul'.[3]

Ignatius provides definitions on the inner movements of consolation and desolation:

Consolations are interior movements in the soul generated by an inflamed love for God. A consolation can result from sorrow for one's sins, passion for Christ, increases in hope, faith, love or joy. In short, a consolation is anything that causes your intention to be focused on God.

Desolations involve all that is contrary to consolations, such as darkness of the soul, internal uneasiness, agitations and temptations, feeling hopeless, and so on. In short, a desolation is anything that takes away from your attention and focus on God.

As you continue through your daily times of meditation, be aware of your internal movements, seeking to determine if they are consolations (leading you to God) or desolations (leading you away from God). Make a note of your internal movements in your journal. Remember, the determining factor in discerning consolation from desolation is not your emotions or feelings, but rather the direction in which your heart is pointed (toward God or away from God).

OPTIONAL EXERCISE FOR THE PREPARATORY SECTION

The blanket exercise is designed to give you a tangible reminder of how God's love surrounds and embraces you every moment of every day. Use this optional exercise in conjunction with any of the exercises during the preparatory prayer sessions.

The only thing you will need for this optional exercise is a warm, cosy blanket. As you sit down to do your daily preparatory exercise, imagine that your blanket is God's love. Simply wrap yourself up in the blanket as you imagine it to be God's love wrapping around you. Take time after you have completed the preparatory exercise for that day to simply sit with the blanket wrapped around you, focusing on always being surrounded by God's love. When you finish, journal about your experience of sitting in the awareness of God's love surrounding and embracing you.

Another way to use this optional exercise is to wrap the blanket around you and take a walk, once again reminding yourself that God's love surrounds you. As you walk around with this awareness, be sensitive to the feelings arising within you and pay attention to how you see the world around you. This is a great exercise for a cold, windy day or early in the morning around a lake, near the ocean or in a park. Feel free to use this once or twice during the preparatory section. You could also use it on a review day. When you have finished your walk, journal about your experience.

The information above could feel overwhelming, but do not worry; you will be prompted when to make use of the components listed above. I have provided them so you are not caught off-guard when they make their appearance during the daily exercises and to provide additional information regarding these components, without interrupting the flow of the Exercises.

As you enter into and journey through the following exercises, my prayer for you is this:

I pray that God in God's glorious grace would strengthen you with power, so that you who are rooted and established in love may be able to internally grasp and hold on to the width, the length, the height and the depth of Jesus' love for you—not only to know this love but to live a life informed, shaped and sustained by the magnificent love that Jesus has for you.

ADAPTED FROM EPHESIANS 3:16–19

—— 2 ——

GOD'S LOVE

——⊰ SECTION 1 OF 3 ⊱——

GOD LOVES YOU

The grace you are seeking is a deeper awareness of God's love for you.

Examen questions
(the examen questions for the entire preparatory section)

- When and how did I experience God's love for me today?
- How did my awareness of God's love for me affect the way I interacted with others, my circumstances and myself today?

Process

- ☐ Opening
- ☐ Daily exercise
- ☐ Journalling

- ☐ Closing
- ☐ Noontime examen
- ☐ Evening examen

DAY 1

Read 1 John 3:1; 4:19.

Remember, before you begin your time in the exercise for today, take time to slow down and be present to God. Come before God, letting go of your worries, concerns and expectations, seeking to be open to the moving and invitations of God this day. Do not rush through this time; take as much time as you need to ready yourself for your encounter with God and God's word. (See the two slowdown methods in 'Slowing Down' on pages 26–28.)

Neither knowing God nor knowing self can progress very far unless it begins with a knowledge of how deeply we are loved by God. Until we dare to believe that nothing can separate us from God's love—nothing that we could do or fail to do, nor anything that could be done (has been done) by anyone else to us (Romans 8:31–39)—we remain in the elementary grades of the school of Christian spiritual transformation. [1]

Genuine transformation requires vulnerability. It is not the fact of being loved unconditionally that is life changing. It is the risky experience of allowing myself to be loved unconditionally. [2]

Journal about your feelings and thoughts regarding the above passages and quotes. To what are you drawn? Why? Spend time sitting in the truth of God's love for you. After you have sat in the thoughts of God's love, consider these questions:

- How does this make you feel about God?
- About yourself?
- Do you truly feel that God loves you (as opposed to just knowing the truth of God's love)? Why, or why not? Spend some time talking this through with God.

DAY 2

Read Psalm 107:43; Ephesians 3:17–19.

Below are words that various writers have used to describe God's love. Read through the list, sitting with and reflecting on each word. Come up with words of your own. Using these words, write a psalm or poem that celebrates and declares God's wondrous love for you.

Unfailing
Lavish
Extravagant
Wastefully abundant
Wondrous
Indiscriminate
Boundless
Unconditional

You are the chosen one, the beloved of God!

- What is your reaction to this statement?
- Can you embrace these realities? If yes, how does this make you feel? If no, why is this difficult for you? Allow this to lead you into a time of prayer.

Spend time pondering the fact that you are rooted and established (grounded) in love. What does this stir within you?

....

Love, anger, frustration and sadness
Some who journey through this portion of the Exercises do not feel God's love but instead feel emotions such as anger, frustration and sadness. Do not try to force yourself to feel a certain way; instead allow yourself to feel what you are feeling and bring those feelings, as well as the issues that may give rise to these emotions, to God, because God will meet you in that place. God is not afraid of your questions or emotions. Remember, God desires honesty, so be honest and be real with God.

....

DAY 3

Read Romans 5:6–8.

- What does the above passage from Romans remind you of, about the nature of God's love for you?
- What does this tell you about the unconditional nature of God's love for you?
- How do the truths of this passage make you feel about God and about how God loves you?
- What feelings are stirred within you as you reflect on the truth that God chose to demonstrate God's love to you while you were still a sinner?
- What does all this tell you about God's ability to love you and God's desire to love you, no matter what?

DAY 4

Review the past three days.

- In the past three days, which passages were you drawn to or resistant toward? Why?
- How are these passages shaping your image of God and your sense of God's love?
- How has your awareness of God's love been changing?

You may want to use one of the optional blanket exercises today (see page 62).

DAY 5

Read Ephesians 2:1–5.

Spend time considering the spiritual reality of your life before and after God made you alive in Christ, as expressed in the passage above.

- What does this passage tell you about God's love, mercy and grace?
- How do the truths of these passages make you feel about who God is and God's love for you?

. . . .

'I believe; help me in my unbelief'

As you spend time pondering the marvellous love that God has for you, you may begin to realise that you 'know' this, but at a deeper level you do not fully believe it. Do not let this trouble you, but instead repeat the prayer 'I believe; help me in my unbelief.' This is a prayer that Jesus heard and answered. The love of God is a one-of-a-kind, nothing-can-separate-you-from-it love that is hard if not impossible to fully embrace, so give yourself time and grace as your ability to hold on to God's love for you grows. The good news is that God's love is always embracing you, wooing you and indwelling you.

. . . .

DAY 6

Read Psalm 103:1–14.

Quickly compile a list enumerating at least ten of the benefits God has bestowed on you as a result of choosing and redeeming you. Once you have completed your list, go back over it and choose the three benefits that mean the most to you. When you have chosen your three, sit in the reality of these truths, considering how they impact you emotionally. Then reflect on how these truths make you feel about God and yourself. Why did you choose these specific three from your list? Consider why each is so important to you. Spend time remembering 'all God's benefits' bestowed on you.

DAY 7

Review this past week.

- Which passages were you drawn to or resistant toward? Why?
- How are these passages shaping your image of God and your sense of God's love?
- How has your awareness of God's love been changing?

Keeping in mind that baby steps are OK, ask yourself how many times you did the prayer of examen this week. If you struggled with the examen, what might you do differently next week to help you have more success with this component of the Exercises? (See 'Noontime and evening examen' on page 25.)

Trying too hard

If you have been feeling yourself pressing to make something happen during your time in the Exercises, go out and buy a bubble bottle with a wand, and keep them near your journal. The next time you feel yourself pressing to make something happen, pressing to do each exercise 'right', take out the wand and gently start blowing bubbles. As you blow your bubbles, watch them dance on the currents, and ask God to help you to enter these exercises freely and lightly, dancing on the unforced rhythms of God's grace.

⬥ SECTION 2 OF 3 ⬥

GOD REALLY LOVES YOU

There is an optional exercise for Day 1. To do it, you will need at least one can of whipped cream. Please feel free to do this optional exercise on another day if you would like.

The grace you are seeking is a deeper awareness of God's love for you.

Examen questions

- When or how did I experience God's love for me today?
- How did my awareness of God's love for me affect the way I interacted with others, my circumstances and myself today?

Process

❑ Opening   ❑ Closing
❑ Daily exercise   ❑ Noontime examen
❑ Journalling   ❑ Evening examen

DAY 1

Read 1 John 3:1–2.

I am convinced that God loves each and every one of us with depth, persistence and intensity beyond imagination.[3]

God's love is beyond our ability to fully comprehend. In the passage above, John uses a word translated 'lavished': God's love has been lavished upon you. The word 'lavish' can mean 'superabundant', 'generous', 'plentiful', 'over the top' and even 'wasteful'. Spend time pondering the magnitude of God's love for you.

Optional exercise

For this optional exercise, you will need at least one can of whipped cream, a coffee mug and a saucer. Imagine that the cup represents you, and the whipped cream represents God's love for you. Place the cup on the saucer and begin to fill the cup with the whipped cream. Continue to fill the cup until the can of whipped cream is empty. As you empty the can, remember that the cup represents you and the whipped cream is God's love for you. Be aware of what feelings arise within you as you empty the can and fill the cup.

- What were your feelings as you emptied the can and as you looked at the mountain of whipped cream and reflected on God's love being lavished upon you?
- How does this make you feel about God's love for you?

DAY 2

Read Romans 8:38–39.

We have the formula of the spiritual life: a confident reliance *on the immense fact of His Presence.*[4]

Lie down and rest in the loving presence of the triune God. Close your eyes and, if you are outside, listen to the sounds of nature and feel the warmth of the sun or the cool of the breeze. Be still and know God, and know yourself as one loved by God.

....

Examen review

How are you doing at making the noontime and evening examen a part of your daily rhythm? Ask yourself what steps you could take to make this a more regular practice as you go through the Exercises. For tips regarding this, refer back to 'Noontime and evening examen' on page 25).

....

DAY 3

Read Psalm 32:1–5.

Spend time focusing on God's forgiveness of you. Let this lead into a time of thanksgiving. How does God's forgiveness of you make you feel toward God? Conclude your time by confessing to God any sins of omission and commission.

Are you able to receive and internalise God's forgiveness of you? Why, or why not?

DAY 4

Review the past three days.

- Which passages were you drawn to or resistant toward? Why?
- How are these passages shaping your image of God and your sense of God's love?
- How has your awareness of God's love been changing?

You may want to use one of the optional blanket exercises today.

DAY 5

Read Mark 1:40–41.

Divine love is absolutely unconditional, unlimited and unimaginably extravagant.[5]

Reread the above passage, and put yourself in the story as the leper. Imagine that you have been viewed with disdain and disgust all your life, that you have been and are an outcast. People turn away from you and keep their children away from you. You are viewed as one cursed by God. Now you come face to face with Jesus.

• What do you see in Jesus' eyes as he looks into yours?
• What does it feel like to be touched by Jesus, touched for the first time in years, touched by the One who can heal you?
• What does this touch mean to you, communicate to you?
• What does it mean to you that, while you are still a leper, Jesus feels compassion for you?
• How does this make you feel toward Jesus' love for you?
• What does this tell you about how God sees you?
• How does that make you feel about God, about yourself?

Conclude your time by talking with Jesus about the feelings that arose within you toward him as you imagined your encounter with him as the leper. Now stop imagining you are a leper, and go back to being you.

Is it more difficult for you to internalise Jesus' love for you as yourself than it is when you imagined yourself as a leper? Why, or why not?

DAY 6

Read Isaiah 43:1–7.

Read the above passage as if it was written to you.

- What is God's message to you in this passage?
- What feelings arise within you as you read through it and hear to what lengths God is willing to go in order to be your God?
- How does this make you feel toward God?

DAY 7

Review this past week.

- Which passages were you drawn to or resistant toward? Why?
- How are these passages shaping your image of God and your sense of God's love?
- How has your awareness of God's love been changing?

••

Perfectionism

If you are a perfectionist or a recovering perfectionist, please be on guard. The structure of the daily exercises can tap into your strong desire to 'do it right' and then stir up negative messages of self-condemnation when you feel you are not 'doing it right'. If you feel yourself stressing about this or you begin hearing internal voices that call up shame or condemnation within you, stop and ask God to help you be gracious and patient with yourself. These voices are not coming from God but are lies that will distract you and keep you from the journey.

••

—◀ SECTION 3 OF 3 ▶—

GOD REALLY, REALLY LOVES YOU

There is an optional exercise for Day 5. There are no materials or preparation needed for this optional exercise. Please feel free to do this optional exercise on another day if you would like.

The grace you are seeking is a deeper awareness of God's love for you.

Examen questions

- When or how did I experience God's love for me today?
- How did my awareness of God's love for me affect the way I interacted with others, my circumstances and myself today?

Process

- ❏ Opening
- ❏ Daily exercise
- ❏ Journalling
- ❏ Closing
- ❏ Noontime examen
- ❏ Evening examen

DAY 1

Read Romans 8:1.

'There is no condemnation.' Pause and let these words sink deep within you.

- What do these words mean to you?
- Are you able to believe these words? Why, or why not?

Make a list of the things that tend to evoke condemnation within you. Read through your list line by line and, after each entry, say out loud, 'There is no condemnation for me in Christ.' If you have trouble internalising the truth of there being no condemnation for you, add the phrase 'I believe; help me in my unbelief.'

Which of the entries on your list are the easiest or hardest for you to internalise as the truth of there being 'no condemnation' for you in Christ?

DAY 2

Read Matthew 20:1–16.

As you read this passage, imagine you are one of the workers who were hired first.

• What are your reactions to the payments made by the owner at the end of the day? Why?

Now read through the passage imagining you are one of the final group of workers hired.

• What are your reactions regarding the payments made to the workers from the groups who were hired prior to you?
• What are your reactions regarding the payment you receive at the end of the day?
• What are your feelings toward the owner regarding the payments made to the other workers and to you?
• What is the difference between your reactions? Why?
• As a Christian, with which group of workers do you identify? Why?
• How does this impact your view of God and God's grace?

....

Your space
The space you use for your prayer times can be a help or a hindrance to your time with God. Choose a space that

has a minimum of distractions. Keep all the materials you use together and, if possible, in the area where you enter into these exercises each day. These simple tips can make a dramatic difference in your ability to be present to God during your prayer time each day.

....

DAY 3

Read John 10:14–15.

Jesus chose to die for you. Spend your time sitting with and pondering this truth: Jesus died for you.

- How does that make you feel about Jesus?

Reflect on what it meant for Jesus to come and die for you. Write a letter to Jesus, thanking him for taking your sins upon himself and dying for you. Read your letter while imagining Jesus is sitting across from you.

- What is Jesus' reaction to your letter?
- What, if anything, does he say or do?

DAY 4

Review the past three days.

- Which passages were you drawn to or resistant toward? Why?
- How are these passages shaping your image of God and your sense of God's love?
- How has your awareness of God's love been changing?

You may want to use one of the optional blanket exercises today (see page 62).

DAY 5

Read 1 Corinthians 13:4–7.

Since God is love (1 John 4:19), read the above passage, replacing the word 'love' with the word 'God', 'Jesus' or a title of God that you especially like.

- What does this passage tell you about God's love for you?
- How does this make you feel toward God?

Share your feelings with God.

Optional exercise

You are invited to come before God and express to God, through dance as prayer, your thanks for God's forever love and caring involvement in your life. I have found it helpful to wrap my 'God loves me' blanket around me as I do this. It helps calm my insecurities (I am not a great dancer) and brings me greater freedom to express myself to God through dance.

DAY 6

Read 1 John 4:16.

And so we know *and* rely *on the love God has for us. God is love. Whoever lives in love lives in God, and God in him. (1 John 4:16, emphasis added)*

In order for our knowing of God's love to be truly transformational, it must become the basis of our identity. Our identity is who we experience ourselves to be—the 'I' each of us carry within. An identity grounded in God would mean that when we think of who we are, the first thing that would come to mind is our status as someone who is deeply loved by God.[6]

- What would it mean for you to rely on and live in God's love for you?
- How would your life be different if you were able to rely on and live out of a place of having internalised God's love for you?
- What keeps you from embracing your identity as one deeply and unconditionally loved by God?

DAY 7

Review this past week.

- Which passages were you drawn to or resistant toward this week?
- How are these passages shaping your image of God and your sense of God's love?

Review the past 21 prayer sessions.

- How has your image of God and your internalised sense of God's love developed during these sessions?
- How is your awareness of God's love now shaping your sense of self, God and your daily circumstances?
- How has your awareness of God's love been changing as you have journeyed through these prayer sessions? If you feel it has not changed or you are having difficulty embracing God's unconditional love for you, see the closing comments below.

Keeping in mind that baby steps are OK, ask yourself the following questions:

- How many times did I do the prayer of examen this week?
- How does that compare to last week and the week before that? Why was this week different?
- How has my experience of the prayer of examen changed over the past three weeks?

If you are still struggling with the examen, ask yourself why.

- What is making it difficult for you to make the examen a part of your day?
- Is it more of an external or an internal reality?
- How might you deal with the issues that have surfaced as you have explored this?
- What might help you have success with this important component of the Exercises?

CLOSING COMMENTS

If you are still having difficulty internally embracing God's unconditional, nothing-can-separate-you-from-it, one-of-a-kind love, I would suggest three things:

1. Choose to go through one or all of the preparatory sections again. I cannot stress enough the importance and life-transforming power of coming to a place where you know deep within the recesses of your being that you are uniquely loved, valued and delighted in by God and that nothing—no thing— can ever change that. If all you do is spend an entire nine months seeking to internalise God's love for you, it will be time well spent. That may be the very thing God would be inviting you to do for those nine months.
2. Read two excellent books that will help you to internalise God's love for you, both of which are written by David Benner: *The Gift of Being Yourself* and *Surrender to Love*. I have read them each more than once and have been immensely helped by them. In fact, I give away *The Gift of Being Yourself* more than any other book.
3. Talk with your spiritual director or listener about your difficulty in embracing God's unconditional love.

Please do not feel that you have to move on to the next section. There is no rush to get through the Exercises. Remember, it is about the journey. Be open to the invitation of God to pitch your tent in the preparatory section for a while longer, sitting alongside the cool stream and in the spacious meadows of God's love for you.

Before moving on, this might be a good time to reread Part 1, 'Getting the Most Out of the Exercises'. You might want to incorporate additional ideas from page 46: 'Tips on How to Approach the Exercises', to help your experience in the Exercises flow more smoothly and to help you get the most out of your daily experience.

—— 3 ——

PRINCIPLE AND FOUNDATION

The Principle and Foundation is the second phase of your preparation for entry into the Spiritual Exercises of Ignatius. If you are tempted to skip the Principle and Foundation, don't. This section is the nuts and bolts of your preparation and, though not as initially attractive as focusing on God's love, it has a rugged beauty all its own that will serve you well, not only as you continue your journey through the Exercises but also as you continue your journey through life.

The Principle and Foundation provides the opportunity to expand your image of God while also affording you the chance to bring to the surface some of the issues you have in regard to your image of God. The first phase of your preparation was focused on God's loving involvement in your life and the truth that nothing can ever change that. With that groundwork in place, you are free to sit with and explore your image of God without fear and with abandonment.

In the Principle and Foundation, Ignatius brings you face to face with the fullness of God. You will look at God as creator and explore your own place in God's creation. You will spend time focusing on God as powerful, transcendent and worthy of praise, reverence, honour and service. God is a God of love, but that is not the whole story. The immanence of God that was stressed in the first phase of the Preparatory Exercises now gives way to God as transcendent creator and wholly Other, involved in yet separate from creation.

You will be challenged in your view of God and your role as one created by God to serve God, praise God and honour God.

The Principle and Foundation centres the Exercises within God's plan for those whom God created. The focus on God as creator is an apt reminder of God's initial and ongoing involvement in the world in general and in you in particular. This phase of the Preparatory Exercises serves to remind you that you are a creation of God 'fearfully and wonderfully made' (Psalm 139:14) and God's masterpiece 'created in Christ Jesus' (Ephesians 2:10), while putting the twin attributes of God's transcendence (God beyond us) and immanence (God with us) on display. Your image of God will be dealt with implicitly from a variety of vantage points, as will the purpose for which you were created.

Finally, you will spend the entire last part of this section exploring the essential topic of indifference. The word 'indifference', when used in relationship to interaction with God, life and the world, seems out of place within a Christian context because it brings to mind callousness, an uncaring apathy that is not concerned about much of anything. To mitigate against the negative connotations, some writers have translated 'indifference' in the Principle and Foundation as 'balance'.[1] Though understandable, I think this translation softens the term without bringing clarity to what it means in terms of the Exercises and life. You will ponder and explore indifference in Section 5, but first I want to plant some seeds regarding indifference, trusting God to cause them to germinate and even begin to sprout near the time you actually get to that section.

'Indifference', as used by Ignatius and other mystic writers, is not a lack of desire but a freeing of desire, and the developing of your ability to say yes to God and the expressed purposes of God. Indifference is about freedom to be and to live in a way that honours and affirms who God created you to be. A helpful way to think about indifference is that it involves a twofold freedom: freedom from those things that would hold you back from saying yes to God (disordered attachments) and freedom to say a more robust and resounding yes to God.

Indifference is a much misunderstood and maligned but significant component of spiritual formation and one worthy of taking the time provided in this section to fully understand and personally embrace. Many have commented on the invaluable benefits of spending seven prayer sessions unpacking and processing the concept of indifference. Their ability to understand and embrace God-honouring indifference was a life-changer.

As I have led people through the Principle and Foundation, I have found it to be a valuable time for allowing issues regarding their image of God to surface. Many were initially surprised by what they discovered but were able to process through it and left this portion of the Exercises at a better place with God and ready to enter into Week 1.

The Principle and Foundation is as follows:

Human Beings are created to praise, reverence, and serve God our Lord… for this it is necessary to make ourselves indifferent to all created things in all that is allowed to the choice of our free will and is not prohibited to it; so that, on our part, we want not health rather than sickness, riches rather than poverty, honour rather than dishonour, long rather than short life, and so in all the rest; desiring and choosing only what is most conducive for us to the end for which we are created.[2]

You will spend the next 35 prayer sessions exploring five key concepts found in the Principle and Foundation, which serve as final preparation for entry into the Weeks section of the Exercises. In the Principle and Foundation, Ignatius shares his answer to these questions: How did we get here (created by God)? Why are we here (praise, reverence and serve God)? What is a key attitude to cultivate to help us order our lives in such a way as to say yes to God in all situations (indifference)?

SUMMARY OF PRINCIPLE AND FOUNDATION:

1. There is an original purpose (praise, reverence, service) established by the creator God.
2. Every created thing exists to help us to live in the original purpose(s).
3. We are to embrace that which furthers the original purpose(s) for which we were created and turn away from those things that hinder us from embracing the original purpose(s).
4. We are to keep ourselves free from a preference for the temporal world so we are free to choose what enables and empowers us to say yes to God.

GETTING STARTED

Note that the 'grace' will change with each new week, relating to the theme for that week. Make sure that each week you familiarise yourself with the new grace for that week.

The examen questions will also be changing almost weekly. They are crafted to reflect the theme for each section of the Principle and Foundation. Please take time at the beginning of each week to familiarise yourself with the new examen questions so you can make use of them during your noontime and evening examen.

Each time you get to a new section while making your way through the Exercises, there will be new pieces ('additions') incorporated into that section. These will be found under the heading 'Additions to Exercises'. It is important that you read these, because they are designed to help you more fully partner with what God is doing in and through the Exercises as you journey through them.

For this section, you will be incorporating the use of your senses. Ignatius strongly believes that you are to bring all of who you are to the Exercises, including your five senses. There will be more on this when you reach Week 2, but for now please seek to incorporate your senses as promoted in the exercises below. Do so while keeping in mind that you cannot force something to happen or 'do it right'. Instead, enter into the use of your senses freely, lightly and openly, recalling that all is a gift.

The Principle and Foundation is the last piece of your preparation before you enter the Weeks. As you enter into these meditations, earnestly seek to be open to God and the invitations of God's Spirit. Be determined to look at areas of resistance that arise within you (see 'Resistance' on pages 49–50) as well as areas that resonate with you.

As you enter into and journey through the Principle and Foundation, my prayer for you is this:

God help this one to know beyond knowing and understand beyond understanding something of the depths of your riches, the incomprehensibility of your knowledge and wisdom, and the impenetrability of your judgments. In accordance with your grace help this one to be moved to praise, honour and service as he or she begins to glimpse your creative power, magnificent splendour and awe-inspiring holiness. (Adapted from Romans 11:33–36)

SECTION 1 OF 5

CREATED

Earth's crammed with heaven,
And every common bush afire with God;
But only he who sees, takes off his shoes;
The rest sit round it and pluck blackberries.
ELIZABETH BARRETT BROWNING, POET

Let us leave the surface and, without leaving the world, plunge into God.
PIERRE TEILHARD DE CHARDIN, JESUIT PRIEST

The world is charged with the grandeur of God.
GERARD MANLEY HOPKINS, POET AND JESUIT PRIEST

The grace you are seeking this week is the ability to internalise the great love, power, wisdom and faithfulness of God as revealed in creation in general and God's creation and re-creation of you in Christ in particular.

Examen questions

- When were you aware of the love, power, wisdom and faithfulness of God as revealed in creation today, and how did that impact how you lived (the choices you made) and interacted with others?
- What did you purpose to carry with you throughout the day?
- How successful were you in bringing it to mind from time to time?
- What impact did this prayer of recollection have on you?

Process

- ❏ Opening
- ❏ Daily exercise
- ❏ Journalling
- ❏ Closing
- ❏ Noontime examen
- ❏ Evening examen

Special instructions: During your time this week, begin each day by pondering the passage for the day using *lectio divina* (see '*Lectio divina*' on pages 36–37). When you are finished, move into a time of using your senses as a means of connecting with and learning about God. You may want to know a day ahead what sense you will be exploring so that you can be somewhat prepared to enter more fully into the experience.

....

Art time
This could be a great week to get your art supplies out
and have some fun during your journalling time using
paints, markers, construction paper or other supplies to
communicate your feelings, record the meaningful images
that may arise or just see what happens when you get arty.
Let go of the need to do it well or right. Jump in with both
feet and see what emerges.

....

DAY 1

Read Genesis 1:1–3; John 1:1–5.

Use your ears to listen to the sounds around you.

- As you are quiet, what do you hear?
- Now listen to some music, to the chirps of a bird, a water fountain, children playing.
- How do your ears help you to discover God and draw close to God?
- How does hearing impact your heart and mind?

DAY 2

Read Psalm 19:1–4.

Use your eyes to take in creation. Take a walk and give yourself
permission to stop and look along the way as things grab your
attention.

- How does seeing impact your heart and mind?
- How do these things you are seeing speak without words to you about God and God's love and care?

DAY 3

Read Genesis 1:27; Psalm 139:1–16.

Look at your body, your hand, your foot, your eyes, and ponder how they work.

• What do these tell you about God?

DAY 4

There is no scripture to read today. Instead, explore your sense of taste. Choose some things sweet, sour and spicy to taste and savour.

• How does taste impact your heart and mind?
• What does your ability to taste tell you about God and about God's love and care?

Review your past three days.

• Which verses touched you? Why?
• How are these passages shaping and strengthening your image of God?
• What has been your experience of your senses as a vehicle for connecting with God?

DAY 5

Read 2 Corinthians 5:17.

Initially spend time reflecting on being a 'new creation in Christ'.

What do these words mean to you? What feelings do these words stir within you? Why?

Spend a few moments leaning into your identity as a 'new creation in Christ'.

When you are finished, use the remaining time to explore your sense of touch. Touch a variety of surfaces. Explore how water makes you feel when it is cold, then warm. Go outside and pick up various things, exploring them with your hands. Take off your shoes and walk around, becoming aware of what you feel with your feet.

- How does touch impact your heart and mind?
- What does your ability to touch and feel tell you about God and about God's love and care?

DAY 6

Read Ephesians 2:10.

Initially spend time reflecting on being God's workmanship, created in Christ Jesus, but instead of 'workmanship', use the word 'masterpiece'.

As you think of yourself as God's one-of-a-kind masterpiece, what feelings arise within you? Why?

Spend a few moments soaking in the truth of you being a one-of-a-kind 'masterpiece of God created in Christ Jesus'.

When you are finished, use the remaining time to explore your sense of smell. You might want to go to a coffee shop, bakery or garden just to enjoy the smells. Grab some things around your house, such as garlic, an orange, coffee or perfume, and spend time taking in the scents of each.

- How does smell impact your heart and mind?
- What does your ability to smell tell you about God and about God's love and care?

DAY 7

Review this past week.

- Which verses really touched you? Why?
- How are these passages shaping and strengthening your image of God, your image of yourself, your image of others?
- What has been your experience of your senses as a vehicle for connecting with God?
- How has focusing your attention on the creative power of God changed your awareness of God's transcendent power, immediate presence, love and care?
- How have your feelings about God begun to change this week?

....

Resistance

Whenever you become aware of resistance, respond to it as a warning light and seek to discover the source of the resistance. Resistance is a gift from God that invites you to a deeper discovery concerning God and yourself, so internally pause and ponder when you become aware of resistance. Ask God to help you discern where the resistance is coming from. What does it reveal about your image, level of belief, love and trust of God? What does it tell you about your sense of self, your identity? Take the time to reflect and unpack your resistance, for over time the results can be life-changing. (See 'Resistance' on pages 49–50.)

....

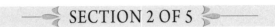

SECTION 2 OF 5

PRAISE

Looking ahead: On Day 5 you will be invited to take a walk with God. Please plan ahead so you do not feel rushed. Also, feel free to swap Day 5 with another day if that would work better for you (for example, do the walk on Day 2 and then do Day 2 on Day 5). If you are able, take your walk at a time and place you enjoy (a park, the beach, a lakeside, on city streets).

There is an optional exercise for one or both of your review days. If you choose to do it, you will need a bottle of bubbles.

The grace you are seeking this week is the ability to enter more fully and freely into the sacrifice of praise as you become aware of the character of God.

Examen questions

- When were you moved to praise God today?
- What prompted you to praise God today?
- What hindered you from praising God today?
- What did you purpose to carry with you throughout the day?
- How successful were you in bringing it to mind from time to time?
- What impact did this prayer of recollection have on you?

Process

- ☐ Opening
- ☐ Daily exercise
- ☐ Journalling

- ☐ Closing
- ☐ Noontime examen
- ☐ Evening examen

Use the *lectio divina* method as you read through the passage for each day (see 'Lectio divina' on pages 36–37). Some days do not have written exercises (prompt questions), so, on those days, sit with whatever God brings forth for you during your time in the passage using the *lectio divina* method of reading.

DAY 1

Read Psalm 96.

Spend time praising God for who God is and for what God has done for you—past, present and future.

DAY 2

Read Psalm 103:1–14.

Spend time praising God for the benefits that have flowed into your life as a result of the death and resurrection of Christ.

DAY 3

Read Psalm 136.

Drawing from your life experience, write your own Psalm 136 by replacing the first line of each verse with an event from your own life. When you have finished, share your psalm with God.

DAY 4

Review your past three days.

- Which verses really touched you? Why?
- How are these passages shaping or strengthening your image of God?

- What themes in these passages most easily move you to praise God? Why?

Optional exercise

This exercise, which can be used today and/or on Day 7, seeks to provide a reminder that God is your creator and that you are called merely to be in harmony with the winds of God's Spirit in your life.

Using a bubble bottle and wand, begin to blow bubbles. As you blow the bubbles, imagine the breath of God creating those bubbles and that those bubbles are you—God is breathing life into you. The wand is Christ, reminding you that all things were made in and through Christ. Now pay attention to your bubbles, watch them float and dance, and experiment with how you blow to create the bubbles.

- How are the bubbles like you?
- What do these bubbles teach you about yourself, about God and about you and God?

Watch as the wind takes them.

- How is your life like the bubbles on the wind?
- What keeps you from floating on the wind of God's Spirit?
- How is indifference modelled by the bubble?
- How much responsibility does a bubble have in terms of its flight?

DAY 5

Take a walk today, seeking to make use of all five senses together and individually. Allow creation and your senses to move you into times of praising God as you walk.

DAY 6

Read Romans 11:33–36.

Spend your time pondering the greatness of God. How does pondering God's greatness make you feel about God? Yourself? Why?

DAY 7

Review this past week.

- Which verses really touched you? Why?
- How are these passages shaping or strengthening your image of God and your love for God?
- How has focusing on praising God impacted your life and how you view and interact with your world?

Optional exercise

See Day 4 above.

....

Reminder
Remember to make use of your examen questions each day at noontime and evening. The consistent use of the examen questions will dramatically increase the transforming power in your life.

....

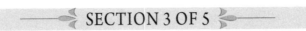

SECTION 3 OF 5

REVERENCE

The grace you are seeking this week is the ability to be in awe of God.

Examen questions

- When were you wowed by the person of God today? What were the circumstances?
- What was your response? Why?
- How did that moment make you feel about God?
- If there was not a moment of being wowed by God, why do you think that was?
- What did you purpose to carry with you throughout the day?
- How successful were you in bringing it to mind from time to time?
- What impact did this prayer of recollection have on you?

Process

☐ Opening   ☐ Closing
☐ Daily exercise   ☐ Noontime examen
☐ Journalling   ☐ Evening examen

Use the *lectio divina* method as you read through the passage for each day. Some days do not have written exercises (prompt questions), so, on those days, sit with whatever God brings forth for you during your time in the passage using the *lectio divina* method.

DAY 1

Read 1 Chronicles 16:23–35.

DAY 2

Read Revelation 1:12–18.

DAY 3

Read Proverbs 1:7; 9:10; Hebrews 10:31.

DAY 4

Read 1 John 4:18.

DAY 5

Review your past four days.

- Which verses really touched you? Why?
- How are these passages shaping or strengthening your image of God?

DAY 6

Read Revelation 4:6–11.

Imagine the scene and enter into it.

- What are you feeling or experiencing?

DAY 7

Review this past week.

- Which verses really touched you? Why?

- How are these passages shaping or strengthening your image of God?
- How has focusing your attention on the greatness of God changed how you view and interact with your world?

··

Putting in the time

One of the greatest and most consistent of the temptations that will come your way as you journey through the Exercises is that of cutting your prayer time short. In the Exercises, Ignatius emphasises on two occasions the importance of spending the full time in prayer. This temptation to cut the prayer time short will be especially strong during times of desolation. But endeavour to spend the time, for it is of great value for your heart and soul.

··

SECTION 4 OF 5

SERVICE

The grace you are seeking is the ability to own your role as one who serves others.

Examen questions

- When did you proactively serve others today?
- How did you feel when you decided to serve someone, as you served him or her, and after you were finished?
- Was there a time when you chose not to serve someone today? Why?
- As you reflect back on your choice not to serve someone, how does it make you feel? Why?

Process

- ☐ Opening
- ☐ Daily exercise
- ☐ Journalling

- ☐ Closing
- ☐ Noontime examen
- ☐ Evening examen

Use the *lectio divina* method as you read through the passage for each day. Some days do not have written exercises (prompt questions), so, on those days, sit with whatever God brings forth for you during your time in the passage.

DAY 1
Read Matthew 20:28.

DAY 2
Read John 13:12–17.

After you have spent time in *lectio divina* with the above passage, meditate on the ancient prayer below that focuses on serving Jesus.

> *Teach us, good Lord, to serve thee as thou deservest;*
> *to give, and not to count the cost,*
> *to fight, and not to heed the wounds,*
> *to toil, and not to seek for rest,*
> *to labour, and not to ask for any reward,*
> *save that of knowing that we do thy will.*
> ST IGNATIUS OF LOYOLA

- To what are you drawn? Why?
- What are you resistant toward? Why?
- What might be God's invitations and challenges to you in this prayer?
- Do you have the desire to pray this prayer? Why, or why not?

DAY 3

Read Romans 12:1–2.

DAY 4

Review your past three days.

- Which verses really touched you? Why?
- Around which verses did you feel resistance? Why?
- How are these passages shaping or strengthening your image of Jesus?
- How are these verses shaping your awareness of Jesus' role and, in turn, your role in the lives of others?
- Does Jesus' role as a servant empower you to serve others? Why, or why not?

DAY 5

Read Philippians 2:3–8.

After you have spent time in *lectio divina* with the above passage, meditate again on the ancient prayer below that focuses on serving Jesus.

> *Teach us, good Lord, to serve thee as thou deservest;*
> *to give, and not to count the cost,*
> *to fight, and not to heed the wounds,*
> *to toil, and not to seek for rest,*
> *to labour, and not to ask for any reward,*
> *save that of knowing that we do thy will.*
> ST IGNATIUS OF LOYOLA

- To what are you drawn? Why?
- What are you resistant toward? Why?

- What might be God's invitations and challenges to you in this prayer?
- Do you have the desire to pray this prayer? Why, or why not?

DAY 6

Read Ephesians 2:10.

What might be the good works that God has uniquely created you in Christ to accomplish?

DAY 7

Review this past week.

- Which verses really touched you? Why?
- Around which verses did you feel resistance? Why?
- How are these passages shaping or strengthening your image of Jesus?
- How are these verses shaping your awareness of Jesus' role and, in turn, your role in the lives of others?
- Does Jesus' role as a servant empower you to serve others? Why, or why not?

After you have spent time in *lectio divina* with the above passage, meditate another time on the ancient prayer below that focuses on serving Jesus.

Teach us, good Lord, to serve thee as thou deservest;
to give, and not to count the cost,
to fight, and not to heed the wounds,
to toil, and not to seek for rest,
to labour, and not to ask for any reward,
save that of knowing that we do thy will.
ST IGNATIUS OF LOYOLA

- To what are you drawn? Why?
- What are you resistant toward? Why?
- What might be God's invitations and challenges to you in this prayer?
- Do you have the desire to pray this prayer? Why, or why not?

—◄ SECTION 5 OF 5 ►—

INDIFFERENCE

It is necessary to make ourselves indifferent *to all created things in all that is allowed to the choice of our free will and is not prohibited to it; so that, on our part, we want not health rather than sickness, riches rather than poverty, honour rather than dishonour, long rather than short life, and so in all the rest;* desiring and choosing only what is most conducive for us to the end for which we are created.[3]

The term 'indifference' is an important term for Ignatius. Often 'indifference' is used to speak of not caring about something or having a lack of passion. But for Ignatius, this word was a critical component that, when properly understood and embraced, led to freedom—a freedom to say yes to God and the invitations of God, and to say no to those things that would draw us away from God. This freedom, born of indifference, is a desired outcome expressed by Ignatius. His Exercise 21 states the goal as the ability to order one's life in such a way that no decision is made resulting from a disordered attachment.

Reflecting on indifference, or, as he refers to it, 'detachment', Gerald May writes:

Detachment is the word used in spiritual traditions to describe freedom of desire. Not freedom from desire, but freedom of desire... An authentic spiritual understanding of detachment devalues neither desire nor the objects of desire. Instead, it 'aims at correcting one's own anxious grasping in order to free one's self for committed relationship to God'.

According to Meister Eckhart, detachment 'enkindles the heart, awakens the spirit, stimulates our longings, and shows us where God is'.[4] This freedom from attachment leads to a freedom of desire that is characterised by 'great unbounded love, endless creative energy and deep pervasive joy', according to May.[5]

For Ignatius, indifference (detachment) was for the purpose of spiritual freedom. The opposite of indifference for him would be a disordered love that would exert authority over an individual to such a degree that he would be incapable of choosing to say yes to God and to God's purpose for his life. Ignatius' Exercises are 'structured for the purpose of leading a person to a true spiritual freedom. To grow into a freedom by gradually bringing an order of values into the lives of individuals so that they may find at a moment of choice or decision that they are not swayed by any disordered love.'[6]

As you spend this week reflecting on the concept of indifference, remember, it is not saying no to desires but rather seeking a healthy balance where no thing has power over you. Indifference is about freedom to live the kind of life that at any moment can say yes to the invitations and person of God.

The grace you are seeking is the ability to identify those areas and desires in your life that hinder you from freely being able to choose God's purpose for you (that purpose being praise, honour, service of God).

Examen questions

- Look back over your day, seeking to identify the areas and desires that made it difficult for you to say yes to God. What were they?
- What is the source of their power over you?

Share your insights with God, asking for God's help and wisdom.

Process

☐ Opening ☐ Closing
☐ Daily exercise ☐ Noontime examen
☐ Journalling ☐ Evening examen

Use the *lectio divina* method as you read through the passage for each day.

DAY 1

Read Philippians 4:11–13; Psalm 23:1.

Spend time thinking through how Paul's contentment helped him to be able to embrace the strength of Christ in his life.

- What do these verses teach about the place and power of contentment (indifference, detachment)?
- Look at your own life. Can you say with Paul, 'I have learned to be content whatever the circumstances,' or with the psalmist, 'The Lord is my shepherd; I shall not want'? Why, or why not?

Ask God to show you areas in which you need to learn contentment and embrace indifference.

DAY 2

Read 1 John 2:15–17.

Meditate on the following phrases, asking God to speak to you regarding struggles you may be having in any of these areas. Journal any insights God gives you. Conclude this time with a prayer of commitment to respond to the insight(s) God has given you during this time.

- Do not love the world or anything in the world.
- If anyone loves the world, the love of the Father is not in him.
- The cravings of sinful man
- The lust of his eyes
- The boasting of what he has and does
- Comes not from the Father but from the world
- The world and its desires pass away

DAY 3

Read Matthew 6:19–25.

We cannot see things in perspective until we cease to hug them to our own bosom.[7]

Read the passage for today and consider these questions:

- What do you treasure?
- How do these treasures lead you to God or away from God?
- Who or what is your master? Explain your answer.

Spend time sitting before God, asking God what you are treasuring, depending on or trusting in that is taking your attention and your heart away from God and lessening your desire for God.
Read Matthew 6:25 and consider these questions:

- What are the things you worry about?
- Why are you concerned about those things?
- Why are they important to you—that is, what do they represent to you (such as security, significance, power, love)?
- What does this show you about your level of trust in God?

Spend time prayerfully processing your responses with God.

DAY 4

Review your past three days.

- What have you discovered regarding the link between indifference and freedom to say yes to God?
- What have you learned about inordinate attachment and enslavement to the world? To self?
- What might it mean for you to 'seek first the kingdom of God'?

DAY 5

Read Psalm 63:1; Psalm 42:1–2; Philippians 3:8.

Spend time pondering the level of your desire for God. Share your thoughts and feelings with God. Ask God if there is anything in your life that is quenching your desire for God.

DAY 6

Read John 21:15–17.

Imagine you are standing before Jesus, and he looks you in the eye and asks you, 'Do you love me more than these?'

- What might 'these' refer to in your life?
- Do you love Jesus more than these?

Julian of Norwich prayed that she would let God be enough for her. This notion is extremely challenging. Reflect on the following two questions, and journal your response.

- Is God enough for you?
- Can you be satisfied with just having God and not having whoever or whatever is being emptied out of your life?

DAY 7

Review this past week.

- Which verses really challenged you? Why?
- Around which verses did you feel some resistance? Why?
- What have you discovered regarding the link between indifference and freedom to say yes to God?
- What have you learned about inordinate attachment and enslavement to the world? To self?
- What might it mean for you to 'seek first the kingdom of God'?

CONCLUDING COMMENTS AND REFLECTIONS

You have now completed the preparatory section of the Exercises. You have spent the past several weeks soaking in God's love and working through the Principle and Foundation. This section was designed to help you develop an internalised sense of God as one involved and as one whose interaction with you is characterised by love, care and grace. This awareness of God, which may not be fully developed, is nonetheless a critical internalised awareness for those continuing on into Week 1 of the Exercises.

Before choosing to enter Week 1, it is extremely important that you determine if you are in a spiritually healthy place in terms of your sense of God and self. You also need to be in a place where you have an internalised sense of faith and hope. Week 1 is one of the most difficult sections of the Exercises, and, if you do not feel ready to proceed, feel free to go back and revisit the previous exercises.

Remember, the goal is not to reach the end of the Exercises but to experience God in the midst of them. Therefore, it does not matter if you now move to Week 1 or if you spend more time in the Preparatory Exercises. What is important is entering into the exercises each day with openness to the invitations and promptings of God.

Take a day or two to work through the following reflection and questions before making your choice to enter or not enter Week 1. I strongly suggest that you work through this with your spiritual director or listener.

- Take time to think about God. What images of God come to mind? Come up with three to five images of God, and write them down. Now explore each of these images. Do they seem to have a predominantly positive or negative sense to them? Why?
- What is your internalised sense of God's love for you? Do you believe (not just give theological assent) that God loves you and accepts you just as you are in this moment? Why, or why not?
- Where would you place yourself on the following continuums?

positive sense of self   negative sense of self
|—————————————————————————————————————|

positive sense of God   negative sense of God
|—————————————————————————————————————|

strong faith   weak faith
|—————————————————————————————————————|

strong sense of God in life   weak sense of God in life
|—————————————————————————————————————|

strong hope   weak hope
|—————————————————————————————————————|

indifference   disordered attachments
|—————————————————————————————————————|

As you have interacted with the questions and worked through each continuum, what has been your sense concerning your view of God? Is it a more positive—God is there for me, loving and caring—sense? Or is it more negative: God is against me, judging and demanding? Also, what is your level of faith and hope? Would you characterise the level of your faith and hope more toward the strong or weak end of the continuum? Finally, where are you on the indifference/disordered attachment continuum? Do you sense that your desire to be free from disordered attachments in order to say yes to God is growing? Why?

As you honestly look at where you are in terms of God as well as your levels of faith and hope, it is important that you are brutally honest with yourself. If you do not have a positive internalised sense of God and a level of faith and hope that is on the strong end of the continuum, I encourage you to spend more time in the preparatory sessions.

Before making your final decision regarding moving on to Week 1, reentering the Principle and Foundation, or concluding your journey through the Exercises, speak with your spiritual director or listener, sharing your insights from the questions and continuums above.

If you are feeling as if you are in a good place internally for moving forward, do one more thing: take time to recommit to your journey through the Exercises, pledging to give yourself wholly to God (as you are able). Seek to gain nothing from God, but rather purpose each day to present yourself to God as 'your spiritual act of worship', which is 'holy and pleasing to God' (Romans 12:1).

PART 3

THE SPIRITUAL EXERCISES

SIN, ME AND GOD'S LOVE

You have now reached what is officially known as Week 1 of the Spiritual Exercises of Ignatius.[1] The preparatory section was designed to equip you to enter this Week. It is critically important before beginning this section that you have internalised the truths of the prior weeks. You need to have come to a place where you know in your heart at an experiential level, not just a knowledge level, that God loves you, cares for you and stands with you. If this is not the case, return to the preparatory weeks, and work through those exercises again and/or read one of the books suggested at the end of the section on 'God's Love' before moving on (see page 80).

If you feel that you have been able to internalise God's love for you, I welcome you to Week 1. As you enter this Week, you may be taken by surprise by its subject matter: sin. You will be spending time pondering the sin of the angels and the sin of Adam and Eve, and then you will be invited to take a look at your own sin. You will also be asked to ponder hell.

Much of the material in Week 1 is reminiscent of Ignatius' experience in Manresa, Spain. Manresa was the place Ignatius travelled to after making his profession of faith. He journeyed there to spend a couple of days praying and fasting before continuing on to secure passage to Jerusalem. These couple of days turned into an eleven-month period that God used to mould and shape Ignatius in incredibly profound and transforming ways—heart, soul and spirit. Later he would refer to this as a time when God taught him 'like a little school boy'. It was during these eleven months that he became deeply aware of and wrestled with his sin and brokenness.

It was a time of deep personal anguish, self-loathing and torment that ultimately led to great spiritual freedom. During that time he learned the power of detachment, humility and absolute trust in God. Because of his experience at Manresa, Ignatius had a strong conviction that without a deep sense of your own sinfulness and your absolute need for the salvation rendered in Christ, you will not truly be able to know and appreciate in a transformative way the cost God expended on your behalf.

So during this section, Ignatius takes you to a preconversion mindset in which you once again feel the confusion and sorrow regarding your sins that led you to make the decision to turn away from those sinful choices and actions and turn toward God. These twin experiences of repentance (becoming aware of your condition as a sinner) and conversion (embracing anew your experience of salvation) will be entered into throughout this week. As you go through this section, you will be asking God for confusion (why did I and do I choose to sin?), intense sorrow and even tears because of your sins.[2]

This remembering, examining and detailing of your sins and sinfulness can easily lead to desolation and despair. The exercises of Week 1 are designed in part to bring you to a place of feeling naked, vulnerable and sorrowful in your own sin, but you are not left there. Ignatius built into this week four particular prayer practices, referred to as colloquies.[3] These colloquies take you into the presence of God, Jesus and the Holy Spirit, seeking to tether you to their love for you and forgiveness of you even as you look at your own sin and sinfulness. You are invited to move into a consideration of the wondrous gifts of God's grace and mercy, which God offers to you as a sinner. For while you were still a sinner, God demonstrated God's love for you.

A series of meditations based on the Ten Commandments is provided to aid you in unpacking and naming your sins.[4] These are given to help you get to a place of sorrow for your sins. The type of sorrow you are expected to experience is a godly sorrow, which brings repentance and leads to salvation while leaving no regret; not the worldly sorrow, which leads to death (2 Corinthians 7:10).

Please pay attention to yourself, asking yourself if these exercises are ultimately leading you to God or if you are getting stuck in feelings of shame and worthlessness that are sending you into a downward spiral of self-loathing and condemnation. If the latter is the case, step away from these exercises for a few days and make use of the alternative passages at the end of this section (page 157).

The goal of this section is that you will be enabled to acknowledge and embrace the destructive nature of sin globally and personally as you also realise and embrace the transforming power of God's love, grace and mercy. As you reflect on your sin, you may come to realise that it wasn't your sin that drove Jesus to the cross, but Jesus' love for you that led him to the cross and kept him on the cross. Ultimately this section helps you fix your eyes on Jesus, the author and perfecter of your faith, who 'for the joy that was set before him endured the cross' for you (Hebrews 12:2).

It is extremely important to be aware of your internal movements during this Week. Take time to ask yourself, 'Where is my sorrow taking me?' If your sorrow is taking you into places of self-loathing, condemnation, darkness of the soul, internal uneasiness and feelings of hopelessness, this is not what God desires for you. It is a worldly self-preoccupied sorrow that leads you away from God and toward internal destruction. If your feelings of self-loathing, condemnation and hopelessness persist, talk to your listener or spiritual director.

If your sorrow for your sins takes you to the cross of Christ and ultimately to the assurance of God's love, grace, mercy and faithfulness, which is what the Exercises were designed to do, continue on through Week 1. But as you continue, be vigilantly aware of your internal movements. Ignatius himself got caught in the downward spiral of self-loathing, condemnation and hopelessness as he wrestled with his own sin.

Remember, the goal of this section is to purge from your life the lie that because of your sin you are unlovable. There is no need for you to continually try to prove you are lovable by doing things for God, by parading around as one without struggles, doubts and sin, to save yourself. You are a forgiven and beloved sinner. Keep yourself tethered to the truth of the unconditional, nothing-can-separate-you-from-it love that God has for you. This is the same truth you have been soaking in throughout the preparatory section leading up to Week 1.

SUMMARY OF WEEK 1

1. Sin has historical roots (angels, Adam and Eve) and universal consequences.
2. Sin has had a grip on your life and has caused you and others pain and suffering.
3. Jesus loves you and died for you while you were a sinner and offers you forgiveness, grace, mercy and love.
4. Your sin can lead you to God/Jesus or away from God/Jesus.
5. Sin brings confusion and is an indication that you have turned from God to disordered attachments.

The grace you will be seeking throughout Week 1 is the gift of a growing sorrow, even to the depth of tears (if grace so moves you) for all your sins, as well as confusion over your choices to sin in light of God's limitless love, grace, mercy and faithfulness.[5]

Resist the temptation to judge or evaluate your experience of Week 1 based on the amount of tears you shed or do not shed. Many people who journey through Week 1 do not experience the shedding of tears for their sins. There are a number of reasons for this, such as their personal history with sin, personality or theological upbringing. The bottom line is for you to enter into Week 1 as you are able, trusting God to guide and direct as God sees fit. Seek to trust God and trust the process.

EXAMEN QUESTIONS

The questions for noontime and evening examen remain the same throughout Week 1.

- How did your meditation on the destructive nature of sin impact the way you lived your life today (choices you made, interaction with others, and so on)?
- When were you aware of the love, grace and forgiveness of God in your life?

OPENING TIME

This Week you will add an additional component to the beginning of your time in the exercises. This addition flows out of the Principle and Foundation section that you have just completed. You are encouraged to come to prayer, conscious of the reverence God deserves while asking God that everything in your day may lead you to divine praise and service. This will be added to the initial activities leading you into your time in the daily exercises. Please feel free to place it where you feel it fits best. For the purpose of the book, it will be placed right before the slowdown.

COLLOQUY

As you begin this first Week of the Exercises, you will discover another addition: the colloquy. There are four colloquies for this section. The term colloquy is derived from the Latin word for 'conversation'. Ignatius describes the practice of it as speaking as one friend speaks to another, or as a servant to his master—

now speaking, now asking for some grace, now confessing some misdeed, now communicating thoughts and feelings, and asking for wisdom.[6]

Reciting the Lord's Prayer often follows the colloquy. As you proceed through Week 1, you will be instructed on certain days to conduct a colloquy as part of your prayer time. You will receive instructions regarding the what, how and to whom of your colloquy on the days when it is part of your time in the daily exercises.

THE LORD'S PRAYER (OUR FATHER)

Do not rush through the Lord's Prayer; let yourself linger with each phrase. If you practise this way of saying this prayer, you will be able to make use of the Lord's Prayer in other areas of your life as a tool to centre you and reconnect you with God, no matter what your circumstances. Do not rush through your recitation of the Lord's Prayer, but give God the freedom to stop you along your way through the prayer. Just as with the Exercises, the goal is not to get through the prayer but to open yourself up to God through the Lord's Prayer.

SUGGESTIONS FOR PRAYER

In the course of giving instructions to the director, Ignatius provides seven helps for prayer. These are found in his Exercises 73–79. Please read through the following summary of the tips for prayer, and make use of them as you see fit.

1. As you go to bed at night, briefly call to mind what you will be meditating on during the following day.

2. When you awake, focus your thoughts on the subject of your meditation for that day.
3. As you enter into your prayer time, remind yourself that you are entering the presence of God. Do so with reverence and humility.
4. Experiment with different postures while praying, such as kneeling, sitting, standing or lying prostrate. Seek to choose positions that seem to be helpful in reinforcing your internal mood or capturing the feeling of the prescribed meditation.
5. After finishing your prayer time, take a few moments to review what happened during that time, such as consolations, desolations, fear, drowsiness, anxiety or boredom.
6. Seek to remain in the feelings that surface during the time of meditation.
7. As you are able, create an environment that helps to reinforce the focus of your meditation. Since the heart of your prayer times during the next few weeks will be sin and hell, keeping the room dark and avoiding the pleasantness of sunlight and the beauties of nature during your prayer time will be in keeping with the mood.

Once again, the above tips are given as possible aids to your daily times of prayer. They are not a list of things you are required to make use of, but I would suggest you experiment with these tips from time to time and see if they are at all helpful to you.

USE OF THE ANIMA CHRISTI (SOUL OF CHRIST) PRAYER

Soul of Christ, sanctify me.
Body of Christ, save me.
Blood of Christ, inebriate me.
Water from the side of Christ, wash me.
Passion (suffering) of Christ, strengthen me.

O good Jesus, hear me;
Within thy wounds hide me;
Suffer me not to be separated from thee;
From the malignant enemy defend me;
In the hour of my death call me,
And bid me come to thee,
That with thy saints I may praise thee
Forever and ever. Amen

Although this prayer has been a part of the Exercises for centuries (first appearing in the 1576 edition of the Exercises) and is attributed by many to Ignatius, it actually dates back to the 15th century. This was most probably a prayer with which Ignatius had become familiar and found helpful during his spiritual journey and thus eventually incorporated into the Exercises.

RULES OF DISCERNMENT

Ignatius provided key insights for discernment for those journeying through the Exercises. He referred to this section as 'rules for perceiving and knowing in some manner the different movements which are caused in the soul'. Hopefully you have already familiarised yourself with these rules during your time in the Preparatory Exercises and the Principle and Foundation.

Even if you have already read over the rules for Week 1, as you were encouraged to do before entering into the Preparatory Exercises, I would invite you to do so again.

The material in Week 1 is capable of stirring up desolation, and so it is extremely important to have a keen awareness of Ignatius' insights regarding dealing with desolation and using consolation.

OVERVIEW OF THE RULES OF DISCERNMENT

The Rules of Discernment resulted from Ignatius' experiences during his time convalescing at Loyola and his eleven-month sojourn in Manresa. The incident leading to Ignatius' need to convalesce at his brother's castle in Loyola occurred during a battle at Pamplona, Spain (May 1521). It was in the midst of this battle that his leg was shattered by a cannon ball. Eventually he was transported to Loyola, where he recuperated from June 1521 to February 1522. During this time Ignatius began to turn his thoughts from being an earthly knight to imagining what following Jesus and the saints might entail. The following rules are a byproduct of when Ignatius alternated times of meditating on being an earthly knight, seeking personal honour and glory, with times of meditating on the lives of Jesus, St Francis and St Dominic. As he meditated, he became aware of the impact that consolations and desolations had on him, and he formulated the insights that he gleaned into rules of discernment.

The rules, which are probably best understood as principles, are divided into two sections. The first is for those just entering the Exercises. Its overarching focus is desolation—defining it as well as giving reasons for it and aids to combat it. The second section is designed for those entering Week 2 and beyond.[7] Its focus is on the subtlety of spiritual attacks and the uncertainty that experiences of consolation are a trustworthy indicator of God's presence.

Timothy Gallagher came up with an excellent paradigm for understanding the role played by the Rules of Discernment in the life of the retreatant. He writes that these rules help the retreatant to 'be aware' (notice what is going on within), 'understand' (whether this is from God or not) and 'take action' (accept or reject what you have noticed and understood).[8] This threefold paradigm succinctly conveys the goal which both sections of the Rules of Discernment were designed by Ignatius to accomplish.

In these Rules of Discernment, Ignatius stressed the importance of paying attention to the emotional affect (inner movement) that arises as you journey through the Exercises. Ignatius' concern was not with the thoughts of the retreatant but rather with the affect beneath the thoughts. This emphasis on feelings is evident from the feeling terms in the rules that Ignatius used to describe consolation (joy, love, peace) and desolation (darkness, dryness, disturbance, lack of peace, absence of God). It is your feelings that will help to reveal where your thoughts originated, namely, the 'good spirit' or the 'evil spirit'.

'GOOD SPIRIT' AND 'EVIL SPIRIT'

There has been much written concerning what is actually represented by the good spirit and the evil spirit as employed by Ignatius in the Exercises. Those who write concerning this identify the good spirit as referring to God, the Holy Spirit and angels. This designation is generally agreed on.

The identity of the evil spirit has been much more problematic. Ignatius referred to the evil spirit as 'the evil one' and 'the enemy' or 'our enemy'. From this it would seem clear that Ignatius meant the devil. However, the question is, does this represent the entire scope of the term 'evil spirit', or is there more to it? Did Ignatius' understanding allow for other factors to be included under the umbrella of the term 'evil spirit'? The simple answer would be no; Ignatius did not see a broader scope to the term 'evil spirit'. This is not surprising, because Ignatius was a person fully entrenched in his own time and place. But if we change the above question slightly to 'Would Ignatius allow his definition of evil spirit to be expanded based on the further knowledge of the inner workings of the human psyche?' I believe the answer would then be an emphatic yes! This yes reflects the elements of flexibility, adaptation and accommodation that are characteristic of the Exercises in particular and Ignatian spirituality in general.

In response to this, Gallagher writes, 'The word further signifies the weakness of our humanity.'[9] In 'the weakness of our humanity' Gallagher includes the flesh, with its desire against the Spirit, as well as the world around us (society, culture). I would add to this list the false self, 'the lust of the flesh and the lust of the eyes and the boastful pride of life' (1 John 2:16, NASB).

Thomas Green, who would be in agreement with what has been written above regarding the expanded scope of the term 'evil spirit', writes, 'From the point of view of discernment we can take the "evil spirit" of the "devil" to mean whatever forces are working against God, whether they be "natural" or strictly diabolical.'[10] For the purposes of this book, the evil spirit, the evil one and so on will refer to anything that seeks to take people away from following God's call or invitation in their life.

With the above background laid, it is time to focus on the Rules of Discernment for Week 1.

RULES OF DISCERNMENT: WEEK 1

These rules are given to help you during encounters with the evil spirits during your initial time in the Exercises.[11] Before diving into the Rules of Discernment, it is helpful to make some general observations. The major focus of the Rules of Discernment in this section is desolation. There are 14 rules, of which six deal solely with desolation, two deal solely with consolation, three deal with consolation and desolation, and three deal with temptation.

Based on my experience with those making their way through the Exercises, the first few weeks in the Exercises can be a time of significant desolation and temptation. This may or may not be the case for you, but it would behove you to be ready for this possible eventuality. The Preparatory Exercises and Week 1 are a time of purgation, which can be very demanding. Taking the time to become familiar with the insights from the Rules of

Discernment below can be very helpful as you begin your journey.

Note that Ignatius was not so concerned with the surface manifestation of a feeling or emotion but would encourage you to explore what is beneath that feeling to determine if it is from the good spirit or the bad. This is much more involved than a superficial inventory of what you may or may not be feeling.

The Rules

1. If the flow or focus of your life is away from God, you will experience the evil spirit as something positive, bringing you pleasures and delight, and you will experience God as harsh and stinging.
2. If the flow or focus of your life is toward God, you will experience God as positive, bringing you pleasures and delight, and will experience the evil spirit as harsh and stinging.

The key discernment insight found in Rules 1 and 2 does not concern feelings but rather the flow of your life. Your feelings, though important, are not to be judged solely at face value but need to be interpreted in light of inner movements of your heart—toward God or away from God. Only when you are aware of this inner reality can you accurately discern what is happening. Because the easiest person to fool is always yourself, it is important to have a trusted spiritual director or listener to journey with you and help you discern.

3. Consolation is characterised by being inflamed with the love of God, growing in faith, love and hope, being strengthened and encouraged, interior joy and a desire to serve God and connect with God in all things. Ignatius also wrote that pain and tears may also be a consolation if these take you to the feet of Jesus, praising and worshipping God.

4. The affects for desolation are darkness, emptiness, slothful complacency, inner turmoil, sadness, despair, selfishness, rebelliousness, discouragement and feeling distant from God.

On the surface it would appear that when you are feeling good, it is consolation, and when you are feeling bad, it is desolation. But such a reading of these two rules is not congruent with what was stated in them regarding taking into account the flow of your life as an aid to deciding if your affect is pointing to consolation or desolation. Consolation is an outflow of your interior movement toward God, while desolation has to do with interior movement away from God, regardless of your feelings of pain or peace, comfort or confusion. Think of the focus of your life as being a computer screen. A simple way to remember the difference between consolation and desolation is this: consolation means that God is on the computer screen, while desolation means God is not on the computer screen. The critical question becomes not 'What am I am feeling?' but 'Who is on my screen?'

Rules 5–9 deal with desolation.

5. When in desolation (your life flow is away from God), do not change a decision that was made during a time of consolation (God was on your screen).
6. When in desolation, continue in prayer, meditation and the examen with more resolve.
7. Though you will feel alone and separated from God during your time of desolation, remember that God is with you.
8. Be patient in the midst of your desolation, knowing that this is not the end. God is faithful, and consolation will come in time. Also seek to determine the possible reason for your desolation (see Rule 9).
9. Reason for desolation:
    a. You are lazy, careless, lukewarm or caught up in sin.
    b. It is allowed by God to show you how closely your faith-

fulness is tied to your experiences of consolation and greater graces.

c. It is a gift from God to demonstrate to you that yours is not a causal, tit-for-tat spirituality. All is gift. Everything that comes your way as you pray is because of God's grace. This gift of dryness can be used to purge you of pride (I am making myself grow and experience God) and vainglory (I am great because of my experiences of God).

These last two reasons for desolation (9b and c) serve to remind you that desolation can be a gift from God that can become fodder for your continuing spiritual development and will equip you so that you can continue through the Exercises. It is important to determine the 'why' behind your experience of desolation so you can respond accordingly.

Next Ignatius provided insight regarding what to do when you are experiencing consolation:

10. Garner strength from your consolation for your continuing journey, preparing for the time when desolation will come. Journalling about periods of consolation can help you during times of desolation.

11. Receive your consolation as a gift from God and not as a result of your spiritual striving or accomplishment. Endeavour to humbly accept the consolation while fighting the urge to think it was your own doing.

Ignatius concluded this section by delineating three ways that the evil spirits attack:

12. The first is the spoiled child.[12] The evil spirit will whine, scream, beg, make promises and pursue you relentlessly to give in to its demands. You need to stand firm in your resolve, employing courage and determination.

13. Second, the evil spirit will be like a secret lover: something is going on that only you know about. You need to bring your sin into the light of day; share it with your spiritual director, listener, pastor or a trusted friend. The power of that sin is linked to its secrecy and, when revealed, the power will be greatly lessened.

14. Third, the evil spirit is a brilliant military commander who will attack you again and again at two points: your personal weakness and places of internal complacency and spiritual pride. To withstand these attacks, you need a degree of self-knowledge and self-awareness, which can be cultivated through the daily use of the General Examen of Conscience, accompanied with the commitment to be absolutely honest and open with God and yourself.

The three lines of attack by the enemy outlined above can provide you with insights of how to combat them if you are willing to take an honest look at your own life to discern how you tend to be attacked. Take time to consider in which of these ways you are primarily attacked, bearing in mind that there are often multiple modes of attack.

As you continue through the Exercises, you will struggle with desolation, times of dryness in prayer and attacks by the enemy. The above rules will help you to fight the good fight. Remember from these rules that, first, consolation and desolation have little to do with what you are feeling and much more to do with the direction of your mind, heart and spirit—if toward God, consolation; if toward the enemy and the deeds of the flesh, desolation. The key question remains: who is on your screen? Second, when in desolation, use the tools God has given you—the prayer of examen and prior consolations—and continue the course you have set by presenting yourself to God daily through the material found in the Exercises.

CONFESSION

At the end of this section, you are encouraged to make a confession. The purpose of the confession is to acknowledge to another your grief and sorrow for your sins and revulsion over its consequences in your life and the lives of others. Please take time to carefully and prayerfully consider making a formal confession, in accordance with James 5:16 and 1 John 1:9. If you decide to make a confession, choose wisely the person to whom you will confess. Ask God to show you someone you can trust, someone who truly cares about you and will not judge or condemn you. Although this is scary, I strongly encourage you to step out in this way. Remember, confessing your sins is about acknowledging before God that you have done wrong and agreeing with God that, indeed, it was wrong.

OPTIONAL EXERCISE: THE JESUS PRAYER

Although the Jesus Prayer was not part of the original Exercises, I believe it fits well into this section. It can help you to maintain the tension between your own sins and God's love, while also helping to deepen your ability to find God in all things. The Jesus Prayer is part of a larger category of prayers called breath prayers.

Breath prayer arose out of a desire to pray without ceasing. It is a short, simple prayer of petition that would be spoken in one breath, thus the name 'breath prayer'. Breath prayers are brief, seldom more than seven or eight syllables. They express love, dependency, meekness and trust. This type of prayer is a very helpful tool in refocusing your entire being back to God in a single moment.

The most famous breath prayer is the Jesus Prayer: 'Lord Jesus Christ, have mercy on me.' Later it was lengthened to 'Lord Jesus Christ, Son of God, have mercy on me, a sinner.' This prayer was derived from Jesus' parable on self-righteousness, in which the tax collector beat his chest and prayed, 'God, have mercy on me, a sinner!' (Luke 18:13). It was used extensively in the sixth century, and in the 14th century it was revived in the Eastern church.

The Jesus Prayer involves turning aside from images and concentrating your attention on, or rather within, the words. It is not a hypnotic incantation but a heartfelt cry seeking a living connection with God.

The optional exercise over the next 35 days is to make the Jesus Prayer a part of your experience. If you choose to participate in this, please endeavour to practise the prayer from time to time throughout your day. The Jesus Prayer will be an aid, reminding you of your need for Jesus and his mercy. Here are three forms of the Jesus Prayer:

- Jesus Christ, Son of God, have mercy on me.
- Jesus Christ, Son of God, have mercy on me, a sinner.
- Lord Jesus Christ, Son of God, have mercy on me, a sinner.

Remember, optional means optional. It is up to you if you make this a part of your experience during Week 1 or not. This practice has been found helpful for many with whom I have journeyed through the Exercises.

A final word of wisdom: Be on guard as you work your way through Week 1. As you seek to hold on to the seemingly contradictory realities of your sinfulness and God's love, and you sense you are landing on the side of your sinfulness, and feelings of self-condemnation are gaining a foothold within you, stop and refocus on God's unconditional love and forgiveness while reciting this prayer: 'I believe; help me overcome my unbelief' (Mark 9:23–25). Jesus heard and answered this prayer.

The above section containing all the additions for Week 1 could be overwhelming to you, but do not worry; you will be prompted when to make use of the components listed above. I have discussed them first so that you are not caught off-guard when they make their appearance and to provide additional information regarding these components without interrupting the flow of the Exercises.

As you enter into and journey through Week 1, my prayer for you is this:

God, as this precious chosen one of yours walks through Week 1, coming face to face with sin, help him or her to remember your grace, bathe your beloved in your love and free her or him from the prison of guilt and shame, from which you have delivered this one by the shedding of your blood. (Adapted from Ephesians 1:3; Romans 3:23; 5:12; Ephesians 1:7; Romans 8:1)

EXERCISES FOR WEEK 1

SECTION 1 OF 5

The grace you are seeking this week is the ability to experience sorrow, tears and confusion over your choices to sin in light of God's limitless love, grace, mercy and faithfulness.

Examen questions

- How did your meditation on the destructive nature of sin impact the way you lived your life today (choices you made, interaction with others and so on)?
- When were you aware of the love, grace and forgiveness of God in your life?

Come to prayer, conscious of the reverence God deserves, while asking God that everything in your day may more and more lead you to divine praise and service.

Process

- [ ] Opening
- [ ] Daily exercise
- [ ] Journalling
- [ ] Closing
- [ ] Noontime examen
- [ ] Evening examen

....

Be aware

One of the struggles of Week 1 will be the tendency to enter the exercises intellectually rather than with your heart. This is understandable but not helpful. It is important for you to enter into these exercises emotionally so that you can feel sorrow and confusion arise within you as you explore the pervasive reality of sin in the world and in your own life. It will be hard not to want to protect yourself from the pain that this week may bring to the surface within you, but it is this pain that will take you to God and to freedom, and it will lead you to experience God's love in a deeper way.

....

DAY 1

Read Jude 6.

Angels: The sin of the angels (led by Satan) involved a radical choice of self before God, a rejection of the very source of all life and love, a turning from God.

Spend time pondering the sin of the angels, letting its decisiveness and consequences strike deep within your heart.

Consider how you have turned from God, rejecting the life and love that God offers you.

Conclude by slowly reciting the *Anima Christi* (Soul of Christ) prayer:

Soul of Christ, sanctify me.
Body of Christ, save me.
Blood of Christ, inebriate me.
Water from the side of Christ, wash me.
Passion (suffering) of Christ, strengthen me.
O good Jesus, hear me;
Within thy wounds hide me;
Suffer me not to be separated from thee;
From the malignant enemy defend me;
In the hour of my death call me,
And bid me come to thee,
That with thy saints I may praise thee
Forever and ever. Amen

DAY 2

Read Genesis 3:1–13.

Adam and Eve: Their sin is a direct rejection of God's love. They seek to escape the responsibility of their choice by blaming someone or something. Through their sin, we see the personal and cosmic consequences of sin.

Spend time pondering the sin of Adam and Eve, letting its pervasive and destructive consequences become fully present to your mind and heart.

Consider this: if one sin can wreak so much havoc, what about your own sins?

DAY 3

Read Romans 6:23.

Sin: An act that leads to separation from God, from life, from love, bringing destruction and death to all of creation.

Spend time thinking through the results of sin in the world, your country, your city, your family and your life. Glance through the newspaper or surf the internet, and see the results of the destructive, corrupting power of sin.

Remember, the purpose of Week 1 is not self-loathing, condemnation or hopelessness but a deep awareness of sin in yourself and the world, along with a deeper appreciation and realisation of God's love for you.

DAY 4

Review your past three days.

- How has meditating on the sins of the angels, Adam and Eve, and your own sin impacted your heart and your appreciation of God's love and grace?
- Have you felt sorrow or confusion, or been moved to tears? Why, or why not?

Colloquy

Approach Jesus, and ask him for three favours:

- A deep realisation of the sin in your life and a sorrow for your sinful acts.
- An understanding of and feeling for the havoc in your life due to your sin and sinful tendencies, as well as wisdom regarding how to bring order into your life.
- An awareness of the ways in which the world actively and passively stands in opposition to Christ, so that you may distance yourself from all that is worldly and vain.

Conclude this time by slowly reciting the Lord's Prayer.

DAY 5

Read Ephesians 2:1–3.

Your own sin: See yourself as a sinner, helpless and alienated before a loving and holy God. Let the sins (of commission and omission) and sinful tendencies of your life float through your mind.

Let the weight of your sins be felt throughout your entire being.

Reflect on the evil that has flowed from you, one among billions of people living on the earth. Feel the combined weight and horror of your sinful acts multiplied by billions.

DAY 6

Read Luke 12:4–5.

Hell: Choosing to say no to God's love, turning away from God to self and rejecting the life and love God offers through Jesus is to condemn oneself to hell for all eternity.

Consider the number of times you have said no to God up to this point in your life. Spend time talking to God about those choices.

Colloquy

Spend time thanking Jesus for the love and mercy he has shown you throughout your life.[13]

Conclude this time by slowly reciting the Lord's Prayer.

DAY 7

Review this past week.

- Which day's meditations touched you? Why?
- How did these meditations impact your heart and your appreciation of God's love and grace?

- Have you felt sorrow or confusion, or been moved to tears? Why, or why not?
- Did these meditations increase your ability to make more God-honouring choices? Why, or why not?

....

You are loved
As you focus on your own sin and brokenness, remember that your sin does not define you. You are forgiven. You are a saint uniquely loved by God. If you struggle with this, pray this prayer: 'Jesus, I believe; help me overcome my unbelief.'

....

──◄ SECTION 2 OF 5 ►──

The grace you are seeking this week is the ability to experience sorrow, tears and confusion over your choices to sin in light of God's limitless love, grace, mercy and faithfulness.

Examen questions

- How did your meditation on the destructive nature of sin impact the way you lived your life today (choices you made, interaction with others and so on)?
- When were you aware of the love, grace and forgiveness of God in your life?

Come to prayer, conscious of the reverence God deserves, while asking God that everything in your day may more and more lead you to divine praise and service.

Process

- ☐ Opening
- ☐ Daily exercise
- ☐ Journalling

- ☐ Closing
- ☐ Noontime examen
- ☐ Evening examen

DAY 1

Read Joshua 7.

The sin of Achan: Achan chose to disobey the commands of God and follow the inner voices of his own desires.

Spend some time pondering Achan's sin, letting its pervasive and destructive consequences become fully present to your mind and heart.

Pay special attention to Joshua 7:20–21, looking at the sequence of Achan's sin, then exploring your own heart. Are there things you are coveting? Are there sins that you are hiding from God? If so, take some time to be open and honest with God.

Conclude by slowly reciting the *Anima Christi* (Soul of Christ) prayer:

> *Soul of Christ, sanctify me.*
> *Body of Christ, save me.*
> *Blood of Christ, inebriate me.*
> *Water from the side of Christ, wash me.*
> *Passion (suffering) of Christ, strengthen me.*
> *O good Jesus, hear me;*
> *Within thy wounds hide me;*
> *Suffer me not to be separated from thee;*
> *From the malignant enemy defend me;*
> *In the hour of my death call me,*
> *And bid me come to thee,*
> *That with thy saints I may praise thee*
> *Forever and ever. Amen*

....

Desolation

There is probably an up-and-down dynamic to your experience as you travel through the Exercises. Seek to continue your journey, spending your allotted time in the prayer times, giving special attention to praying the examen while seeking to discern what is the cause of your desolation (see Rule 9 in the 'Rules of Discernment' list above). When in the grip of desolation, it will be hard to continue moving through the Exercises, but that is exactly what you need to do, recalling to mind that this is just a season and God is faithful and ever-present, no matter what you are feeling.

....

DAY 2

Read Genesis 3:17–19.

Spend your time pondering the consequences of Adam's sin, letting its pervasive and destructive consequences become fully present to your mind and heart.

Consider this: if one sin can wreak so much havoc, what about your own sins?

Special instructions for journeying through the Ten Commandments: As you journey through the Ten Commandments over the next few days, ask God for the grace to know how you have failed to keep them and for a deeper understanding of what they most truly convey, so that you are better able to live in internal harmony with them. As you ponder each commandment, reflect both on how you have been faithful in living out the commandment and on how you have failed to live out the commandment. As you become aware of your failings, ask God for forgiveness. Conclude your time in the commandment by speaking intimately with God (colloquy), sharing with God whatever arises within you.

Conclude this time by slowly reciting the Lord's Prayer.

DAY 3

Spend your time reviewing your life using the commandments listed below.

'You shall have no other gods before me.

'You shall not make for yourself an idol in the form of anything in heaven above or on the earth beneath or in the waters below. You shall not bow down to them or worship them; for I, the Lord your God, am a jealous God, punishing the children for the sin of the fathers to the third and fourth generation of those who hate me, but showing love to a thousand [generations] of those who love me and keep my commandments.

'You shall not misuse the name of the Lord your God, for the Lord will not hold anyone guiltless who misuses his name.

'Remember the Sabbath day by keeping it holy. Six days you shall labour and do all your work, but the seventh day is a Sabbath to the Lord your God. On it you shall not do any work, neither you, nor your son or daughter, nor your manservant or maidservant, nor your animals, nor the alien within your gates. For in six days the Lord made the heavens and the earth, the sea, and all that is in them, but he rested on the seventh day. Therefore the Lord blessed the Sabbath day and made it holy.

'Honour your father and your mother, so that you may live long in the land the Lord your God is giving you.' (Exodus 20:3–12)

- How have you lived them out?
- How have you gone astray?
- What has lured you away from God? What have you desired more than God? Why?

Colloquy

Approach Jesus, and ask him for three favours:

- A deep realisation of the sin in your life and a sorrow for your sinful acts.

- An understanding of and feeling for the havoc in your life due to your sin and sinful tendencies, as well as wisdom regarding how to bring order into your life.
- An awareness of the ways in which the world actively and passively stands in opposition to Christ, so that you may distance yourself from all that is worldly and vain.

Conclude this time by slowly reciting the Lord's Prayer.

....

Prayer postures
If you have not yet done so, I encourage you to experiment with different prayer postures (kneeling, lying face down or face up, standing, arms raised, head bowed and so on). Prayer postures can be an aid in helping us move from head to heart as we come before God. Also, with a prayer posture, you may be able to communicate to God what your words fail to convey. Give it a try.

....

DAY 4

Spend your time reviewing your life using the verses listed below.

'Honour your father and your mother, so that you may live long in the land the Lord your God is giving you. You shall not murder. You shall not commit adultery.' (Exodus 20:12–14)

'You have heard that it was said to the people long ago, "Do not murder, and anyone who murders will be subject to judgment." But I tell you that anyone who is angry with his brother will be subject to judgment. Again, anyone who says to his brother, "Raca", is answerable to the Sanhedrin. But anyone who says, "You fool!" will be in danger of the fire of hell.' (Matthew 5:21–22)

'You have heard that it was said, "Do not commit adultery." But I tell you that anyone who looks at a woman lustfully has already committed adultery with her in his heart. If your right eye causes you to sin, gouge it out and throw it away. It is better for you to lose one part of your body than for your whole body to be thrown into hell. And if your right hand causes you to sin, cut it off and throw it away. It is better for you to lose one part of your body than for your whole body to go into hell.' (Matthew 5:27–30)

- How have you lived them out?
- How have you gone astray?
- What has lured you away from God? What have you desired more than God? Why?

Colloquy

Spend time thanking Jesus for the love and mercy he has shown you throughout your life.

Conclude this time by slowly reciting the Lord's Prayer.

DAY 5

Spend your time reviewing your life, using these commandments.

'You shall not steal.

'You shall not give false testimony against your neighbour.

'You shall not covet your neighbour's house. You shall not covet your neighbour's wife, or his manservant or maidservant, his ox or donkey, or anything that belongs to your neighbour.' (Exodus 20:15–17)

- How have you gone astray? What has lured you away from God?
- What have you desired more than God? Why?

It is not happening
During Week 1 of the Exercises, some people get discouraged because they are not moved to tears because of their sin or do not feel as if they are able to fully connect emotionally with their sinfulness. Be patient with yourself and trust God and the process. God is at work!

DAY 6

Read 2 Thessalonians 1:9.

Hell: Choosing to say no to God's love, turning away from God to self, and rejecting the life and love that God offers through Jesus is to condemn oneself to hell for all eternity.

Imagine what it would be like in hell as it is described in the above passage.

Colloquy

Spend time thanking Jesus for the love and mercy he has shown you throughout your life.

Conclude this time by slowly reciting the Lord's Prayer.

DAY 7

Review this past week.

- How has meditating on the sins of the angels, Adam and Eve, and your own sin impacted your heart and your appreciation of God's love and grace?
- Have you felt sorrow or confusion, or been moved to tears? Why, or why not?

Colloquy

Place yourself before Jesus as he hangs on the cross. Talk to him regarding his love for you and his choice to die for your sins. While reflecting on your life, let these questions penetrate your heart and mind:

- In the past, how have you responded to God's love, to the sacrifice of Jesus?
- How are you currently responding to God's love, to the sacrifice of Jesus?
- How might God be asking you to deepen your response to God's love, to the sacrifice of Jesus?

As you look at Jesus hanging on the cross, spend time reflecting on and interacting with Jesus about whatever God may bring to your attention.

Close this time by slowly reciting the Lord's Prayer.

Journalling

It is very helpful to journal through these exercises. Journalling helps you to see patterns in your prayer times, to recall what God has spoken to you. Often, as you journal, God expands on what you have discovered or been made aware of. Journalling will deepen your experience with the Exercises.

◄ SECTION 3 OF 5 ►

The grace you are seeking this week is the ability to experience sorrow, tears, and confusion over your choices to sin in light of God's limitless love, grace, mercy and faithfulness.

Examen questions

- How did your meditation on the destructive nature of sin impact the way you lived your life today (choices you made, interaction with others and so on)?
- When were you aware of the love, grace and forgiveness of God in your life?

Come to prayer, conscious of the reverence God deserves, while asking God that everything in your day may more and more lead you to divine praise and service.

Process

☐ Opening   ☐ Closing
☐ Daily exercise   ☐ Noontime examen
☐ Journalling   ☐ Evening examen

....

Forgiven and loved by God

As you are looking at your own sin, recall to mind that nothing can separate you from the love of God and that there is no condemnation for those who are in Christ Jesus. If you are feeling condemnation during Week 1, it is not coming from God.

....

DAY 1

Read James 1:13–15.

What is the birthing process of sin conveyed in this passage?

Ask God to show you the desires and disordered attachments in your heart that tend to take you away from God and give birth to sin, death and destruction in your life. Confess to and grieve before

God your ongoing sins that are brought to birth by the counterfeit fulfilment of the desires of your heart.

Colloquy

Spend time thanking and praising God the Father, Jesus the Son, and the Holy Spirit for the grace, mercy, love and forgiveness you have been given.

Close this time by slowly reciting the Lord's Prayer.

DAY 2

Read 1 Corinthians 10:13; James 4:17.

What do these passages reveal about temptation, sin and God?

Take a look at some of the past times of sin in your life, and ask God to help you to see how God was faithful in those times to provide you with a way of escape. Why did you not avail yourself of God's provision in those instances?

Ask God for help in the future to take the ways of escape that God graciously provides for you.

Think back over your life in the past few months, and ask God to show you when you knew the 'good thing' to do and did not do it. What led to your decision not to do the 'good'? Share your insights with God.

DAY 3

Read Romans 8:19–22.

Spend time thinking through the results of sin in the world, your country, your city, your family and your life. Glance through the newspaper or surf the internet, and see the results of the destructive, corrupting power of sin in the world.

DAY 4

Review your past three days.

- How has meditating on your own sin and temptation impacted your heart and your appreciation of God's love, grace and faithfulness?
- Have you felt sorrow or confusion, or been moved to tears? Why, or why not?

Close this time by slowly reciting the Lord's Prayer.

Colloquy

Approach Jesus, and ask him for three favours:

- A deep realisation of the sin in your life and a sorrow for your sinful acts.
- An understanding of and feeling for the havoc in your life due to your sin and sinful tendencies, as well as wisdom regarding how to bring order into your life.
- An awareness of the ways in which the world actively and passively stands in opposition to Christ, so that you may distance yourself from all that is worldly and vain.

Close this time by slowly reciting the Lord's Prayer.

DAY 5

Spend your time reviewing your life using this passage:

The acts of the sinful nature are obvious: sexual immorality, impurity and debauchery; idolatry and witchcraft; hatred, discord, jealousy, fits of rage, selfish ambition, dissensions, factions and envy; drunkenness, orgies, and the like. (Galatians 5:19–21)

- How have you gone astray? What has lured you away from God?
- What have you desired more than God? Why?

DAY 6

Confession: Drawing from your reflections on the Ten Commandments and the Galatians 5 passage above, write out a confession.

Conclude by slowing reciting the *Anima Christi* (Soul of Christ) prayer:

> *Soul of Christ, sanctify me.*
> *Body of Christ, save me.*
> *Blood of Christ, inebriate me.*
> *Water from the side of Christ, wash me.*
> *Passion (suffering) of Christ, strengthen me.*
> *O good Jesus, hear me;*
> *Within thy wounds hide me;*
> *Suffer me not to be separated from thee;*
> *From the malignant enemy defend me;*
> *In the hour of my death call me,*
> *And bid me come to thee,*
> *That with thy saints I may praise thee*
> *Forever and ever. Amen*

DAY 7

Review this past week.

- Which day's meditations touched you? Why?
- How did these meditations impact your heart and your appreciation of God's love and grace?
- Have you felt sorrow or confusion, or been moved to tears? Why, or why not?
- Did these meditations increase your ability to make more God-honouring choices? Why, or why not?

Colloquy

Spend time thanking and praising God the Father, Jesus the Son, and the Holy Spirit for the grace, mercy, love and forgiveness you have been given.

....

Spiritual director or listener
If you haven't done so, please meet with your spiritual director or listener soon. This can be a difficult time for some, a time that may become destructive and not life-giving, especially if experienced alone.

....

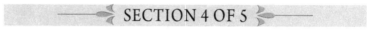

SECTION 4 OF 5

The grace you are seeking this week is the ability to experience sorrow, tears and confusion over your choices to sin in light of God's limitless love, grace, mercy and faithfulness.

Examen questions

- How did your meditation on the destructive nature of sin impact the way you lived your life today (choices you made, interaction with others and so on)?
- When were you aware of the love, grace and forgiveness of God in your life?

Come to prayer, conscious of the reverence God deserves, while asking God that everything in your day may more and more lead you to divine praise and service.

Process

- [ ] Opening
- [ ] Daily exercise
- [ ] Journalling

- [ ] Closing
- [ ] Noontime examen
- [ ] Evening examen

DAY 1

Read Psalm 32:1–5.

Your own sin: See yourself as a sinner, helpless and alienated before a loving and holy God. Let the sin (sins of commission and omission) and sinful tendencies of your life float through your mind.

Colloquy

Spend time thanking and praising God the Father, Jesus the Son, and the Holy Spirit for the grace, mercy, love and forgiveness you have been given.

DAY 2

Read Matthew 15:10–11, 17–20.

Spend time thinking through the root of sin in your life.

What internal desires lead you away from God rather than toward God? Why?

DAY 3

Read Mark 9:43–48.

What does this passage communicate concerning the seriousness of sin?

Do you take the destructive nature of your own sin seriously? Why, or why not?

Are there sins in your own life that need to be cut out? If yes, ask God to help you discover the desires within that are giving birth to those sins.

Colloquy

Spend time thanking and praising God the Father, Jesus the Son, and the Holy Spirit for the grace, mercy, love and forgiveness you have been given.

Close this time by slowly reciting the Lord's Prayer.

DAY 4

Review your past three days.

- How have these times of meditation touched your heart?
- Have you felt sorrow or confusion, or been moved to tears? Why, or why not?

Colloquy

Today, use your time thanking and praising God the Father, Jesus the Son, and the Holy Spirit for the grace, mercy, love and forgiveness you have been given.[14]

Close this time by slowly reciting the Lord's Prayer.

DAY 5

Read Luke 18:9–14.

Your own sin: See yourself as a sinner, helpless and alienated before a loving and holy God. Using imaginative reading, place yourself into this Gospel story.

Spend time repeating the famous breath prayer taken from the one in this passage: 'Lord Jesus, have mercy on me, a sinner.' Say the prayer two to three times, letting the words find a home in your soul. Now say the prayer slowly, lingering before God with each separate word.

What is the invitation or challenge for you in this prayer?

Make use of this breath prayer, praying it again and again as you go through your day.

DAY 6

Read Psalm 51:1–10.

Your own sin: See yourself as a sinner, helpless and alienated before a loving and holy God. Let the sin (sins of commission and omission) and sinful tendencies of your life float through your mind.

Colloquy

Spend time thanking and praising God the Father, Jesus the Son, and the Holy Spirit for the grace, mercy, love and forgiveness you have been given.

DAY 7

Review this past week.

- Which day's meditations touched you? Why?
- How did these meditations impact your heart and your appreciation of God's love and grace?
- Have you felt sorrow or confusion, or been moved to tears? Why, or why not?
- Did these meditations increase your ability to make more God-honouring choices? Why, or why not?

Conclude by slowly reciting the *Anima Christi* (Soul of Christ) prayer:

> *Soul of Christ, sanctify me.*
> *Body of Christ, save me.*
> *Blood of Christ, inebriate me.*
> *Water from the side of Christ, wash me.*
> *Passion (suffering) of Christ, strengthen me.*
> *O good Jesus, hear me;*
> *Within thy wounds hide me;*
> *Suffer me not to be separated from thee;*
> *From the malignant enemy defend me;*
> *In the hour of my death call me,*
> *And bid me come to thee,*
> *That with thy saints I may praise thee*
> *Forever and ever. Amen*

SECTION 5 OF 5

Looking ahead: Day 3 and Day 4 are a little different in Section 5. Take a look ahead so that you can come up with a plan. Please feel free to switch these days to another time during this week if doing so would make it easier for you to enter into these exercises.

The grace you are seeking this week is the ability to experience sorrow, tears and confusion over your choices to sin in light of God's limitless love, grace, mercy and faithfulness.

Examen questions

- How did your meditation on the destructive nature of sin impact the way you lived your life today (choices you made, interaction with others and so on)?

- When were you aware of the love, grace and forgiveness of God in your life?

Come to prayer, conscious of the reverence God deserves, while asking God that everything in your day may more and more lead you to divine praise and service.

Process

☐ Opening   ☐ Closing
☐ Daily exercise   ☐ Noontime examen
☐ Journalling   ☐ Evening examen

DAY 1

Take your confession from Section 3, Day 6, and share it with someone and/or with God.

Please take time to carefully and prayerfully consider making a formal confession. If you decide to make a confession to another, choose the person to whom you will confess carefully. Ask God to show you someone you can trust, someone who truly cares about you and will not judge or condemn you. Although this is scary, I strongly encourage you to step out in this way. Remember, confessing your sins is about acknowledging before God that you have done wrong and agreeing with God that indeed these things were wrong.

You can also make your confession before God. After you are finished, I suggest burning or shredding your confession as an indication that these sins are forgiven and God has removed them as far as the east is from the west.

Colloquy

Spend time thanking and praising God the Father, Jesus the Son, and the Holy Spirit for the grace, mercy, love and forgiveness you have been given.

DAY 2

Read Romans 8:1, 38–39.

Imagine yourself underneath a giant waterfall of God's love. God's love is rushing over you, drenching you. Imagine that instead of hearing the roaring of the water as it cascades down on you, you hear the gentle whisper of God saying to you, 'There is no condemnation in Christ; nothing can or will ever separate you from my love for you.' Spend time soaking in God's love, being caressed by God's loving touch, and hearing God whisper to you, 'There is no condemnation in Christ; nothing can ever separate you from my love.'

What feelings does this stir within you? Share your feelings with God.

Use all or part of the sentence 'There is no condemnation in Christ; nothing can separate you from my love' as a breath prayer throughout your day.

DAY 3

Take a walk, sit outside, lie down on your couch, get something to eat or grab a cup of coffee, and spend your time being open to God. This time is about intentionally being with God. Share with God any feelings that arise.

DAY 4

Have a relaxed day with God, doing something you enjoy, and share your experience with Jesus.

DAYS 5–6

Review these past 35 prayer sessions.

- What meditations really touched you? Why?
- How have these meditations impacted your heart and your appreciation of God's love and grace?
- Have you felt sorrow or confusion, or been moved to tears? Why, or why not?
- Did these meditations increase your ability to make more God-honouring choices? Why, or why not?

Colloquy

Spend time thanking and praising God the Father, Jesus the Son, and the Holy Spirit for the grace, mercy, love and forgiveness you have been given.

DAY 7

Spend time recalling those who have shown you God's love, carried you to Jesus, prayed for you and chosen to journey with you during certain legs on your adventure of faith—those whom God has used to help grow, sustain and deepen your faith.[15] Ponder their involvement in your life even as you were broken, struggling and messy.

- What feelings arise as you recall these individuals?
- What are the gifts they gave you through their presence with you?
- What does their love, care and involvement reveal to you about God?

Give thanks to God for these individuals. Pray for them and be open to God leading you to write one or more of these instruments of God a note of thanks and appreciation.

CONCLUDING COMMENTS AND REFLECTIONS

You have completed Week 1 of the Exercises. They were designed to help you cultivate a deep conviction of your sinfulness while reminding you of your absolute need for the salvation rendered in Christ and God's eagerness to forgive you, love you and be gracious toward you. Hopefully you have been able to move through this section without trivialising your sin or feeling overwhelmed by the immensity of it. It is important that you were able to sit with the seemingly paradoxical realities of your sin and God's love, your absolute poverty and God's immeasurable riches provided to you in Christ, your brokenness and God's transformation of you into a one-of-a-kind masterpiece. When all is said and done, the above twin realities are to be embraced and internalised before you continue your journey through the Exercises.

Now is the point when you begin to discern with God if it is time for you to move on to Week 2. As you are making your decision, please remember that the point is not to get through the Exercises but to interact with God and yourself through them. During the almost 500 years of the Spiritual Exercises of Ignatius, there have been many who did not continue beyond Week 1. That is OK. So, as you begin your discernment process, let go of internal pressure to move on to Week 2. Instead, open yourself to God's leading regarding moving on.

Begin by pondering where you find yourself on the continuums below. These are designed to help you explore how you have been able to internalise God's love and forgiveness, even as you have been focused on your sin. As you work through the continuums, endeavour to answer from your heart and not merely your head. Seek to embrace indifference.

Where would you place yourself on the following continuums?

naked, broken, alienated   loved, forgiven, accepted

|————————————————————————|

SIN/grace   GRACE/sin

|————————————————————————|

sinner   sinner radically loved by God

|————————————————————————|

intellectual sense   strong heartfelt sense
of need for God   of need for God

|————————————————————————|

my abject poverty   God's radical love

|————————————————————————|

self-condemnation   no condemnation in Christ

|————————————————————————|

conditional love of God   unconditional love of God

|————————————————————————|

preoccupied with my sin   eyes fixed on Jesus

|————————————————————————|

- As you look at each continuum, what do you think has changed in your view of God and of yourself during Week 1?
- Have you seen your ability to internalise God's love, grace, mercy and forgiveness through Jesus deepen during Week 1? Why, or why not?

- Are you able and comfortable living in the tension of being a forgiven sinner who is also the one-of-a-kind masterpiece of God created in Christ Jesus and dearly loved by God? Why, or why not?

If you feel that you are predominanty on the left side on the above continuums, consider taking six days to do the exercise below, under 'Additional exercises'. If you find yourself predominantly on the right side of the continuums, please move on to the exercises in the following 'Important' section.

Important: Take a moment to consider with head and heart the reality of sin (commission/omission) in your life—your past sins, your present sins and the fact that you will sin again.

Now add to your pondering of the pervasive reality of sin in your life the idea of your brokenness.

What are the overriding feelings that well up in your heart as you consider these two realities of your life? Why?

However, if your overriding feelings were of love and not condemnation, skip past the following 'Additional exercises' to the paragraph marked 'Moving on'.

If your overriding feeling was self-condemnation, shame or hopelessness—or any combination of these—I would encourage you to spend a week in the additional exercises below. These exercises will provide extra time and opportunity for you to sit with God's forgiveness, unconditional love, acceptance and embrace of you just as you are in this moment, even as God knows all that you have done and will do in terms of sin.

The rhythm for these six days is this: on Days 1, 3 and 5, you will be involved in working through a normal formatted exercise with slowdown, and so on. On Days 2, 4 and 6, you will spend time soaking in the love, grace, mercy and forgiveness of God.

ADDITIONAL EXERCISES

DAY 1

Read Ephesians 2:1–3.

Your sin: See yourself as a sinner, helpless and alienated before a loving and holy God. Let the sins (of commission and omission) and sinful tendencies of your life float through your mind.

Now read and focus all your attention on Ephesians 2:4–5. Allow the truths found in these verses to speak to you concerning who you are now as a result of God's great love and mercy.

- How does this make you feel?
- Which verses have more power in your heart: 2:1–3 or 2:4–5? Why?

Colloquy

Spend time thanking and praising God the Father, Jesus the Son, and the Holy Spirit for the grace, mercy, love and forgiveness you have been given.

DAY 2

Spend your time soaking in the love, grace, mercy and forgiveness of God.

DAY 3

Read Romans 5:6–11.

Spend time with this passage, considering when Jesus died for you. It was not when you had your act together but when you were powerless, ungodly, a sinner and an enemy of God. That is when Jesus died for you.

- What does this passage reveal to you regarding the nature of God's love for you?
- How does that make you feel?
- Are you able to hang on to the extraordinary love God has for you? Why, or why not?

Colloquy

Spend some time thanking and praising God the Father, Jesus the Son, and the Holy Spirit for the grace, mercy, love and forgiveness you have been given.

DAY 4

Spend your time soaking in the love, grace, mercy and forgiveness of God.

DAY 5

Read Romans 8:1, 38–39.

Imagine yourself underneath a giant waterfall of God's love. God's love is rushing over you, drenching you. Imagine that instead of hearing the roaring of the water as it cascades down on you, you hear the gentle whisper of God saying to you, 'There is no condemnation in Christ; nothing can or will ever separate you from my love for you.' Spend time soaking in God's love, being caressed by God's loving touch, and hearing God whisper to you, 'There is no condemnation in Christ; nothing can ever separate you from my love.'

What feelings does this stir within you? Share your feelings with God.

Use all or part of the sentence 'There is no condemnation in Christ; nothing can separate you from my love' as a breath prayer throughout your day.

DAY 6

Spend your time soaking in the love, grace, mercy and forgiveness of God.

DAY 7

Read through and interact with the material contained in the section above beginning with 'Important'.

MOVING ON

If you have not talked to your spiritual director or listener about moving on to Week 2, please do so now. Walk through the above continuums together, and make sure you have truly internalised the love and forgiveness of God as provided for through the death and resurrection of Christ.

If you are feeling that you are in a good internal place for moving forward, do one more thing: take time to recommit to your journey through the Exercises, pledging to give yourself wholly to God (as you are able) and to seek to gain nothing from God. Determine to present yourself each day to God as 'your spiritual act of worship', which is 'holy and pleasing to God' (Romans 12:1).

FINAL REMARKS

These past few sections (the Preparatory Exercises, the Principle and Foundation, and Week 1) have all been building up to the rest of the Exercises. This has been bringing you to a place of deep realisation and internalisation of the greatness and love of God.

In Week 1, as you pondered the global and personal realities of sin, spending significant time naming and exploring your own sins, the goal was to realise the unlimited, unreserved and unconditional love of God in spite of your own sin and brokenness. This love of God is not some kind of warm fuzzy feeling that God has toward you but an engulfing love that propelled Jesus from the freedom of heaven to the confines of a human body and a cross on your behalf. This is a transforming love that meets you right where you are and yet also transforms and reshapes you even as your sin seeks to deform and destroy you.

It is only with this love of God in mind that you can fully and honestly enter into the next phase of the Exercises, known as Week 2. Week 2 plunges you squarely into the life of Jesus and confronts you with questions concerning your willingness to follow Jesus and the depth of your commitment to him. As you enter Week 2, it is critically important for you to experience yourself as one uniquely and unconditionally loved by God, so that you are able to honestly explore where you currently are in regard to your heartfelt desire to follow Jesus.

When you are ready to enter Week 2, read Mark 1—10 in one sitting as your final preparation.

WALKING WITH JESUS

You have now reached what is traditionally known as Week 2 of the Spiritual Exercises of Ignatius. This marks the beginning of your time in the Gospel narratives. This section's focus—the life of Jesus up to the Passion Week—is the heart and soul of the Exercises and comprises the largest single section. This emphasis on the life of Jesus as the focal point for the Exercises is not at all surprising given Ignatius' spiritual journey, for the seeds of his conversion experience were planted as he spent time reading the *Life of Christ* by Ludolph of Saxony, while recuperating from the damage suffered when a cannon ball hit his leg during the battle at Pamplona.

That was just the beginning. In his autobiography Ignatius spoke of special encounters with Jesus, his long and arduous journey to Jerusalem to walk where Jesus walked and his strong desire to return with his followers to Jerusalem before pledging his allegiance to the church. For Ignatius and those with him who founded the Society of Jesus, Jesus was the nucleus that everything else revolved around.

As you move into Week 2, your focus shifts from the sins of the world, Adam and Eve, the angels and your own sin and brokenness to the life of Jesus. Your prayer time each day will involve walking with Jesus, listening to Jesus and interacting with Jesus as you enter into the Gospel narratives. Your desire will now be focused on deepening your knowledge of Jesus and your love for him as well as on walking more closely with him.

To put this week within the framework of the classical stages of spiritual development, you have moved from the Purgative

Way of Week 1 and entered into the Illuminative Way of Week 2. The Purgative Way in the Exercises has been concerned with naming, resisting and overcoming disordered passions globally and personally and, at the same time, seeking to nourish and strengthen your awareness of God's love for you and your trust of God for your salvation while stimulating your love for God. In Week 2, the Illuminative Way is focused on enlightening you to spiritual things and fostering a life orientated to the person and teachings of Jesus while continuing to realise a deepening love for God/Jesus.

In Week 2 you will be seeking to know and embrace Jesus, his values and his mission. From this week on, and through the rest of the '19th Annotation', you will be setting your eyes, heart and mind on Jesus, the author and perfecter of your faith. You will be invited into life with Christ, and Christ will become the prototype and inspiration for your ongoing journey through the Exercises and through life itself.

This Week and those that follow (Weeks 3 and 4) help you to move toward a more Christ-centred life. It is the living out of the apostle Paul's words found in Galatians 2:20: 'I no longer live, but Christ lives in me.' As you work through the daily exercises, you will be fixing your attention on Jesus, which, according to Paul, brings transformation: 'We all, with unveiled face, beholding as in a mirror the glory of the Lord, are being transformed into the same image from glory to glory, just as from the Lord, the Spirit' (2 Corinthians 3:18, NASB).

In Week 2, you will see and experience the Gospel narratives as never before. You will discover things about yourself, about Jesus, about your faith and about your level of commitment that you did not know. You will be walking, talking and being with Jesus. The method for interacting with the narratives will primarily involve the imaginative reading of scripture.[1] You will be encouraged to implement the 'application of the senses', which involves using your senses along with your imagination to be more fully present and involved in the Gospel narratives.[2]

This section leads to a deepened awareness regarding who Jesus is for you and who you are as a follower of Jesus. As you journey through Week 2, you will explicitly and implicitly be confronted by a few questions from Jesus: Who do you say that I am? What is the level of your desire and willingness to follow me? Will you follow me?

Ignatius designed four different meditations with the purpose of helping you discover and gauge the level of your desire to be involved with Christ and to gauge your commitment to him. You will be spending time in three of these meditations: the 'Call of the King',[3] the 'Two Standards'[4] and the 'Three Classes of Persons'.[5] The subject matter of the first two is taken from the life of Ignatius and thus reflects the political system (kings) and violent reality of his times (war). Therefore, these two meditations have been recast to keep intact the original intention of helping you explore your willingness to follow Jesus. The third meditation, 'Three Classes of Persons', remains much the same as it appears in the original Exercises.

The purpose of these three meditations is not to make you choose but rather to help you discern where you currently are in regard to who you are following and your level of commitment. As you make your way through these meditations, you may become aware of how the desire for honour, security, possessions, health, wealth, peace, happiness and so on blinds you to the invitations of Jesus or renders you powerless to say yes to him. A key question in these meditations is, 'What will it cost me to follow (say yes to) Jesus, and am I willing to pay that price?'

Although the three meditations can be powerful and challenging, they play only a small role in your overall experience of Week 2. The majority of your time will be spent entering into the Gospel narratives in a holistic way that encourages you to use your imagination and the application of your senses. Incorporating the imagination and the senses as a means to enter into the Gospel narratives is the genius of the Exercises and, once again, flows out of Ignatius' own conversion experience, which resulted from hours spent imaginatively journeying with Jesus through the Gospel narratives as he recuperated. Ignatius came to realise that employing the imagination and senses helps people to involve their feelings and creativity as well as the cognitive aspects of their being, while opening themselves to God in deeper and more profound ways.

If you have concerns about using your imagination, I encourage you to revisit the biblical rationale for the use of your God-given imagination (under 'Imaginative Prayer' on pages 37–41). Also remember that as you enter the Gospel narratives, you are not trusting your imagination but you are ultimately trusting God, the one who created your imagination. God will be the one you are depending on to guide, lead and teach you through the daily exercises as you utilise your God-given imagination.

Please remember, as you enter into these Gospel narratives using your God-given imagination, to resist the inner voices that pressure you to do it 'right' or 'well'. Instead, just have fun with it and let your ability grow and develop over time. As you enter the text in this way, your time will be transformed from knowing about Jesus to experiencing Jesus and yourself in life-giving and transforming ways. Since it is children who readily use their imaginations, it would make sense that when we use our God-given imagination to walk through the Gospels with Jesus, we find freedom and playfulness.

REMINDER AND ENCOURAGEMENT

JOURNALLING

Journalling through these exercises will help you to see patterns in your prayer times and to recall what God has spoken to you. Often, as you journal, God expands on what you have discovered or been made aware of. I strongly encourage you to journal. It will deepen your experience with the daily exercises.

PRAYER OF EXAMEN

Please continue to strive to make the daily examen part of your time in the Exercises. This is a very important part of the Exercises. If you are still struggling to incorporate this practice into your life, go back and review the section 'Prayer of examen' (pages 29–32).

THE LORD'S PRAYER

Once again, the Lord's Prayer will play a part in this section. When you pray the Lord's Prayer, please do so slowly, lingering with each of the words or phrases. Do not feel compelled to complete the prayer, but rather be open to the inner prompting of the Holy Spirit, seeking to be sensitive to God's invitations and challenges as you pray this prayer. You may find yourself concentrating on a single phrase for your entire time. Just as with the Exercises, the goal is not to get through the Lord's Prayer but to be open to God as you pray the prayer.

ADDITIONS TO EXERCISES

As you enter into Week 2 of the Exercises, there are a number of additions besides the imaginative reading of scripture, the employing of your senses and the three meditations that Ignatius designed for use during this Week. These additions are briefly described below to help you be better prepared as you enter Week 2, so you can fully enter into the experience of it.

BOWING

Bowing will become a part of your opening sessions during this entire Week. The practice of bowing builds on the use of the body in prayer that was mentioned during Week 1. You will bow to begin your time with God. It is a physical declaration of respect, honour, even humility. For centuries, bowing has also been used in religious practices as a sign of submission, adoration, gratitude, reverence and trust. It demonstrates trust when we bow before another, because we render ourselves helpless and fully vulnerable to their attack.

TWO NEW GRACES

The second addition to this Week is two new graces. The first grace will be used only in conjunction with the three meditations mentioned above. You will be asking to not be deaf to Jesus' call and to be ready and willing to do what Jesus asks.[6] This will be the grace for sections 1 and 6 of this Week. The rest of the time you will be asking to know Jesus intimately, to love him more intensely and to follow him more closely.[7] Remember to ask God for the suggested grace each day as you begin your time in the exercise for that day. It can also be helpful to recall the grace to your mind as you rise in the morning and to make it a prayer throughout your day.

NEW COLLOQUIES

The third addition during Week 2 is occasionally to end your prayer time with a couple of new colloquies. These colloquies will move you on from activity to quiet presence, from striving to being still and being with God. In Week 2 there is a definite move to a time of resting in God as a part of your daily experience. During those times, seek to just be.

TWO PRAYERS

On a number of days, you will be invited to sit with the words of two prayers, seeking to discern whether they express your heartfelt desires. Be honest with yourself and God as you ponder the words of the prayer, seeking to discover why the prayers do or do not truly express your inner desires regarding following Jesus. These two prayers take the place of the *Anima Christi* (Soul of Christ) prayer of Week 1.

Eternal Lord and King of all creation, humbly I come before you… I am moved by your grace to offer myself to you and your work. I deeply desire to be with you in accepting all wrongs and all rejections and all poverty, both actual and spiritual—and I deliberately choose this, if it is for your greater service and praise.[8]

Lord Jesus,
Help me to know you, to love you, to follow you.
Help alleviate my fears
and fan the embers of trust within me.
Give me the strength to say yes to your invitations,
the courage to continue my journey with you.
Remind me that you are
the Way,
the Truth
and the Life,
and apart from you there is no life,
but with you
and you alone
is fullness of life,
life everlasting.

Ignatius also suggests, if you are so inclined, that you do some spiritual reading. A book that he recommended for this very purpose is *The Imitation of Christ* by Thomas à Kempis. Ignatius used this book devotionally throughout his life. If you have the desire to make it a part of your Week 2 experience, consider buying a copy or downloading the entire book and listening to it as you drive or exercise.[9]

RECALLING THE FOCUS

The final new addition involves recalling to your mind the focus of your morning meditation throughout your day.[10] This simple practice can have a radical impact on your experience through this section of the Exercises. It helps you to be more open and aware of your desires and of what God may be up to in and through you. It is a way of continually presenting yourself to God throughout the day and reminding yourself that you are living with God, in God, and that God is living in you.

THREE CAUTIONS

First, please keep in mind that this may not be an easy section to make your way through. You will be challenged internally in terms of your own 'stuff', but also externally. It seems that during this section of the Exercises, distractions more readily arise, such as the temptation to say no to the exercises and yes to something else, something that is not bad but is not the focus of your time with God.

As I have journeyed with others, I have seen many abandon their journey during this Week of the Exercises, even though they were initially very excited about focusing on the life of Jesus. I believe a spiritual battle intensifies in Week 2 because of the transforming power that flows from time spent with Jesus in the ways incorporated in this section.

As you enter into this Week, you enter more fully into a spiritual battle between the flesh and the spirit and the principalities and powers of this world. Be on guard, for there is often a level of spiritual warfare that arises as you intentionally focus on the person of Jesus, seeking to love him more dearly and follow him more closely, which is exactly the grace you will be seeking this Week. This is a good time to come before God and recommit yourself to the journey, not just now, but weekly and even daily.

Second, as you work your way through Week 2, you will soon discover that you know, or are at least familiar with, most if not all of the Gospel narratives that will make up your daily experiences through this Week. Please be aware that you may be tempted not to enter fully into the narratives or prepare yourself to enter into them because you may assume that you know how God will meet you in the story or teach you from the story. Let go of all expectations, and endeavour to truly use your imagination and senses as you enter into the story and let the Spirit guide and direct your time.

Finally, beware of the expectations and feelings that may spontaneously arise within you as you enter Week 2, knowing you are going to spend your prayer times walking with Jesus through the Gospel narratives. You may expect powerful emotional times, or you may be anticipating some jaw-dropping experiences and mind-blowing insights. But you need to embrace indifference, endeavouring to be present to and trusting of God and the process. Seek to enter each prayer experience expectation-free and desiring simply to 'show up', presenting yourself as a living sacrifice, 'holy and pleasing to God—this is your spiritual act of worship' (Romans 12:1). Resist the temptation to evaluate your daily times on the basis of your felt experience or what you feel you 'got out of' your prayer time.

If the new additions seem overwhelming, do not worry. You will be prompted when to make use of them, so that you are not caught off-guard and to provide additional information regarding these components without interrupting the flow of the Exercises. Please also seek to incorporate journalling and the prayer of examen into your day. And do take heed of the cautions above, even rereading them from time to time.

RULES OF DISCERNMENT: WEEK 2

Ignatius provides key discernment insights for those entering into Week 2.[11] These new Rules of Discernment deal with the subtleties of spiritual attacks—the danger of taking consolations at face value and the tendency of the enemy to appear disguised as 'an angel of light' (2 Corinthians 11:14). The tactics of the evil spirit may become much more subtle as you continue to journey through the Exercises. It is important to have a keen awareness of Ignatius' insights regarding discerning the source of consolations you experience.

These new Rules of Discernment are for you who are maturing in your faith as you continue your journey through the Exercises. These rules presuppose that you are walking with God, that you are choosing to say yes to God and that praising, worshipping and serving God is the desire of your heart.

Unlike the first set of Rules of Discernment, which dealt primarily with desolation, these rules focus on the ambiguity of consolation. Consolation, which was the realm of the good spirit in the Rule of Discernment for Week 1, is now portrayed as a likely weapon of the evil spirit. The concern addressed with the Rules of Discernment for Week 2 is the subtlety of the evil spirit's new strategies. These rules, like the first set, help you to 'be aware' (notice what is going on within), and 'understand' (whether this is from God or not) your inner movements (feelings) and then prepare you to 'take action' (accept or reject what you have noticed and understood).[12]

Just like the first set of rules, these too arose out of Ignatius' experiences. It was during his time in Manresa that Ignatius discovered that the evil spirit not only uses desolation but also makes use of consolation for his own purposes. While in Manresa, Ignatius would go to bed for much-needed sleep and begin to receive great enlightenment and consolation that would rob him of sleep. Over time he came to realise that these were not coming from God but from the evil one. Additionally, while he was studying

Latin, he received great spiritual delights and insights into spiritual matters that hindered his ability to continue his studies. Once again he realised that these consolations were not from God but from the evil one. Through these two experiences and the help of his spiritual director, Ignatius became convinced that consolations did not always have their source in God but could be used by the evil spirit against those who seek to follow after God.

Because you are changing, the strategies of the enemy are changing too. Now the evil one will not tend to tempt you with something overtly evil, but will come under the appearance of good. The brilliant military commander will now become subtler, cleverer and craftier, making use of Trojan horses and all sorts of evil camouflaged as good to ensnare you. Jesus warned regarding wolves in sheep's clothing (Matthew 7:15), and the apostle Paul admonished that Satan himself masquerades as an angel of light (2 Corinthians 11:14).

THE RULES

1. When you are living with Jesus on the screen of your life, you will tend to experience God's presence as supportive, encouraging, even joy-filled, and you will tend to experience the presence of the evil one as bringing dissatisfaction, anxiety, self-doubts, even feelings of pride concerning your walk with God.[13]
2. If you experience the rising of consolation without an external catalyst, this is a consolation you can trust as coming from God. It is called 'a consolation without previous cause'. This type of consolation is not given because of anything you did but as a gracious gift from God. This is the only type of consolation that can be fully trusted and entered into without reservation. (However, in Rule 8 below, Ignatius will even give some cautionary advice about the period immediately following this type of consolation.)[14]

3. When you experience consolation that has an external cause to it (music, scripture, a sunset, a child's smile, a work of art, a sermon, a passage in a book), its source can be the good or evil spirit. Ignatius advised that the source of consolation, even if it flows from something good, may not be from God but can just as easily be from the evil spirit and used for his ends.
4. In case you did not get the message in Rule 3, Rule 4 clearly states that the evil one can and does appear as an angel of light and will even use good and holy thoughts to achieve his ends. The days of being tempted solely with something overtly evil are over. Wisdom and discernment are now the order of the day.[15]

This is a tactic experienced by those in Week 2 and beyond. As you go through the Exercises, you may be tempted to use your entire hour in the slowdown or feel the need to ponder something that has arisen within you during that time instead of entering into the Exercises that day. Be careful: this is exactly how the evil one may get you off track. These things are not wrong, but they do take you away from the Exercises.

5. A good, God-honouring beginning that brings consolation does not guarantee a good, God-honouring ending. Here you are cautioned to be self-aware and discerning, not only as you make a decision but as you proceed with that decision. You may make a decision based on wisdom that seems like a good decision, but that does not mean you will not fall into the snare of the evil one. The angel of light can begin to subtly divert your attention and course from where you began. If at some point you discover that your heart and mind are far from God, the evil spirit has derailed you.

The prayer of examen can be a great tool in this discernment process when used in the prescribed way at noontime and night. A few good questions for use during your examen in order to discern the source of a consolation are, 'Where is this leading me: God, evil, distraction, less good? Am I currently experiencing harmony, distress, peace or disturbance in my heart? What changes have taken place regarding the beginning trajectory of the consolation and where it is now leading me?'

6. When you realise that you have been deceived, retrace your steps. Go back to the beginning, middle and end of your choice, exploring your attitudes to see where the evil spirit got its hooks into you.
7. When you are proceeding from good to better, you will experience God's touch as light and gentle, like a drop of water falling on a sponge, but you will experience the evil spirit like a drop of water hitting a stone. However, if you are proceeding from good to bad, your experience of God and the evil spirit will be the opposite of what is stated above.
8. Beware of the afterglow of consolation without previous cause. Although consolation without previous cause is without a doubt from God, all that follows from that experience is not necessarily from God. Be careful about making heartfelt commitments and vows to God after such a time; this could very well be the evil spirit sidetracking a holy moment for his own ends. These afterglow feelings are not directly connected to the consolation without previous cause and can be used by the evil spirit to lead you to make decisions that appear to be God-honouring but are not what God is inviting you into. So be determined not to make any decision immediately after an experience of consolation without previous cause.

These Rules of Discernment for Week 2 serve to warn you that the strategies of the evil one are becoming more subtle and sophisticated. It is extremely important for you to be vigilant, evaluating and reevaluating perceived consolations and good and holy thoughts to discern their origin and determine if they should be embraced and followed or not.

I have seen this twisting of consolations for the enemy's purpose again and again as I have journeyed through the Exercises with others. It can be very subtle and always seems like a good thing, even a God-honouring endeavour, yet it gradually leads the person away from God, away from the very journey into which God invited her to enter. Be on guard! The Rules of Discernment for Week 2 serve to remind you of the perils of your journey and hopefully reinforce the value of having a spiritual director or listener to accompany you. As your journey continues, so the attacks continue to grow in their devious subtlety.

FINAL REMARKS

The above could very well feel overwhelming to you, but do not worry. You will be prompted below when to make use of those components listed above. They are provided so you are not caught off-guard when they make their appearance during the daily exercises and to provide additional information regarding these components without interrupting the flow of the Exercises.

If you have not yet done so, please read Mark 1—10 in one sitting before entering Week 2. This will provide you with a brief overview of much that you will be exploring during this section of the Exercises.

As you enter into and journey through Week 2, my prayer for you is this:

God grant this one strength in accordance with your incredibly great power at work within him or her to continue the journey; give this precious one your wisdom that she or he would come to know Jesus more intimately, love Jesus more intensely and be emboldened in faith to follow him more closely. (Adapted from Ephesians 1:19; 1:17; 2 Timothy 1:7)

EXERCISES FOR WEEK 2

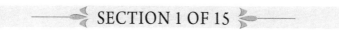

SECTION 1 OF 15

The grace you are seeking is not to be deaf to Jesus' call and to be ready and willing to do what Jesus asks.[16]

Examen questions

When and how did you choose to follow Jesus and embrace his call today?

Start your time with a bow—slowly bending from your waist—as a visible sign of your reverence for and honouring of God, while asking God that everything in your day may more and more lead you to divine praise and service.[17]

Process

- ☐ Opening
- ☐ Daily exercise
- ☐ Journalling
- ☐ Closing
- ☐ Noontime examen
- ☐ Evening examen

DAY 1

Will you?[18]

Part 1: In your imagination, stand before a truly good and powerful person who says, 'It is my will to rid all lands of injustice and bring them peace, rest, healing, hope and love. I would like you to join me. If you agree to join me, and I hope you do, you would have to be content to eat as I do, and to drink and dress and live as I do. Likewise, you will labour with me in the day and watch with me in the night, being alert and ready at all times to do my bidding. And you will have a place at my table, a part with me in the victory. And I will call you friend.'

Consider how you would respond to such a request.

Part 2: In your imagination, stand before Jesus and hear him say to you, 'It is my will to bring all the world into the glory of my Father's kingdom, to rid all lands of injustice and bring peace, rest, healing, hope and love. I would like you to join me. If you agree to join me, and I hope you do, you will walk as I walk and live as I live, labouring with me, being alert and ready at all times to do my bidding, following me in the pain so that you may also follow me in the glory. And you shall have a place at my table, a part with me in my victory. And I will call you friend.'

Consider how you would respond and how you are currently responding to this call of Christ.

DAY 2

Read Matthew 8:18–22.

Imaginatively enter into this passage at least twice. The first time, picture yourself as one who comes to Jesus, moved by Jesus' teaching and pledging to follow him wherever he goes.

- What are your expectations as you approach Jesus?
- What do you feel as you hear Jesus' reply?
- What do you do?

The second time, picture yourself as the disciple who asked Jesus to allow him to travel home 'to bury my father'.

- What are your expectations as you approach Jesus?
- What do you feel as you hear Jesus' reply?
- What do you do?

Ask God to show you if there are any things in your life that may either hinder your ability to hear Jesus' call to follow or hamper you from actually following Jesus.

Sit with the words of the following prayer.

Eternal Lord and King of all creation, humbly I come before you... I am moved by your grace to offer myself to you and your work. I deeply desire to be with you in accepting all wrongs and all rejections and all poverty, both actual and spiritual—and I deliberately choose this, if it is for your greater service and praise.

- What do these words stir within you?
- Are you willing to pray this prayer in a heartfelt way? Why, or why not?

DAY 3

Read Matthew 10:1–15.

Read through this passage a couple of times, being open to verses, words or phrases to which you are drawn. Once you have gathered a number of these, spend the rest of your time pondering them.

- Is there a theme that connects them?
- What feelings do these verses, words or phrases stir within you?
- What are you feeling about saying yes to Jesus and going out with the Twelve?

Share your thoughts and feelings with God.

DAY 4

Review Part 2 of the Kingdom Meditation from Day 1.

Consider how you are currently responding to this call of Christ to embrace his life and follow him.

- Has your level of desire and commitment to follow Jesus changed at all? Why, or why not?

Colloquy

Spend time expressing thanksgiving and gratitude to God the Father, Jesus the Son, and the Holy Spirit individually.

DAY 5

Read Matthew 10:16–24.

Read through this passage a couple of times, being open to verses, words or phrases to which you are drawn. Once you have gathered a number of these, spend the rest of your time pondering them.

- Is there a theme that connects these words?
- What feelings do they stir within you?
- What are you feeling about saying yes to Jesus and going out with the Twelve?

Share your thoughts and feelings with God.

....

Recall to mind
Recall the focus of your morning meditation throughout your day.[19] This simple practice can have a radical impact on your experience through this Week of the Exercises. It can help to open you up to God, providing an opportunity for you to present yourself to God throughout your day, and serve to remind you that you are living with God and in God, and that God is living in you.

....

DAY 6

Sit with the words of this prayer.

Eternal Lord and King of all creation, humbly I come before you... I am moved by your grace to offer myself to you and your work. I deeply desire to be with you in accepting all wrongs and all rejections and all poverty, both actual and spiritual—and I deliberately choose this, if it is for your greater service and praise.

- What do these words stir within you?
- Are you willing to pray this prayer in a heartfelt way? Why, or why not?

If not, take some time to write your own prayer that would communicate your desire to follow Jesus.

Conclude your time by slowly praying the Lord's Prayer.

DAY 7

Review.

Read your journal entries from this Week and part 2 of the Kingdom Meditation from Day 1. Consider how you are currently responding to this call of Christ to embrace his life and follow him.

Has your level of desire and commitment to follow Jesus changed at all? Why, or why not?

Slowly pray the Lord's Prayer.

....

Opening time in prayer
Make sure you make full use of the slowdown and commitment time at the beginning of your time in prayer each day. Do not rush through the opening time, which is

designed to help you slow down and foster respect for God as you come into God's presence. This opening involves a conscious effort to present yourself before God as a living and holy sacrifice (Romans 12:1) and to ready yourself to be present to God. It can be an aid in helping you enter fully into the Exercises and experience God throughout your day.

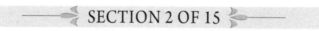

SECTION 2 OF 15

The new grace you are seeking today is to know Jesus intimately, to love him more intensely and to follow him more closely.

Examen questions

- How and when did I demonstrate my trust in God today?
- How and when did I demonstrate my lack of trust in God today?

Start your time with a bow—slowly bending from your waist—as a visible sign of your reverence for and honouring of God, while asking God that everything in your day may more and more lead you to divine praise and service.

Process

- ☐ Opening
- ☐ Daily exercise
- ☐ Journalling
- ☐ Closing
- ☐ Noontime examen
- ☐ Evening examen

DAY 1

Read Matthew 1:18–25.

Imagine you are Joseph.

- What are you feeling?
- What is your reaction? What would you do?
- What do Joseph's responses reveal about his faith and trust in God?
- What about your responses? What do they reveal about your faith and trust in God?

DAY 2

Read Matthew 1:23.

Spend your time today pondering and journalling about the implications of the name Immanuel, which was given to Jesus.

What does this name convey to you and stir within you?

DAY 3

Read Luke 1:26–39.

Imagine you are Mary, an unwed but pledged young girl in a male-dominated culture, where you can rightfully be killed for being unfaithful to your husband-to-be. You have been told by an angel that you are with child.

- What are you feeling after the angel leaves you?
- What are your fears, concerns and doubts?
- Will you tell anyone? Why, or why not?

DAY 4

Review.

Read through your journal entries from the past couple of days, seeking something that resonated deep within you, something that was either drawing you or stirring resistance in you. Spend your prayer time pondering, unpacking and exploring whatever you come up with.

DAY 5

Read Luke 1:37–38.

Sit with these words of the angel to Mary (to you).

- Do you believe these words to be true?
- Do you currently live in a way that would confirm or deny your answer? How?
- How might your life be different if you really believed these words?
- What is your level of trust in God (not trust in God doing what you want God to do for you, but trust in the person and character of God, come what may)?

Sit with Mary's response to God, a response that springs from a deep place of trust and little understanding.

Would your response be different from or the same as Mary's? Why?

DAY 6

Read Luke 2:1–7.

Imagine you are Joseph.

- What are you feeling as Mary's labour begins?
- What are you feeling as you hear the baby's first sounds, as you hold Immanuel, God with us, in your arms and you feel his heart beating?
- As you look into the eyes of the Lord your God?
- As you remember the angel's words to you?
- As you watch the Creator of heaven and earth get his first mouthfuls of nourishment at Mary's breast?

Imagine you are Mary.

- What are you feeling as labour begins?
- What are you feeling as you hear the baby's first sounds, as you hold Immanuel, God with us, in your arms and you feel his heart beating?
- As you look into the eyes of the Lord your God?
- As you remember the angel's words to you?
- As you watch the Creator of heaven and earth get his first mouthfuls of nourishment at your breast?

DAY 7

Review your week.

- Which passages really touched you? Why?
- How are these passages shaping and strengthening your ability to trust God and your appreciation of the gift of Jesus and the faith of Mary and Joseph?

When you are finished, just be with Jesus, resting in his love for you and acknowledging his presence with you. Take a few moments to cease from striving and to be still in the presence of the One who is with you and within you.

....

I am not doing this right
If you feel that you are not journeying through the Exercises correctly, please seek to trust God and trust the process. God is at work. The Exercises are bringing you into the presence of God with intentionality; the rest is up to God. Do not try to make something happen. Trust God and trust the process, focusing not on what is seen, but on what is unseen and thus eternal (2 Corinthians 4:18).

....

SECTION 3 OF 15

The grace you are seeking this week is to know Jesus intimately, to love him more intensely and to follow him more closely.

Examen questions

- How and when did I demonstrate my trust in God today?
- How and when did I demonstrate my lack of trust in God today?

Start your time with a bow—slowly bending from your waist—as a visible sign of your reverence for and honouring of God, while asking God that everything in your day may more and more lead you to divine praise and service.

Process

☐ Opening   ☐ Closing
☐ Daily exercise   ☐ Noontime examen
☐ Journalling   ☐ Evening examen

DAY 1

Read Luke 2:8–14.

Imagine you are a shepherd.

- What are you feeling as you see the angels and hear the message they bring?
- What does it feel like to have the angel tell you, a lowly shepherd, this good news? What does this tell you about God?
- What is it that drives you to the manger (such as curiosity, hope, boredom, peer pressure, fear)?
- What are you feeling and thinking as you look up and see the star in the sky?
- What are you feeling and thinking as you run to the manger?
- Why doesn't anything else matter to you except going to see this newborn baby?
- When you arrive at the manger, where do you stand? What do you do, think, feel and say?
- Imagine Mary calling you to come closer, and, as you approach, she gently hands Jesus to you. What goes on in your heart? What do you feel?
- What is it like to hold in your arms the Creator and Sustainer of all that is seen and unseen, to see his little hands and feet, to feel him gripping your finger, to feel the warmth of his body against your chest?
- What do you see in his eyes?
- What do you say to the Lord your God as you cradle him in your arms?

DAY 2

Read Luke 2:22–39.

Imagine you are Simeon.

- What are you feeling about this child? About God?
- What does this event demonstrate about the character of God?

DAY 3

Read Matthew 2:13–18.

Imagine you are Mary, who becomes aware that although she is safe with her child, many mothers in Israel are weeping over the deaths of their children.

- What are you feeling?
- What questions do you have for God?
- What goes through your mind as you hold Jesus, knowing that others no longer have a child to hold?

DAY 4

Review.

Read through your journal entries from the past couple of days, seeking something that resonated deep within you, something that was either drawing you or stirring resistance in you. Spend your prayer time pondering, unpacking and exploring whatever you come up with.

Slowly pray the Lord's Prayer.

DAY 5

Read Matthew 1:23.

Think over all you have pondered about Jesus thus far. In light of all this, spend your time today pondering and journalling about new awareness, insights and implications of the name Immanuel, which was given to Jesus.

- What does this name now convey to you?
- What does it stir within you?

Spend time thanking God the Father for the gift of his Son, and thanking Jesus for his willingness to become a child, to be Immanuel, God with us. Slowly pray the Lord's Prayer.

DAY 6

Read Luke 2:41–52.

Spend time imagining Jesus at the following ages: infant to two years, three to five years, and six to twelve years. Try to appreciate his development, his vulnerability and his challenges at each age.

Conclude your time by thanking God for sending Jesus, and thanking Jesus for choosing to come to earth, clothed in the flesh of an infant who had to grow and develop like the rest of us.

DAY 7

Review your week.

- Which passages really touched you? Why?
- How are these passages shaping or strengthening your ability to trust God and your appreciation of the gift of Jesus?

Spend time thanking God the Father for the gift of the Son, and thanking Jesus for his willingness to become a child, to become Immanuel. When you are finished, just be with Jesus, resting in his love for you, acknowledging his presence with you. Take a few moments to cease from striving and be still in the presence of the One who is with you and within you.

Slowly pray the Lord's Prayer.

You and Jesus
As you meditate on these various passages of scripture, focusing on the life of Christ, please be aware of what draws you to Christ, challenges you, amazes you or gives you pause. Please take time to journal about and ponder these internal movements.

SECTION 4 OF 15

The grace you are seeking this week is to know Jesus intimately, to love him more intensely and to follow him more closely.

Examen questions

- How and when did you experience Immanuel (God with you) today?
- When were you aware of your love for Jesus today?
- When do you 'follow Jesus' in your relationships, circumstances, reactive and proactive responses, and actions?

Start your time with a bow—slowly bending from your waist—as a visible sign of your reverence for and honouring of God, while asking God that everything in your day may more and more lead you to divine praise and service.

Process

- ☐ Opening
- ☐ Daily exercise
- ☐ Journalling
- ☐ Closing
- ☐ Noontime examen
- ☐ Evening examen

DAY 1

Read Matthew 3:13–17.

Read through this passage, keeping in mind the circumstances surrounding the birth of Jesus, who as a child grew up as one who was conceived out of wedlock.

- What must it have been like to grow up among the whispers, condemnation and ridicule of others?
- What do you think God's words, 'This is my Son, whom I love; with him I am well pleased,' meant to Jesus?
- What do you think they made him feel?
- What are the words you long to hear from God? Spend some time listening for the still small voice of God.

DAY 2

Read Matthew 4:1–11.

Imagine you are looking on from afar.

- What do you notice about Jesus before Satan comes to tempt him, during the temptation and after the temptation?

When the temptations are over, go and speak to Jesus. Journal your interaction with Jesus. What do you say, and why? How does Jesus respond to you?

DAY 3

Read John 1:35–42.

Imagine you are with John's disciples as they are following Jesus, and Jesus turns around and asks, 'What do you want?' Sit before God, before Jesus, and answer that question as if it is addressed to you right now. Spend time pondering, journalling about and unpacking your response. Conclude your time by expressing your desire to God the Father and then to Jesus.

....

Expectations and Jesus

Be aware of expectations and feelings that may spontaneously arise within you, knowing you are going to keep spending your prayer times walking with Jesus through the Gospel narratives. You may anticipate powerfully emotional times, you may be anticipating some jaw-dropping experience or mind-blowing insights—but you need to come seeking to embrace indifference, endeavouring to be present to and trusting of God and the process. Seek to enter each prayer experience expectation-free and desiring simply to 'show up', presenting yourself as a living sacrifice, 'holy and pleasing to God—this is your spiritual act of worship' (Romans 12:1).

....

DAY 4

Review.

Read through your journal entries from the past couple of days, seeking to find something that resonated deep within you, either drawing you or stirring up resistance in you as you spent time in the daily exercises. Spend your prayer time pondering, unpacking and exploring whatever you come up with.

Slowly pray the Lord's Prayer.

DAY 5

Read Mark 1:16–20.

Imagine you are one of those called by Jesus to 'follow me'.

- What do you feel as you hear his words addressed to you?

- What draws you to follow Jesus?
- What fears arise within you?

Colloquy

Seek to end your time 'just being with' Jesus, rather than having a verbal response. Be still and be with God.[20]

....

Imagination
The use of the imagination enables you to incorporate your mind and heart in your times of contemplation or meditation. Do not get discouraged because of what you perceive to be a deficiency in your ability to make use of imagination. The important thing is to do it to the degree you are able and to trust that God will honour your efforts. The use of the imagination is a powerful tool of illumination and formation that Ignatius incorporated in the Exercises (see 'Imaginative Prayer' on pages 37–41).

....

DAY 6

Read Luke 5:1–11.

Imagine you are Peter.

- What do you think and feel as Jesus tells you to put your net on the other side of the boat?
- What do you learn about Jesus as a result of the extraordinary catch of fish?
- Would this be enough for you to realise who Jesus is? Why, or why not?
- Would this be enough for you to leave behind all and follow Jesus? Why, or why not?

- In what ways could this event with Jesus have an impact on how you live your life?

DAY 7

Review your week.

- What qualities of Jesus were you drawn to as you journeyed through the past week?
- What surprised or shocked you about Jesus?
- How has this week helped you to know Jesus more intimately, to love Jesus more intensely and to follow him more closely?
- Was there anything that encouraged you or gave you pause or concern regarding following Jesus? If so, what, and why?
- Are you becoming more in tune with Jesus' call in your life, and is your willingness increasing to say yes to the invitations of Jesus? Why, or why not?

Share your thoughts and feelings with God/Jesus, and, when you are finished, just be with Jesus, resting in his love for you, acknowledging his presence with you. Take a few moments to cease from striving and be still in the presence of the One who is with you and within you.

....

Showing up

Your part is to show up and enter into the Exercises for each day, as you are able. By doing that, you have offered yourself to God and declared your desire to be with God and hear from God. That is all you can do. What happens beyond that is up to God. Rest assured that to come into God's presence is to be changed. You may or may not feel something, but God is at work.

....

SECTION 5 OF 15

During part of this week, you will focus on two extra-biblical meditations found in Week 2 of Ignatius' Exercises. The purpose of these meditations is for you to discern where you currently are in your spiritual life. It is not about deciding where you want to be or think you should be, but about honestly assessing where you currently are in terms of following Christ and making choices. You will spend two days on each of the meditations.

The grace you are seeking this week is not to be deaf to Jesus' call in my life and to be ready and willing to do what he wants.[21]

Examen questions

- When were you not able to be indifferent today? Why?
- What were you attached to today?
- When were you aware of choosing to follow after Jesus? What helped you to make that decision?

Start your time with a bow—slowly bending from your waist—as a visible sign of your reverence for and honouring of God, while asking God that everything in your day may more and more lead you to divine praise and service.

Process

- ☐ Opening
- ☐ Daily exercise
- ☐ Journalling

- ☐ Closing
- ☐ Noontime examen
- ☐ Evening examen

DAYS 1–2

Who will it be? [22]

Imagine that you are at a beautiful setting of your choosing, and there are two people vying for your attention, desiring an alliance with you. The first catches your eye and, with an alluring smile and self-assured manner, begins to flatter you, promising you personal value, riches, fame, power, physical intimacy, the satisfaction of all your desires. The words are intoxicating and seductive. Pay attention to the ways in which you are enticed, seduced, ensnared.

Which is it—flattery, personal value, riches, fame, power, physical intimacy, the satisfaction of all your desires—that entices, seduces or ensnares you? Why?

Spend time asking Jesus to help you fight these battles.

Now imagine Jesus standing in the same setting before you. Hear him calling you away from what has enticed you, and calling you to embrace love, joy, peace, patience, kindness, goodness, faithfulness, gentleness and self-control. Inviting you to embrace an attitude of indifference—not desiring life over death, health over sickness or riches over poverty, but being willing to say yes to God.

Spend time thinking over which of these things might be hard for you to stop seeking after. Explore with Jesus why this might be so.

Colloquy

Seek to end your time 'just being with' Jesus, rather than having a verbal response. Be still and be with God.

DAYS 3–4

Three classes of people [23]

Using your imagination, consider the three types of people described below. People in each of these types have great wealth and consider themselves to be faithful followers of Jesus.

Class 1: These individuals desire to be free from their dependence on their possessions because they see their possessions as hindrances to following fully after Jesus. They have good intentions but remain busy with the daily demands of life. They end their lives still thinking about getting rid of their possessions and fully following Jesus, but have not done so. Their lives are characterised by a lot of talk but no action.

Class 2: These individuals would like to free themselves from all the attachments that get in the way of relating to God. They believe that working harder will bring them freedom. These individuals are willing to do just about anything, but face a block that hinders their ability to fully follow Jesus. They may do any number of good things, all the while avoiding the real issue. Their lives are characterised by doing everything but the one necessary thing.

Class 3: These individuals desire to be rid of attachments that get in the way of fully following Jesus. Their desire is to be sensitive to the movements of God's Spirit in their lives and to be ready and willing to follow God's lead. These individuals seek to arrive at a place where they want neither to retain their possessions nor to give them away, unless God directs them to do so. Their lives are characterised by a desire to hear and respond to God's invitation.

- As you look at your life, which of these types of people would best characterise how you live your life?
- What can you point to in your life that would confirm your choice?

Share your insights with God the Father, Jesus the Son, and the Holy Spirit.

Colloquy

Seek to end your time 'just being with' Jesus, rather than having a verbal response. Be still and be with God.

Emotions

Beware of what you are feeling about God, yourself and the exercise of the day. We are often taught to ignore our emotions, but Ignatius found that our emotions are an aid in our spiritual formation as we become aware and unpack them. As you pay attention to your emotions—such as resistance—and unpack them, you will learn more about yourself and your image of God in the process. Your emotions will prove to be an excellent source of material for journalling.

DAY 5

Review the previous four days.

What insights have you gained about you and about your desire and commitment to follow Jesus?

DAY 6

Read Luke 14:25–34.

Imagine Jesus speaking the words of this passage to you. Spend time thinking through what the cost might be that would hinder you from being able to say unequivocally to Jesus, 'Yes, I will follow you.'

- What might it be difficult for you to part with to follow Jesus? Why?

Share your thoughts, feelings and concerns with Jesus.
    Sit with the words of the following prayer.

Eternal Lord and King of all creation, humbly I come before you… I am moved by your grace to offer myself to you and your work. I deeply desire to be with you in accepting all wrongs and all rejections and all poverty, both actual and spiritual—and I deliberately choose this, if it is for your greater service and praise.

- What do these words stir within you?
- Are you willing to pray this prayer in a heartfelt way? Why, or why not?

DAY 7

Review your week.

- How has this week helped you to know Jesus more intimately, to love Jesus more intensely and to follow him more closely?
- What have you learned about your level of trust in God/Jesus and the impact that has on your ability to follow Jesus in your daily life?
- Are you becoming more in tune with Jesus' call in your life, and do you desire to say yes to the invitations of Jesus? Why, or why not?

Share your thoughts and feelings with God/Jesus, and, when you are finished, just be with Jesus, resting in his love for you, acknowledging his presence with you. Take a few moments to cease from striving, and be still in the presence of the One who is with you and within you.

....

About questions and suggestions

The questions given to ponder and suggestions regarding how to enter into the story are just that: questions and suggestions. These are given to help you get started. In my own journey through the Exercises, I found it helpful to enter the same Gospel narrative from various perspectives: as a bystander, as a disciple, as a person interacting with Jesus and even as Jesus. Each different way of entering into the narrative can bring additional insights and opportunity for connection with Jesus. Putting yourself in Jesus' place also can bring great insight and opportunity to discover some aspects of who he is or how he interacts with others. In short, do not feel constrained by the suggestions and questions. Have fun, explore and experiment, always being open to God.

SECTION 6 OF 15

The grace you are seeking this week is to know Jesus intimately, to love him more intensely and to follow him more closely.

Examen questions

- How and when did you experience Immanuel (God with you) today?
- When were you aware of your love for Jesus today?
- When do you 'follow Jesus' in your relationships, circumstances, reactive and proactive responses, and actions?

Start your time with a bow—slowly bending from your waist—as a visible sign of your reverence for and honouring of God, while asking God that everything in your day may more and more lead you to divine praise and service.

Process

☐ Opening   ☐ Closing
☐ Daily exercise   ☐ Noontime examen
☐ Journalling   ☐ Evening examen

DAY 1

Read John 2:1–11.

Imagine you are a bystander who knows what is going on.

- What are you feeling as this story unfolds?
- What is your reaction as you realise Jesus has turned the water into wine?
- What does this miracle show you?
- What does this miracle teach you about God?
- About Jesus?
- About what it might mean to follow Jesus?

Colloquy

Freely speak out your joy, thanks, wonder and praise to the triune God, earnestly beseeching God that God would enable you to know Jesus more closely and follow Jesus more nearly.

....

Imagine freely and lightly

Do not get bogged down trying to imagine the scene perfectly, especially if you, like Ignatius, have travelled to the Holy Land. The composition of the scene is but a small part of what imaginative prayer is about. Its purpose is encounter with the living God through the living Word.

....

DAY 2

Read John 2:13–16.

Imagine you are following Jesus up the steps to the temple. People are coming and going in this time of the Passover. Watch Jesus fashion a whip and turn over tables. Hear his words to those selling goods in the temple.

- What are you feeling?
- What are you learning about Jesus?
- How do Jesus' actions and words change how you see him and feel toward him?

Subtlety of temptations
Be on guard. The tactics of temptations can change drastically during Week 2. The evil one will seek to derail your journey by using even good things: godly thoughts, consolations, spiritual insights. But these will take you away from your time in the Exercises. So be aware. If these things take you from the very thing God has called you to, there is a good chance that they are not from God. (See 'Rules of Discernment: Week 2' on pages 170–174.)

DAY 3

Read Matthew 8:5–13.

Imagine you are the centurion.

- Why do you come to Jesus for help?
- What is stirred within you as Jesus says he will come and heal your servant?
- When Jesus praises your faith, what do you feel?
- What do you learn about Jesus through this story?
- In what ways could this truth about Jesus have an impact on how you live your life?

Pray the following prayer, and spend time sitting with its words:

Lord Jesus,
Help me to know you, to love you, to follow you.
Help alleviate my fears
and fan the embers of trust within me.

Give me the strength to say yes to your invitations,
the courage to continue my journey with you.
Remind me that you are
the Way,
the Truth
and the Life,
and apart from you there is no life,
but with you,
and with you alone
is fullness of life,
life everlasting.

- What are the truths that resonate with you? Why?
- Does this prayer express your desires? Why, or why not?

DAY 4

Review.

Read through your journal entries from the past couple of days, seeking something that resonated deep within you, something that was either drawing you or stirring resistance in you. Spend your prayer time pondering, unpacking and exploring whatever you come up with.

Slowly pray the Lord's Prayer.

DAY 5

Read Matthew 8:23–27.

Imagine you are in the boat. Allow yourself to feel the force of the storm and the fear rising within you as the waves build and begin to crash over the bow of the boat. Look at the faces of the other disciples. Look at Jesus fast asleep.

- What do you feel as you see Jesus asleep while you fear for your very life?
- What do you feel as you hear Jesus say, 'You of little faith, why are you so afraid?'
- What do you feel as you hear Jesus speak and as you see the wind and waves stop?
- What do you learn about Jesus through this story?
- In what ways could this truth about Jesus have an impact on how you live your life?

As you look over your own life in light of this story, can you remember a time when you experienced Jesus as being asleep, seemingly not caring about you and what you were going through? Take time to work through this, looking at and embracing your feelings and bringing all that to Jesus.

....

Different roles
Please enter the narratives taking on different roles, not only in terms of bystander, disciple, Jesus or a person being healed or interacted with, but as someone who is poor, a woman (if you are a man), rich, religious, desperate for help but not helped. Going through the same narrative from different perspectives can be very enlightening.

....

DAY 6

Read Matthew 8:28–34.

Imagine you are one of the owners of the pigs.

- What are your feelings as you see Jesus heal?
- What are you feeling as you watch your pigs run off a cliff?

- Why do you ask Jesus to leave?
- What do you learn about Jesus through this story?
- In what ways could this truth about Jesus have an impact on how you live your life?

Colloquy

Freely speak out your joy, thanks, wonder and praise to the triune God, earnestly beseeching God that God would enable you to know Jesus more closely and follow Jesus more nearly.

DAY 7

Review.

- What qualities of Jesus were you drawn to as you journeyed through the past week?
- What surprised or shocked you about Jesus?
- How has this week helped you to know Jesus more intimately, to love Jesus more intensely and to follow him more closely?
- Was there anything that encouraged you or gave you pause or concern regarding following Jesus? If so, what, and why?
- Are you becoming more in tune with Jesus' call in your life, and is your willingness increasing to say yes to the invitations of Jesus? Why, or why not?

Share your thoughts and feelings with God/Jesus, and, when you are finished, just be with Jesus, resting in his love for you, acknowledging his presence with you. Take a few moments to cease from striving and be still in the presence of the One who is with you and within you.

───◄ SECTION 7 OF 15 ►───

On Day 5 of this section, you will be invited to take a walk with Jesus. Please feel free to do this on another day if it would help you to enter more fully into the experience.

The grace you are seeking this week is to know Jesus intimately, to love him more intensely and to follow him more closely.

Examen questions

- How and when did you experience Immanuel (God with you) today?
- When were you aware of your love for Jesus today?
- When do you 'follow Jesus' in your relationships, circumstances, reactive and proactive responses, and actions?

Process

❑ Opening   ❑ Closing
❑ Daily exercise   ❑ Noontime examen
❑ Journalling   ❑ Evening examen

DAY 1

Read Mark 2:1–12.

Imagine you are one of the individuals in this story (the paralytic, the people who carry the paralytic, one of the crowd or a Pharisee).

- What are you thinking and feeling as this unfolds?
- What really captures your attention as you watch what transpires?
- What do you think or feel when you hear the words of Jesus, 'Your sins are forgiven,' and 'Get up, take your mat and go home'?
- How does this impact your view of Jesus and your love for him and desire to follow him?

Spend a few moments asking Jesus if there is someone in your life whom you need to bring to him. If there is, ask Jesus what he would have you do.

DAY 2

Read Mark 2:13–17.

Imagine you are one of the Pharisees who is following Jesus from a distance, listening but not trusting or believing in Jesus or his teachings.

- What are you feeling and believing to be true about this Jesus as he invites a tax gatherer (sinner) to be one of his followers?
- As he sits down for a meal with so many sinners, what do you feel?
- As you hear his words directed to you, what do you feel?
- What does all this tell you about Jesus and make you feel toward him?

Resistance
As you journey through the Exercises, pay special attention when you experience internal resistance. Whenever you become aware of resistance, respond to it as a warning light and seek to discover the source of the resistance. Resistance is a gift from God that invites you to a deeper discovery concerning God and/or yourself. So pause internally and ponder when you become aware of resistance. Ask God to help you discern where this resistance is coming from. What does it reveal about your image, level of belief, love and trust of God? What does it tell you about your sense of self, your identity? Take the time to reflect and unpack your resistance because, over time, the results can be life-changing.

DAY 3

Read Matthew 9:18–26.

Imagine you are the ruler of the synagogue, the sick woman or a follower of Jesus.

- What do you learn about Jesus?
- In what ways could this truth about Jesus have an impact on how you live your life?

Colloquy

Seek to end your time 'just being with' Jesus, rather than having a verbal response. Be still and be with God.

DAY 4

Review.

Read through your journal entries from the past couple of days, seeking something that resonated deep within you, something that was either drawing you or stirring resistance in you. Spend your prayer time pondering, unpacking and exploring whatever you come up with.

DAY 5

Take a walk with Jesus. Imagine Jesus is with you as you walk, and just talk or be silent. Share a thought or a feeling with Jesus, or point something out and listen as he does the same with you. Do not try to make something happen; just be with Jesus. If you are up to it, continue this practice throughout your day today.

DAY 6

Read Matthew 7:15–23.

Listen to these words of Jesus. What strikes you about them?

Take some time to look over your life as a Christian. What does your life-fruit reveal concerning who you are?

As you spend time mulling this over, share your feelings with Jesus as they arise, and listen to him.

....

Using imagination

Children readily use their imagination, so there should be a playfulness to our endeavour, a freedom to use our imagination. Resist the inner voices that seek to pressure you to do it right or well instead of having fun with it. As you enter into this way of engaging the text, your time will be transformed from knowing about Jesus to experiencing Jesus and yourself in life-giving and transforming ways.

....

DAY 7

Review your week.

- What qualities of Jesus were you drawn to as you journeyed through the past week?
- What surprised or shocked you about Jesus?
- How has this week helped you to know Jesus more intimately, to love Jesus more intensely and to follow him more closely?
- Was there anything that encouraged you or gave you pause or concern regarding following Jesus? If so, what, and why?
- Are you becoming more in tune with Jesus' call in your life, and is your willingness increasing to say yes to the invitations of Jesus? Why, or why not?

Share your thoughts and feelings with God/Jesus, and, when you are finished, just be with Jesus, resting in his love for you, acknowledging his presence with you. Take a few moments to cease from striving and be still in the presence of the One who is with you and within you.

SECTION 8 OF 15

The grace you are seeking this week is to know Jesus intimately, to love him more intensely and to follow him more closely.

Examen questions

- How and when did you experience Immanuel (God with you) today?
- When were you aware of your love for Jesus today?
- When do you 'follow Jesus' in your relationships, circumstances, reactive and proactive responses, and actions?

Start your time with a bow—slowly bending from your waist—as a visible sign of your reverence for and honouring of God, while asking God that everything in your day may more and more lead you to divine praise and service.

Process

- ☐ Opening
- ☐ Daily exercise
- ☐ Journalling

- ☐ Closing
- ☐ Noontime examen
- ☐ Evening examen

DAY 1

Read Matthew 12:1–14.

Imagine you are the man with the shrivelled hand. Watch as Jesus interacts with the Pharisees. Listen to his words, his tone.

- What do you learn about Jesus through this story?
- In what ways could this truth about Jesus have an impact on how you live your life?

....

I don't like Jesus
As you spend time with Jesus day after day, you may begin to discover that there are aspects of his dealings with people that you do not like. If you discover this, do not fret, but bring this to Jesus even as you continue your journey with him. You will discover that he is much more complicated than we make him out to be. His rubbing you up the wrong way indicates that you are being real and honest with Jesus and with yourself.

....

DAY 2

Read Luke 7:11–17.

Imagine you are the mourning mother.

- What are you feeling about life, about God and about your son?
- How do you feel about Jesus when he says, 'Don't cry'?
- When he touches the coffin and tells your son to 'get up'?
- When you see your son alive once again?
- What do you learn about Jesus through this story?
- In what ways could this truth about Jesus have an impact on how you live your life?

DAY 3

Read Luke 7:36–50.

Imagine you are the woman who anoints Jesus' feet.

- What are you feeling as you enter the room and feel all eyes on you?
- Why are you drawn to Jesus in this way?
- What are you seeking to communicate to Jesus through your actions?
- What do Jesus' words mean to you?
- What do you learn about Jesus through this story?
- In what ways could this truth about Jesus have an impact on how you live your life?

DAY 4

Review.

Read through your journal entries from the past couple of days, seeking something that resonated deep within you, something that was either drawing you or stirring resistance in you. Spend your prayer time pondering, unpacking and exploring whatever you come up with.

Slowly pray the Lord's Prayer.

DAY 5

Pray the following prayer.

Lord Jesus,
Help me to know you, to love you, to follow you.
Help alleviate my fears
and fan the embers of trust within me.

> *Give me the strength to say yes to your invitations,*
> *the courage to continue my journey with you.*
> *Remind me that you are*
> *the Way,*
> *the Truth*
> *and the Life,*
> *and apart from you there is no life,*
> *but with you,*
> *and with you alone*
> *is fullness of life,*
> *life everlasting.*

- Did these words express your heart's desire? Why, or why not?
- Try your hand at writing your own prayer.

Sit with the words of the following prayer:

Eternal Lord and King of all creation, humbly I come before you… I am moved by your grace to offer myself to you and your work. I deeply desire to be with you in accepting all wrongs and all rejections and all poverty, both actual and spiritual—and I deliberately choose this, if it is for your greater service and praise.

- What do these words stir within you?
- Are you willing to pray this prayer in a heartfelt way? Why, or why not?

DAY 6

Write a letter to Jesus.

What do you want to tell Jesus, ask Jesus, share with Jesus? Take your time writing your letter, and, when you are finished, prayerfully share your letter with Jesus. Imagine yourself reading him the letter.

- How does Jesus respond?

- What is your sense of Jesus as you come to him with your letter and as you read him your letter?

Pray this prayer if it reflects your desires:

> *Lord Jesus,*
> *Help me to know you, to love you, to follow you.*
> *Help alleviate my fears*
> *and fan the embers of trust within me.*
> *Give me the strength to say yes to your invitations,*
> *the courage to continue my journey with you.*
> *Remind me that you are*
> *the Way,*
> *the Truth*
> *and the Life,*
> *and apart from you there is no life,*
> *but with you,*
> *and with you alone*
> *is fullness of life,*
> *life everlasting.*

Did you pray this prayer? Why, or why not?

DAY 7

Review your week.

- What qualities of Jesus were you drawn to as you journeyed through the past week?
- What surprised or shocked you about Jesus?
- How has this week helped you to know Jesus more intimately, to love Jesus more intensely and to follow him more closely?
- Was there anything that encouraged you or gave you pause or concern regarding following Jesus? If so, what, and why?

- Are you becoming more in tune with Jesus' call in your life, and is your willingness increasing to say yes to the invitations of Jesus? Why, or why not?

Share your thoughts and feelings with God/Jesus, and, when you are finished, just be with Jesus, resting in his love for you, acknowledging his presence with you. Take a few moments to cease from striving and be still in the presence of the One who is with you and within you.

....

Beware of consolations

In Week 2 and beyond, consolations can be used to derail your journey through the Exercises. Be on guard. This often happens during the opening of your prayer time. You will be tempted by insights, worthwhile subjects to ponder or even a desire just to be with God. Though each one of these is good, they can actually take you away from the Exercises. Be alert to this tactic. Remember that the evil one can very well appear as an angel of light, using good and godly thoughts for his own ends. (See 'Rules of Discernment: Week 2' on pages 170–174.)

....

═◄ SECTION 9 OF 15 ►═

The grace you are seeking this week is to know Jesus intimately, to love him more intensely and to follow him more closely.

Examen questions

- How and when did you experience Immanuel (God with you) today?

- When were you aware of your love for Jesus today?
- When do you 'follow Jesus' in your relationships, circumstances, reactive and proactive responses, and actions?

Start your time with a bow—slowly bending from your waist—as a visible sign of your reverence for and honouring of God, while asking God that everything in your day may more and more lead you to divine praise and service.

Process

☐ Opening   ☐ Closing
☐ Daily exercise   ☐ Noontime examen
☐ Journalling   ☐ Evening examen

DAY 1

Read Mark 6:30–44.

Imagine you are following Jesus.

- What are you feeling as Jesus invites you to come 'to a quiet place and get some rest'?
- What are your expectations?
- What excites you about Jesus' plan?
- What do you feel when you notice that the crowd has followed you and that you will not be alone with Jesus and will not be able to rest?
- When Jesus challenges you to feed the crowd, what goes through your mind?
- When you tell Jesus what provisions you have found to feed the crowd (five loaves and two fish) and he responds by telling you to get the people into groups, what are you thinking?
- When you begin to feed the crowd and come back again and again to pick up more food, what is going on within you?

- When you notice the huge amount of food that remains after the five thousand have been fed, what do you feel and think?
- What do you learn about Jesus through this story?
- In what ways could this truth about Jesus have an impact on how you live life?

....

Contemplation

Take time at the end of your prayer time each day just to be with Jesus. Do not seek anything from him; just be still and rest in and with him in silence—knowing that Jesus is with you and is actively loving you in this moment and into the next moment.

....

DAY 2

Read Mark 6:45–52.

Imagine you are following Jesus. After reading the story, sit with these words of Jesus: 'Take courage! It is I. Don't be afraid.'

- What is it that stirs fear within your heart and mind?
- How does the presence of Immanuel help you escape fear and oppression?

Colloquy

Freely speak out your joy, thanks, wonder and praise to the triune God, earnestly beseeching God that God would enable you to know Jesus more closely and follow Jesus more nearly.

DAY 3

Read Mark 7:24–30.

Imagine you are the woman in this story, a Gentile, an outsider.

- What are your feelings as you come to Jesus?
- What are you hoping for?
- What are you afraid of?
- What do you feel as you hear Jesus' initial response to your plea? How did you experience Jesus when he responded as he did? What did you see in Jesus' eyes, hear in the tone of his voice?
- Do you believe Jesus when he says your daughter is healed? Why, or why not?
- What was your overall experience with Jesus like? Why?

If you have time, imagine that you are a disciple or onlooker.

- What do you think of this Gentile woman who dares to approach Jesus?
- What is your response to Jesus' initial words to this woman?
- Do you believe that Jesus actually heals her daughter? Why, or why not?
- What do you learn about Jesus through this interaction?

DAY 4

Review.

Read through your journal entries from the past couple of days, seeking something that resonated deep within you, something that was either drawing you or stirring resistance in you. Spend your prayer time pondering, unpacking and exploring whatever you come up with.

Slowly pray the Lord's Prayer.

DAY 5

Read John 4:1–26.

Imagine you are the woman at the well.

- What are you feeling as Jesus speaks with you?
- What do you feel coming from Jesus as you interact with him?
- What do Jesus' promises, regarding the water that quenches thirst for ever and produces living water welling up to everlasting life, mean to you?
- What do you learn about Jesus through this story?
- In what ways could this truth about Jesus have an impact on how you live life?

DAY 6

Read Matthew 14:22–36.

Focusing on verses 28–36, imagine you are Peter.

- What are the wind and waves in your life that draw you away from knowing Jesus more intimately, loving him more intensely and following him more closely?

Colloquy

Seek to end your time 'just being with' Jesus, rather than giving a verbal response. Be still and be with God.

DAY 7

Review your week.

- What qualities of Jesus were you drawn to as you journeyed through the past week?

- What surprised or shocked you about Jesus?
- How has this week helped you to know Jesus more intimately, to love Jesus more intensely and to follow him more closely?
- Was there anything that encouraged you or gave you pause or concern regarding following Jesus? If so, what, and why?
- Are you becoming more in tune with Jesus' call in your life, and is your willingness increasing to say yes to the invitations of Jesus? Why, or why not?

Share your thoughts and feelings with God/Jesus, and, when you are finished, just be with Jesus, resting in his love for you, acknowledging his presence with you. Take a few moments to cease from striving and be still in the presence of the One who is with you and within you.

SECTION 10 OF 15

The grace you are seeking this week is to know Jesus intimately, to love him more intensely and to follow him more closely.

Examen questions

- How and when did you experience Immanuel (God with you) today?
- When were you aware of your love for Jesus today?
- When do you 'follow Jesus' in your relationships, circumstances, reactive and proactive responses, and actions?

Start your time with a bow—slowly bending from your waist—as a visible sign of your reverence for and honouring of God, while asking God that everything in your day may more and more lead you to divine praise and service.

Process

- [ ] Opening
- [ ] Daily exercise
- [ ] Journalling

- [ ] Closing
- [ ] Noontime examen
- [ ] Evening examen

DAY 1

Read Mark 9:14–29.

Imagine you are following Jesus.

- As you realise your inability to drive the spirit from the boy, what thoughts cross your mind?
- What doubts arise in your heart?
- What goes on inside you as you watch the interchange between Jesus and the boy's father?
- What is stirred within you as you hear Jesus' words, 'Everything is possible for him who believes' and 'This kind can only come out by prayer'?
- What are your internal reactions to the words of the father, 'I do believe; help me overcome my unbelief'?
- What do you learn about Jesus through this story?
- In what ways could this truth about Jesus have an impact on how you live?

DAY 2

Read Luke 10:38–42.

Read this passage two times using imaginative reading. The first time, imagine you are Martha.

- What are you feeling and thinking as you see Mary?
- As you approach Jesus?
- As Jesus responds to your request?

The second time through, imagine you are Mary.

- What are you feeling and thinking as you see Martha?
- As you hear Martha's request?
- As you hear Jesus' response?
- Whom do you most easily identify with—Mary or Martha? Why?
- What is Jesus' invitation to you through this story?

DAY 3

Read Luke 17:11–19.

Imagine you are an onlooker, watching as ten lepers call out and interact with Jesus. You see them healed as they begin to walk away from Jesus. You see that only one comes back to offer thanks.

- What feelings are stirred within you as you watch this scene unfold?
- How has Jesus brought healing change to you?
- How does this affect the way you see and think about Jesus?

Spend some time thanking Jesus for what he has done, is doing and will do on your behalf.

DAY 4

Review.

Read through your journal entries from the past couple of days, seeking something that resonated deep within you, something that was either drawing you or stirring resistance in you. Spend your prayer time pondering, unpacking and exploring whatever you come up with.

Slowly pray the Lord's Prayer.

DAY 5

Read Mark 10:46–52.

Imagine you are blind Bartimaeus.

- What goes on inside you as you realise Jesus is passing by?
- As others tell you to be quiet?
- As still others tell you that Jesus is calling you?
- What goes through your mind and heart as Jesus asks you what you want? What are the fears, dreams and desires that arise within you?
- What was it like to be able to see? What have you gained and what have you lost?
- How has Bartimaeus' story also been your story?
- What have you learned about Jesus from your story?
- In what ways do these truths about Jesus have an impact on how you live?

As you look at your life, ask yourself these two questions: To what am I currently blind? What do I long to see?

DAY 6

Read Matthew 17:1–9.

Imagine you are going up the hill with Jesus.

- As you watch Jesus transfigured right before your eyes, what are you thinking and feeling?
- What are you feeling when you hear Peter's words?
- When you hear the words of God, what do you feel?
- What is going on inside you as you lie face down on the ground?
- When Jesus touches you and says, 'Don't be afraid'?
- What do you learn about Jesus through this story?
- In what ways could this truth about Jesus have an impact on how you live?

Colloquy

Freely speak out of your joy, thanks, wonder and praise to the triune God, earnestly beseeching God that God would enable you to know Jesus more closely and follow Jesus more nearly.

DAY 7

Review your week.

- What qualities of Jesus were you drawn to as you journeyed through the past week?
- What surprised or shocked you about Jesus?
- How has this week helped you to know Jesus more intimately, to love Jesus more intensely and to follow him more closely?
- Was there anything that encouraged you or gave you pause or concern regarding following Jesus? If so, what, and why?
- Are you becoming more in tune with Jesus' call in your life, and is your willingness increasing to say yes to the invitations of Jesus? Why, or why not?

Share your thoughts and feelings with God/Jesus, and, when you are finished, just be with Jesus, resting in his love for you, acknowledging his presence with you. Take a few moments to cease from striving and be still in the presence of the One who is with you and within you.

SECTION 11 OF 15

The grace you are seeking this week is to know Jesus intimately, to love him more intensely and to follow him more closely.

Examen questions

- How and when did you experience Immanuel (God with you) today?
- When were you aware of your love for Jesus today?
- When do you 'follow Jesus' in your relationships, circumstances, reactive and proactive responses, and actions?

Start your time with a bow—slowly bending from your waist—as a visible sign of your reverence for and honouring of God, while asking God that everything in your day may more and more lead you to divine praise and service.

Process

☐ Opening ☐ Closing
☐ Daily exercise ☐ Noontime examen
☐ Journalling ☐ Evening examen

DAY 1

Read Matthew 6:19–24)

Imagine Jesus speaking these words to you, and ponder them. Before answering the following questions, take a moment to become aware of feelings they raise within you. Share your honest answers with Jesus, and listen for his response.

- What are your treasures?
- Who has your heart?
- Who are your masters?

Pray this prayer if it reflects your desires:

Lord Jesus,
Help me to know you, to love you, to follow you.
Help alleviate my fears
and fan the embers of trust within me.
Give me the strength to say yes to your invitations,
the courage to continue my journey with you.
Remind me that you are
the Way,
the Truth
and the Life,
and apart from you there is no life,
but with you,
and with you alone
is fullness of life,
life everlasting.

Did you pray this prayer? Why, or why not?

DAY 2

Read Matthew 19:16–30.

Imagine you are the rich young man who comes to Jesus.

- Why have you come to Jesus? What are you hoping to receive from your encounter with Jesus?
- When you hear Jesus' initial response, 'Do not commit murder, do not commit adultery' and so on, what are you feeling inside?
- What happens inside you when you hear Jesus' request to 'sell all you have'?
- What is the promise that riches hold for you, which gives them so much power over you?

Imagine you are standing before Jesus, and you ask him, 'What do I lack?' What do you fear will be Jesus' response to you? Why?

Share your fear and seek to unpack it with Jesus.

Pray this prayer if it reflects your desires:

Eternal Lord and King of all creation, humbly I come before you… I am moved by your grace to offer myself to you and your work. I deeply desire to be with you in accepting all wrongs and all rejections and all poverty, both actual and spiritual—and I deliberately choose this, if it is for your greater service and praise.

Did you pray this prayer? Why, or why not?

DAY 3

Read Luke 18:15–17.

Imagine you are a child brought by your parent(s) to Jesus.

- When you see Jesus, what do you sense to be true about Jesus? What draws you to Jesus?
- What kind of interaction takes place between you and Jesus?

After a while, imagine you are sitting on Jesus' lap.

- What are you experiencing?
- What does Jesus say to you? What do you say to Jesus? Why?

Finally, imagine Jesus placing his hands on your head and blessing you.

- What does Jesus speak over you and into you?
- Are you able to receive these words of Jesus? Why, or why not?

Colloquy

Seek to end your time 'just being with' Jesus rather than giving a verbal response. Be still and be with God.

DAY 4

Review.

Read through your journal entries from the past couple of days, seeking something that resonated deep within you, something that was either drawing you or stirring resistance in you. Spend your prayer time pondering, unpacking and exploring whatever you come up with.

Slowly pray the Lord's Prayer.

DAY 5

Read John 11:1–44.

Imagine you are one of the disciples with Jesus, and you get word that Jesus' friend is dying.

- What do you think Jesus will do?
- What surprises you about the way Jesus deals with this situation?

Pay close attention to his words.

- What do you think or feel about what Jesus said? Or what is your reaction to what Jesus said?
- Are you surprised by the way Jesus is initially handling this situation? Why, or why not?

Now sit with the words of John 11:35: 'Jesus wept.'

- What do Jesus' tears mean to you?
- What do Jesus' tears tell you regarding who he is?
- Do you think Jesus has ever shed tears for you? Why, or why not?
- If you answered yes, when did Jesus shed tears for you?
- What do Jesus' tears mean to you?
- How does that impact your relationship with Jesus?

- If your answer was no, how does that feel? How does that impact your relationship with Jesus?

Spend time talking all this over with Jesus.

DAY 6

Read Matthew 20:20–28.

Imagine you are hearing the words of Jesus regarding what it means to be a leader.

- What is your internal reaction?
- How do those words impact your desire to follow Jesus, to say yes to Jesus?

Now listen to Jesus' self-description.

- What do his words and example convey about being a follower of Jesus?
- What do Jesus' words stir within you?

Let this lead you into a time of thanksgiving and praise.

DAY 7

Review your week.

- What qualities of Jesus were you drawn to as you journeyed through the past week?
- What surprised or shocked you about Jesus?
- How has this week helped you to know Jesus more intimately, to love Jesus more intensely and to follow him more closely?
- Was there anything that encouraged you or gave you pause or concern regarding following Jesus? If so, what, and why?

- Are you becoming more in tune with Jesus' call in your life, and is your willingness increasing to say yes to the invitations of Jesus? Why, or why not?

Share your thoughts and feelings with God/Jesus, and, when you are finished, just be with Jesus, resting in his love for you, acknowledging his presence with you. Take a few moments to cease from striving and be still in the presence of the One who is with you and within you.

SECTION 12 OF 15

The grace you are seeking this week is to know Jesus intimately, to love him more intensely and to follow him more closely.

Examen questions

- How and when did you experience Immanuel (God with you) today?
- When were you aware of your love for Jesus today?
- When do you 'follow Jesus' in your relationships, circumstances, reactive and proactive responses, and actions?

Start your time with a bow—slowly bending from your waist—as a visible sign of your reverence for and honouring of God, while asking God that everything in your day may more and more lead you to divine praise and service.

Process

- ☐ Opening
- ☐ Daily exercise
- ☐ Journalling
- ☐ Closing
- ☐ Noontime examen
- ☐ Evening examen

DAY 1

Read Matthew 22:34–38.

Sit with the words of Jesus, 'Love the Lord your God with all your heart and with all your soul and with all your mind.'

- How has your love for the triune God changed as you have journeyed through this section of the Exercises?
- Which is more difficult for you to do: to love God in a heartfelt way (all your heart) or in a more intellectual way (with all your mind)? Why?
- Do you find it easier to love God the Father, Jesus or the Holy Spirit with all your heart, soul and mind? Why?

DAY 2

Read Matthew 22:34–40.

Sit with the words of Jesus, 'Love your neighbour as yourself.'

- As you have journeyed with Jesus through the exercises in this section, what have you learned about what it might mean to love your neighbour?

Ask Jesus to reveal to you how you might be able to grow in your ability to love your neighbour. Also ask him to show you 'neighbours' currently in your life whom God may want you to commit to loving.

DAY 3

Review.

- What is it from these passages that draws you to Jesus, challenges you, amazes you, gives you pause, causes resistance in you or causes another reaction? Why?

Slowly pray the Lord's Prayer.

During Days 4, 5 and 6, you will be encouraged to ask God to reveal areas of struggle in your life that correspond to the woes Jesus pronounces over the Pharisees in Matthew 23. If there is something that God reveals to you as a possible growth area, make a note of it and bring it to God during your noontime or evening examen.

DAY 4

Read Matthew 23:1–12.

As you listen to Jesus pronounce these 'woes', ask God to show you which you are susceptible to and any you may currently need to pay special attention to. Think back over your journey with Jesus through the Gospels, and recall incidents or teachings from his life that demonstrate the opposite of the woes he proclaims.

DAY 5

Read Matthew 23:13–28.

As you listen to Jesus pronounce these woes, ask God to show you which you are susceptible to and any you may currently need to pay special attention to. Think back over your journey with Jesus through the Gospels, and recall incidents or teachings from his life that demonstrate the opposite of the woes he proclaims.

DAY 6

Read Matthew 23:29–39.

As you listen to Jesus pronounce these woes, ask God to show you which you are susceptible to and any you may currently need to pay special attention to. Think back over your journey with Jesus through the Gospels, and recall incidents or teachings from his life that demonstrate the opposite of the woes he proclaims.

DAY 7

Review your week.

- What qualities of Jesus were you drawn to as you journeyed through the past week?
- What surprised or shocked you about Jesus?
- How has this week helped you to know Jesus more intimately, to love Jesus more intensely and to follow him more closely?
- Was there anything that encouraged you or gave you pause or concern regarding following Jesus? If so, what, and why?
- Are you becoming more in tune with Jesus' call in your life, and is your willingness increasing to say yes to the invitations of Jesus? Why, or why not?

Share your thoughts and feelings with God/Jesus, and, when you are finished, just be with Jesus, resting in his love for you, acknowledging his presence with you. Take a few moments to cease from striving and be still in the presence of the One who is with you and within you.

SECTION 13 OF 15

During the next two sections (13 and 14) of Week 2, you will be focusing your attention on the seven 'I am' statements of Jesus. A series of questions will help you ponder these statements during your prayer time each day. As you make use of the questions, please remember that the goal is not to get through them, but rather to use them as a means of opening yourself to Jesus and discovering more about who you are as his follower.

- What does this 'I am' statement communicate to you regarding who Jesus is? What are the feelings or thoughts that arise within you as you ponder this?
- Have you experienced Jesus in this way? If yes, take time to recall the experience. How did it make you feel? How did it, or does it, have an impact on your life? If the answer is no, how does this make you feel? Take time to share your feelings with Jesus. Remember to be honest: even raw, angry honesty with God is welcomed by God.
- As you reflect on this 'I am' statement, are there feelings of disappointment, anger, frustration, confusion, hurt or pain that arise within you? What is the 'why' behind these emotions? What is the impact of these emotions on your life and on your relationship with God/Jesus? Bring all this before God/Jesus through prayer, journalling, writing a letter to God, screaming at God—the means is not the important thing. What is important is that you bring all this to God.
- What might be the invitations, promises, encouragements and/ or challenges for you, found in this 'I am' statement?
- What are the needs and desires that this 'I am' statement might meet in your life if you were fully able to embrace its truth in your heart and allow it to shape and mould you?

Allow this to flow into a time of talking with Jesus about whatever has been or is surfacing within you regarding his 'I am' statements.

The grace you are seeking this week is to know Jesus intimately, to love him more intensely and to follow him more closely.

Examen questions

- How and when did you experience Immanuel (God with you) today?
- When were you aware of your love for Jesus today?
- When do you 'follow Jesus' in your relationships, circumstances, reactive and proactive responses, and actions?

Start your time with a bow—slowly bending from your waist—as a visible sign of your reverence for and honouring of God, while asking God that everything in your day may more and more lead you to divine praise and service.

Process

☐ Opening   ☐ Closing
☐ Daily exercise   ☐ Noontime examen
☐ Journalling   ☐ Evening examen

DAY 1

Read John 6:35.

'I am the bread of life.'

DAY 2

Read John 8:12.

'I am the light of the world.'

DAY 3

Read John 10:7.

'I am the gate [or door].'

DAY 4

Read John 10:11.

'I am the good shepherd.'

DAY 5

Choose an 'I am' statement from a previous day, and ponder it further.

DAY 6

Read John 11:25.

'I am the resurrection and the life.'

DAY 7

Review this past week.

- To which of these images are you most drawn? Why?

Reflect on your time in the 'I am' statements of Jesus, and imagine him asking you the question, 'Who do you say I am?' (Mark 8:29). Journal your response.

SECTION 14 OF 15

The grace you are seeking this week is to know Jesus intimately, to love him more intensely and to follow him more closely.

Examen questions

- How and when did you experience Immanuel (God with you) today?
- When were you aware of your love for Jesus today?
- When do you 'follow Jesus' in your relationships, circumstances, reactive and proactive responses, and actions?

Start your time with a bow—slowly bending from your waist—as a visible sign of your reverence for and honouring of God, while asking God that everything in your day may more and more lead you to divine praise and service.

Process

- ☐ Opening
- ☐ Daily exercise
- ☐ Journalling
- ☐ Closing
- ☐ Noontime examen
- ☐ Evening examen

DAY 1

Read John 14:6.

'I am the way.'

DAY 2

Read John 14:6.

'I am the truth.' Spend some time pondering on how John 8:32—'Then you will know the truth, and the truth will set you free'—and Jesus' declaration above might tie together.

DAY 3

Read John 14:6.

'I am the life.'

DAY 4

Review.

Read through your journal entries from the past couple of days, seeking something that resonated deep within you, something that was either drawing you or stirring resistance in you. Spend your prayer time pondering, unpacking and exploring whatever you come up with.

DAY 5

Read John 15:5.

'I am the vine.'

DAY 6

Draw a picture or create a collage that captures the images of the previous two sections (13 and 14). Imagine yourself presenting your creation to God. How does God respond?

DAY 7

Review the past week.

- To which of these images are you most drawn? Why?

Reflect on your time in the 'I am' statements of Jesus, and imagine him asking you the question, 'Who do you say I am?' (Mark 8:29). Journal your response.

SECTION 15 OF 15

The grace you are seeking this week is to know Jesus intimately, to love him more intensely and to follow him more closely.

Examen questions

- How and when did you experience Immanuel (God with you) today?
- When were you aware of your love for Jesus today?
- When do you 'follow Jesus' in your relationships, circumstances, reactive and proactive responses, and actions?

Start your time with a bow—slowly bending from your waist—as a visible sign of your reverence for and honouring of God, while asking God that everything in your day may more and more lead you to divine praise and service.

Process

❏ Opening   ❏ Closing
❏ Daily exercise   ❏ Noontime examen
❏ Journalling   ❏ Evening examen

DAY 1

Read Matthew 21:12–17.

Imagine you are following Jesus.

- What are you feeling as you watch Jesus overturn tables?
- What are your feelings as he heals people?
- What is stirred within you as you hear the children and watch the interaction between Jesus and the Pharisees?
- How does watching all this make you feel about Jesus?
- How does this affect your desire and willingness to follow Jesus?

DAY 2

Read Mark 11:1–11.

Imagine you are one of the disciples.

- What is going through your mind as you hear the shouts of the people and sense the popularity of Jesus, your teacher?

Colloquy

Freely speak out your joy, thanks, wonder and praise to the triune God, earnestly beseeching God that God would enable you to know Jesus more closely and follow Jesus more nearly.

DAY 3

Read Luke 21:1–4.

Imagine you are watching as the woman gives her offering.

- What do you think of her and of her gift?
- What do you think of her and her gift after you hear the words of Jesus?

Now imagine that Jesus addresses his comments to you.

- What do his words touch within you?
- Look at your life, your pattern of giving to God and to others. Do Jesus' words challenge you, encourage you, embarrass you? Why, or why not?

DAY 4

Review.

Read through your journal entries from the past couple of days, seeking something that resonated deep within you, something that was either drawing you or stirring resistance in you. Spend your prayer time pondering, unpacking and exploring whatever you come up with.

Slowly pray the Lord's Prayer.

DAY 5

Read Matthew 26:6–13.

Imagine you are (A) one of the guests at the meal or (B) the woman who anoints Jesus' head with perfume, and answer the questions below that correspond to each option.

A

- What do you think and feel as this woman approaches Jesus?
- As you watch her pour expensive perfume on Jesus' head?
- As you hear the comments of the disciples?
- What, if anything, changes within you in terms of your feelings toward the woman, her actions and the response of the disciples as you hear Jesus' words to this woman? Why?

B

- What are you feeling as you decide to anoint Jesus' head?
- As you are on your way into the home that Jesus is visiting?
- As you enter the room and feel all the eyes of the people there upon you?
- What do you feel as you pour the precious perfume on Jesus' head?
- As you hear the objections voiced by the disciples?
- As you hear the words of Jesus?
- As you look into the eyes of Jesus, and as he looks deeply into your eyes?

DAY 6

Three Kinds of Humility[24]

Read through the three kinds of humility listed below, seeking to name and discover which one would best indicate the level of your desire and commitment to follow Jesus. The goal is not to choose one over the other, but to discern where you currently are and to name and embrace that reality.

1. I desire to do nothing that would cut me off from God, not even if I were put in charge of all creation or given more years of living here on earth. (Obedience)
2. I do not desire riches rather than poverty, honour rather than dishonour, a long life rather than a short life. My desire is to do the will of God my Lord, to honour, praise and serve God. (Indifference)
3. I desire the truth of Jesus' life to be fully the truth of my own life so that I find myself moved by grace, with a love and a desire for poverty, for insults, for being considered a worthless fool for Christ rather than wise and prudent according to the standards of the world. (Transcendence of indifference)

- As you have reflected on the three kinds of humility, where do you currently find yourself?
- How do you feel about being there?
- What is your desire concerning these three kinds (not levels) of humility? Why?

Share your thoughts and feelings with Jesus, remembering that each kind of humility is acknowledging the greatness and supremacy of God and thus brings praise and honour to God.

DAY 7

Review.

- How did your time in Week 2 of the Exercises mould and shape your view of Jesus?
- Have you been able to know Jesus more intimately, to love him more intensely and to follow him more closely? If yes, how can this be seen in your life? If no, why not?
- What has drawn you to Christ, challenged you, amazed you?
- What has given you pause or caused resistance in you?
- Have you become more in tune with Jesus' call in your life and is your willingness to say yes to the invitations of Jesus increasing? Why, or why not?

Share your thoughts and feelings with God/Jesus, and, when you are finished, just be with Jesus, resting in his love for you, acknowledging his presence with you. Take a few moments to cease from striving and be still in the presence of the One who is with you and within you.

CONCLUDING COMMENTS AND REFLECTIONS

You have made it through Week 2, the heart and soul of the Exercises. You have spent the past several months walking with and being with Jesus from his birth up until the Passion Week (Week 3). You have been growing in your experiential knowledge of Jesus, your love for Jesus and your desire to say yes to Jesus and to follow him more closely as you have faithfully journeyed through the daily exercises. You have asked God for the daily grace and practised the prayer of examen. Through the meditations 'Call of the King', the 'Two Standards' and 'Three Types of Humility', you have been challenged to consider the level of your desire for Jesus and your commitment to follow after him and embrace the life he offers. Week 2 has been a time of exploring and deepening your sense of who Jesus is and what it might mean for you to follow him at this stage of your life and during these circumstances of your life.

Now that Week 2 has come to an end, you are faced with another choice: do you continue on to Week 3; do you end your journey here; or do you continue your journey in the Exercises but, instead of moving on to Week 3, go back through Week 2 or portions of it?

For some of you, this may mark the end of your journey, at least for now. For others, this may be an excellent time to go back slowly over your journal or even re-enter a previous Week or section. Remember, the point is not to get through the Exercises, but rather to use them as a tool to open you up to God. If you are not sure where you are with Jesus, if you are unsure of the level of commitment you are willing to make in order to say yes to Jesus, I suggest you do not move forward but spend time going back through Week 2.

As you ponder your decision, I encourage you to work through the following material to discern whether or not you should move on to Week 3. There is nothing wrong with choosing to linger in Week 2 if that is where you are sensing God working in you. The spiritual transformation that God brings about during your journey through the Exercises is the result of time spent with God, not because you have worked your way through the entire Exercises.

As you go through the questions and continuums below to discern God's leading, take your time. Week 3 can be a very difficult journey for some, and it is certainly not meant for everyone. I suggest taking at least two to three days to journal about the following questions and work through the continuums. There is no need to move on to Week 3 if you are not sensing God's invitation to do so, and there is no rush to make your decision.

- How has your sense of Jesus changed during your journey through Week 2?
- What was lost and what has been gained as your image of Jesus changed?
- What is the level of your desire to follow Jesus?
- What price are you willing to pay to follow Jesus (would you be willing to take up your cross and die)?
- Are you more able to hear the call of Jesus in your daily life? Why, or why not?
- Are you more willing to say yes to the challenges and invitations of Jesus to follow? Why, or why not?

Spend time pondering where you find yourself on the continuums below, seeking to let go of internal pressure to move on to Week 3 and choosing to be open to God's leading regarding moving on. As you work through the continuums, endeavour to answer from your heart and not merely your head.

I live   Christ lives in me

|————————————————————————————————|

Self-focused   Christ-focused

|————————————————————————————————|

Follow world's ways   Follow Jesus

|————————————————————————————————|

Earthly treasure   Treasure in heaven

|————————————————————————————————|

Riches, honour,   Humility, dependency,
significance   significance in Christ

|————————————————————————————————|

Disordered attachment   Indifference/freedom
|————————————————————————————————|

Follow Jesus if convenient   Follow Jesus
|————————————————————————————————|

Save life   Lose life
|————————————————————————————————|

Follow Jesus   Deeper identification with Jesus
|————————————————————————————————|

If you are leaning toward entering into Week 3, ask yourself this final question: Am I ready to walk to the cross with Jesus, to suffer with Jesus, to stand by Jesus as all others desert him? Week 3 will challenge you to enter into a new level, from following him to being with him in the midst of his Passion. It involves choosing to pick up the cross of Jesus, walking with him as Simon did on the Via Dolorosa. This is no walk in the park; it can be a gruelling time of experiencing dryness and desolation during your prayer times. It can be a time of profound sorrow but also a time of surprising consolation.

Please consider carefully if God is leading you into Week 3. It is not for the weak, faint-hearted or timid in spirit. Week 3 is for those who feel the draw, call and desire to enter fully into the Passion of Christ, not as an interested spectator but as a participant willingly choosing to enter into the fellowship of Christ's sufferings.

Before making your final decision regarding moving on to Week 3, re-entering Week 2 or concluding your journey through the Exercises, please speak with your spiritual director or listener, sharing your insights from the questions and continuums above.

If you are feeling that you are in a good internal place for moving forward, do one more thing: take time to recommit to your journey through the Exercises, pledging to give yourself wholly to God (as you are able) and to seek to gain nothing from God, but rather determine to present yourself each day to God as 'your spiritual act of worship', which is 'holy and pleasing to God' (Romans 12:1).

ASH WEDNESDAY AND THE SPIRITUAL EXERCISES

If it is a few days or weeks before Lent begins (on Ash Wednesday), I would encourage you to wait before going forward in the Exercises, so you can begin Week 3 on Ash Wednesday. This is not always possible, but, when it works out, it can be a powerful experience as you join millions of other Christians throughout the world who are also focusing on the Passion of Jesus during this time. If your own church intentionally participates in Lent, this can be a double blessing.

If you are able to sync your entry into Week 3 with the Lenten season, go to Appendix 1, where you will find extra exercises for Ash Wednesday, the rest of that week and the final week leading to Easter.

───── WEEK 3 ─────

JOURNEY TO THE CROSS

As you enter into this new unit of the Exercises, you will find yourself in what is traditionally referred to as Week 3.[1] In Week 3, your focus shifts to the Passion Week (from the Last Supper through to Jesus' death on the cross). Your prayer time during each day will involve walking with Jesus to the cross and being with him at the cross (even on the cross). The method for interacting with the scriptures will primarily be imaginative prayer or *lectio divina*. The purpose of praying over the Passion is to experience it. This means you are not just to contemplate it, but to be with Jesus as it happens.

This week harks back to the Kingdom Meditation (Section 1 of Week 2), when you heard Jesus declare, 'It is my will to bring all the world into the glory of my Father's kingdom; therefore, all who would like to come with me must walk as I walk and live as I live, labouring with me, following me in the pain so that they may also follow me in the glory.'[2] This Week you follow Jesus 'in the pain'.

Week 3 might also remind you of Week 1, as the subject matter seems similar: the cross and sin. However, the focus of Week 3 is quite different. Whereas Week 1 was concerned with your ability to experience sorrow, tears and confusion over your choices to sin in light of God's limitless love, grace, mercy and faithfulness, Week 3 leads you into seeking to be able to enter into the sufferings of Jesus (compassion: to suffer with)—feeling the sorrow and pain of Jesus as he bore your sins and the sins of the world.[3]

While this Week's focus does include the personal and cosmic reality of sin that is embedded in the cross of Christ, you are also to walk with Jesus to the cross, seeking to experience what he experienced. This Week is not about personal repentance but personal following of Jesus, who suffered and died because of your sins.

The goal is not to be overwhelmed by feelings of guilt and shame because your actions (sins) led to Christ's death, but to choose to join with Jesus in his suffering for the sins of the world, for your own sins—a grace that Paul deeply desired and wrote about in Philippians 3:10: 'I want to know... the fellowship of sharing in his sufferings.' This Week is about walking with Jesus in a deeper, more personal and intense way than in Week 2. It is entering into Jesus' journey as a companion in all he encounters. In a sense, it is a change of perspective. In the sections leading up to Week 3, you have looked at Jesus. Now you are invited to look using Jesus' eyes to see. This focus continues into Week 4 as well.

Week 3 involves a deeper identification with Christ, an interior participation in his sufferings. This is a natural outflow of Week 2, during which you were asking God for the grace to know Jesus more intimately, to love him more intensely and to follow him more closely. This deeper identification with Jesus in his Passion is an outflow of a desire not only to follow Jesus but also to be with him as a companion, not merely as an observer.

Week 3 is about choosing to enter into solidarity with Jesus, whom you deeply love and care about. You will now walk with him through Week 3 as one walks with a friend—seeking to be present to Jesus, your friend, empathising with him, seeing how he suffers through the words and actions of others. You no longer stand on the sidelines; you enter into the experience with Jesus, no longer watching but participating. This journeying with Jesus to the cross will continue the process of opening yourself to the depth of God's love.

Although Week 3 can lead you into a greater awareness of the depth and scope of God's love, it can also be a very difficult section of the Exercises. The daily exercises can be very dry and even agonising, leading you to feel discouraged. There may be a time when the felt presence of God is nowhere to be found, a time of avoidance, of extreme distraction and even of unhealthy or destructive guilt. Seeing the depth of his pain and suffering, you might begin to assign yourself blame for what Jesus is going through.

As was stated earlier, Week 3 is not for the weak, timid or faint-hearted. This section may lead you into times when you feel powerless, humiliated, stressed and alone. These are the feelings Jesus encountered as he entered into the travails of his journey to the cross, so it should come as no surprise that you may experience these as you choose to journey with him to the cross.

Heed these words: the person ready for the third Week:

... manifests a deepening desire for union with Christ, no matter what, and usually experiences a desire, although sometimes accompanied with hesitation and even fear, to move with Christ into a contemplation of his Passion and to glimpse what this will mean concretely after the retreat... One's desire, one's whole thrust is to become so identified with Christ that suffering is inevitable.[4]

If the above draws you, even though there may be internal resistance within, by all means move into Week 3. But if you are unable even to desire the desire for what is spoken of above, now is not the time for you to move on to Week 3.

If you are continuing on to Week 3, please carefully and prayerfully heed the warnings concerning the difficulties you may encounter. Your experience in Week 3 might mirror the helplessness and hardship that Jesus experienced in his Passion. But there is also great value found in meditating on the cross of Christ, on Christ crucified. Concerning the transforming power of meditating on the passion of Christ, Martin Luther wrote:

If one does meditate rightly on the suffering of Christ for a day, an hour, or even a quarter of an hour, this we may confidently say is better than a whole year of fasting, days of Psalm singing, yes, than even one hundred Masses, because this reflection changes the whole man and makes him new, as once he was in baptism.[5]

The writings of the apostle Paul also bear testimony to the importance and centrality of Christ crucified:

Jews demand miraculous signs and Greeks look for wisdom, but we preach Christ crucified: a stumbling block to Jews and foolishness to Gentiles, but to those whom God has called, both Jews and Greeks, Christ the power of God and the wisdom of God. (1 Corinthians 1:22–24)

For I resolved to know nothing while I was with you except Jesus Christ and him crucified. (1 Corinthians 2:2)

I have been crucified with Christ and I no longer live, but Christ lives in me. The life I live in the body, I live by faith in the Son of God, who loved me and gave himself for me. (Galatians 2:20)

I want to know Christ and the power of his resurrection and the fellowship of sharing in his sufferings, becoming like him in his death. (Philippians 3:10)

May I never boast except in the cross of our Lord Jesus Christ, through which the world has been crucified to me, and I to the world. (Galatians 6:14)

Although the apostle Paul, Martin Luther and others stressed the importance and the transforming power of Christ crucified, this has not been embraced by Protestants as a whole. For Protestants, there is a tendency to ignore or at least minimise the reality of Christ crucified. Crosses in Protestant churches, if we have crosses, are almost always devoid of the pierced body of Christ. The focus tends to be on the resurrected Christ. Because of a lack of emphasis on Christ crucified in Protestant circles, you may have trouble staying with the focus of Week 3 if you are a Protestant.

Ironically, another hindrance to your ability to enter into the Passion narratives in Week 3—to be with Jesus as he walks to the cross—is your familiarity with these narratives. If you are very familiar with these passages, you probably will not be shocked, offended or appalled by the story. You also may find it difficult to name, let alone identify with, the pain Jesus endured on the cross, because it is beyond all our ability to comprehend. You may find yourself struggling to identify with how he suffered as his disciples slept, Judas betrayed him, Peter denied him, his own people turned against him, people bore false witness regarding him and God forsook him.

But do not lose heart. Simply continue to come into the prayer time each day, presenting your body as a living and holy sacrifice, asking for the grace for this Week, while trusting God and the process, endeavouring to receive whatever God has for you each day. If God has led you to continue, Week 3 will ultimately be a life-giving, spiritually transforming time.

ADDITIONS TO EXERCISES

As you work through the daily exercises, in addition to the questions given each day, there will be three considerations to make each day:

- What did Jesus suffer in his humanity in this narrative?[6]
- How did Jesus hide (not use) his divinity in this narrative?
- What is your response to Jesus' sacrifice for you in terms of how you might view life, live life and interact with others?

During your prayer time, create an ambiance conducive to entering into the pain and sorrow of Jesus.[7] For example, close your curtains or blinds, darken the room in which you will be spending the time, and use a candle as your light source. Consider using different postures during this time, such as kneeling or lying prostrate, to help you engage more fully with Jesus as you enter into the Passion narratives.[8]

SIGN OF THE CROSS

Making the sign of the cross will mark the beginning and end of your daily time through the duration of Week 3. This will serve as a physical declaration of your honouring of God and a presenting of yourself to God as you enter the prayer time as well as when you leave your prayer time to enter the world at large. The sign of the cross is yet another way to involve your body in the prayer process.

To make the sign of the cross, use your right hand. Beginning from the middle of your chest, raise your right hand and touch your forehead, saying out loud, 'In the name of the Father'. Then touch your chest (heart) while saying, 'The Son', and touch your left shoulder, saying 'and the Holy' and then your right shoulder, saying, 'Spirit'. (If you are a fan of the Eastern Church, do as they do, going from right shoulder to left shoulder.) Finally, put your hands together at about chest height and say, 'Amen'.

Please make the sign of the cross slowly and prayerfully. One person, commenting on the speed at which many make this sign, said it has appeared to be less a practice of prayer and more a practice of swatting flies. Endeavour to make this an act of honouring the triune God and acknowledging the sacrifice and love of Jesus.

If you are wondering how to hold your fingers on your right hand while making the sign of the cross, there are generally two ways. The first and oldest way to position your fingers is by using your thumb and forefinger or your index and middle finger. Those in the Eastern Church put three fingers together (thumb, forefinger and middle), while the ring and little finger are folded back on the palm. I like this method because it was chosen to symbolise the Trinity (three fingers) and the two natures of Christ: fully God, fully man (the two fingers folded into the palm).

To the making of the sign of the cross, you can add a slow bow, which you incorporated during Week 2, as you are saying 'Amen'.

CRUCIFIX

A crucifix is a cross with a painted or sculpted image of Christ on it. Crucifixes first came into use around the fifth century, after the days of persecution for Christians in the West had come to an end. When the martyrdom ceased, Christians found it important to use crucifixes as a reminder of Jesus' suffering and death. Before this period, there was no need to be reminded, because Christians were martyred regularly. This religious art form developed over time, and, from the ninth century on, the aim of medieval artists was to convey an increasingly realistic portrayal (if not at times a somewhat exaggerated picture) of Jesus' suffering.

Ignatius encouraged those entering and journeying through Week 3, upon rising, to recall to mind the great sorrow and suffering of Jesus and then, throughout the day, to seek to take joyful thoughts or thoughts about the resurrection captive, endeavouring to foster an attitude of sorrow, suffering and heartache as the Passion narrative for the day is reflected upon.[9] Carrying a crucifix can be a great aid in this practice.

I strongly encourage you to purchase a crucifix, which you may choose to carry in a pocket or bag, and finger it as you pray. Display it during your daily prayer times as a reminder of the depth of Jesus' love for you. Use it as an aid to your times of meditation. Finger it as you do your nightly prayer of examen.

RULES FOR EATING

Ignatius provided eight rules regarding eating.[10] Rules 1–4 deal with what we eat and drink, while Rules 5–8 provide suggestions regarding garnering spiritual profit from eating and drinking, bringing to mind Paul's admonition, 'So whether you eat or drink or whatever you do, do it all for the glory of God' (1 Corinthians 10:31). Ignatius pointed out ways to develop a proper disposition toward food as well as ways to regulate the intake of food. He spoke not of extended fasts but rather of planning, focus and moderation regarding food. He encouraged focusing on the presence of Jesus, slowing down and using moderation when eating and drinking.

In short, Ignatius would encourage you to eat contemplatively while journeying through Week 3. You are invited to choose one meal (lunch or dinner) each week and apply any or all of the following: eating slowly, eating in silence, eating in moderation (eating less than you normally do) and drinking water and no other beverage.

Additionally, if you are physically able, fast (if in doubt, please visit your doctor before beginning a fast). I encourage you to seek to fast from food—having just water and fruit juice—for an entire day each week. Consider doing it on Friday each week to commemorate Jesus' death on the cross.

I also encourage you to use the Jewish rendering of a day when you fast, as this can help you to fast in a more meaningful way. Start your fast at sunset on Thursday. In the late afternoon, have a light meal of fruit and vegetables, and then commence your fast. Conclude your fast the next day at sunset, having another light meal.

If you have health problems that would be triggered by not eating for a day, please do not fast from food. Instead, fast from such things as television, internet, music, words, study or work.

Use the time you would normally be eating (or whatever you are fasting from) for prayer and reflection on the sacrifice, obedience and love of Jesus. In addition to food, you might want also to fast from television, music or other electronic distractions during this 24-hour period so that you can be singly focused. This would be a good time to carry around your crucifix or spend time meditating on the crucifixion.

STATIONS OF THE CROSS

The Stations of the Cross (fourth century) is a meditative walk that takes you through various events associated with Jesus carrying his cross to Golgotha, as well as the crucifixion. Most Catholic churches and Catholic retreat centres have Stations of the Cross set up all year, but so do some Protestant churches. These stations can include actual statues, artists' depictions on canvas or simple placards. Each station has a Roman numeral associated with it and corresponding with Jesus' journey to the cross.

If you would like, download a guide for doing the Stations of the Cross and use it instead of following one of the prayer times during Week 3. I would suggest you wait a couple of weeks until you are fully into Week 3 before making use of this optional exercise. If you do decide to do this exercise, be aware that not every station on the Stations of the Cross will be found in your Bible.

These new additions for Week 3 could very well feel overwhelming to you, but do not worry. You will be prompted below when to make use of those components listed above. They are provided so that you are not caught off-guard when they make their appearance during the daily Exercises and to provide additional information regarding these components without interrupting the flow of the Exercises.

ENCOURAGEMENT

Even if you are not doing Week 3 during the Lenten season, I invite you to enter into the spirit of abstinence associated with Lent by choosing to give up something. As you bump up against your desire to partake of what you are choosing to abstain from, recall to your heart and mind Jesus' sacrifice and his own willingness to lay aside what was rightly his—equality with God—to empty himself instead.

Please continue to strive to make the noontime and evening examen part of your time in the Exercises. This is a very important part of the Exercises, so you are missing out if you are not incorporating the examen each day.

Also remember to recall throughout each day the topic of that day's prayer time.

As you enter into and journey through Week 3, my prayer for you is this:

God, in your great mercy and grace, grant this beloved one the ability to enter into the fellowship of your sufferings, to journey with you not from afar but within your heart as you go to the cross, that this one may know something of your pain, your anguish, your suffering, in order to begin to grasp the immeasurable depth of your love and, being filled with that love, spontaneously share it with others. (Adapted from Colossians 3:12; Philippians 3:10; Ephesians 3:18)

EXERCISES FOR WEEK 3

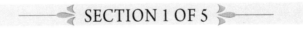 SECTION 1 OF 5

The grace you are seeking is to sorrow with Christ in sorrow, anguish with Christ in anguish, with tears and interior suffering because of the suffering that Christ endured for you.[11]

Examen questions

• Today, did you recall to your mind Jesus' willingness to suffer physical, emotional and spiritual trauma for you? Why, or why not?

- How did the truth of Jesus' willingness to suffer and die for you and others impact the way you interacted with others with whom you came in contact today?
- How did you die to self today?

Three considerations[12]

- What did Jesus suffer in his humanity in this narrative? Enter into Jesus' pain and suffering.
- How did Jesus hide (not use) his divinity in this narrative?
- Consider your response to Jesus' sacrifice for you in terms of how you might view life, live life and interact with others.

Start your time by slowly making the sign of the cross. Conclude with a bow, demonstrating your reverence for and honouring of God, while asking God that everything in your day may more and more lead you to divine praise and service.

Process

☐ Opening   ☐ Closing
☐ Daily exercise ☐ Noontime examen
☐ Journalling   ☐ Evening examen

DAY 1

Read 2 Corinthians 5:21.

Spend time pondering 'him [Jesus] who knew no sin', who became sin so you 'might become the righteousness of God'.

Colloquy

Spend time expressing thanksgiving and gratitude individually to God the Father, Jesus the Son, and the Holy Spirit for their investment, sacrifice and demonstration of love to you and to the world.

DAY 2

Read John 13:1.

Ponder the fact that Jesus knew the time had come, and 'having loved his own who were in the world, he now showed them the full extent of his love'.

Colloquy

Spend time expressing thanksgiving and gratitude individually to God the Father, Jesus the Son, and the Holy Spirit for their invest-ment, sacrifice and demonstration of love to you and to the world.

DAY 3

Read John 13:2–12.

Imagine you are having your feet washed by Jesus.

- How do you feel? What is going on inside you?
- What do you want to say to Jesus?
- What do you desire to hear Jesus say to you?

After Jesus has finished washing your feet, imagine you have an interchange with him.

- What do you say? What does Jesus say?
- How do you feel?

DAY 4

Review the past three days.

- What has really touched you during your prayer times? Why?
- How has the grace for which you have been asking impacted you these past few days?

Do something today for another, something that will cost you (time, money, comfort, security). Remember that Jesus, motivated by love, gave himself up for you.

DAY 5

Read Matthew 26:20–30.

Imagine you are with the disciples.

- What is going through your mind and arising in your heart as you hear Jesus speak of betrayal?
- As Jesus speaks of his body being broken and his blood poured out, what do you feel?
- As Jesus hands you the bread and the cup, your fingers touching his, what do you feel and sense deep within your being?

DAY 6

Read Matthew 26:31–35.

Imagine you are Peter.

- What are you feeling as you make your declaration?
- What do you feel when you hear Jesus' reply to you?

DAY 7

Review this past week.

- What has really touched you during your prayer times? Why?
- How has the grace for which you have been asking impacted you these past few days?
- What has surprised you during your prayer times this past week? Why?

Contemplative eating

Contemplative eating involves eating and drinking with a focus on the presence of Christ. Additionally, Ignatius would encourage you to eat slowly in silence while exercising moderation and drinking water. Please seek to employ these guidelines during one of your meals each week. (See 'Rules for Eating', pages 252–253.)

SECTION 2 OF 5

The grace you are seeking is to sorrow with Christ in sorrow, anguish with Christ in anguish, with tears and interior suffering because of the suffering that Christ endured for you.

Examen questions

- Today, did you recall to your mind Jesus' willingness to suffer physical, emotional and spiritual trauma for you? Why, or why not?
- How did the truth of Jesus' willingness to suffer and die for you and others impact the way you interacted with others with whom you came in contact today?
- How did you die to self today?

Three considerations

- What did Jesus suffer in his humanity in this narrative? Enter into Jesus' pain and suffering.
- How did Jesus hide (not use) his divinity in this narrative?
- Consider your response to Jesus' sacrifice for you in terms of how you might view life, live life and interact with others.

Start your time by slowly making the sign of the cross. Conclude with a bow, demonstrating your reverence for and honouring of God, while asking God that everything in your day may more and more lead you to divine praise and service.

Process

- ☐ Opening
- ☐ Daily exercise
- ☐ Journalling
- ☐ Closing
- ☐ Noontime examen
- ☐ Evening examen

DAY 1

Read Matthew 26:36–41.

Imagine you have been chosen by Jesus to go with him to the garden.

- What are you feeling as you and Jesus go to the garden?
- What are you feeling as you hear Jesus pleading with his Father?
- What do you feel as Jesus rebukes you for falling asleep?

DAY 2

Read Luke 22:39–44.

Imagine that you are with Jesus as he is praying to his Father in heaven. Use the colloquy, asking God to help you experience the depth of feeling, love and compassion for Jesus and to be present with Jesus through everything that happens. Be with Jesus as he prays and as he returns to find those he brought with him sleeping.

- What do you do?
- What do you say?

Conclude your time by saying the Lord's Prayer.

....

Fasting

If you are physically able (if in doubt, please visit your doctor before beginning a fast), I encourage you to seek to fast from food (you can have water and fruit juice) for an entire day each week. I would suggest you do so on Friday each week to commemorate Jesus' death on the cross.

....

DAY 3

Read Matthew 26:47–54.

Imagine you are with the disciples, unsure of what is happening as people are coming toward you with torches and weapons in hand. Listen to the words of Jesus. Watch his actions.

- What are you feeling and thinking?
- What do you want to do?
- What do you want to say to Jesus?
- To Judas?
- To those who have come to arrest Jesus?
- What do you do?

DAY 4

Review the past three days.

- What has really touched you during your prayer times? Why?
- How has the grace for which you have been asking impacted you these past few days?

Do something today for another, something that will cost you something (time, money, comfort, security). Remember that Jesus, motivated by love, gave himself up for you.

DAY 5

Read Matthew 26:55–56.

Imagine you are with Jesus and you hear his words spoken with courage, conviction and confidence.

- What are you feeling about Jesus as you hear him speak to those who have come under cover of darkness to arrest him?

You notice that the disciples are slowly backing away from Jesus and starting to flee. You feel yourself almost involuntarily following their lead.

- How do you feel about deserting Jesus?
- What do you think Jesus is feeling about you as you begin to leave his presence?

As you are leaving, you turn back and catch a glimpse of Jesus. Your eyes and his eyes meet.

- What do you see in his eyes?
- What does he say to you in that look?

DAY 6

Read John 18:12–27.

Imagine you are Peter, following Jesus and the crowd from a distance. As Jesus is taken inside, you are standing around the fire, waiting to see what will happen.

- What do you feel as you are asked if you are a disciple?
- What are you feeling as you deny that you are a disciple?
- What do you feel as you remember your words to Jesus: 'Even if all fall away on account of you, I never will' (Matthew 26:33)?

- What do you feel as he replies, 'I tell you the truth, this very night, before the cock crows, you will disown me three times' (v. 34)?
- How do you feel the second and third time you deny being a disciple of Jesus?
- What do you feel as you hear the cock crow after your third denial?

DAY 7

Review this past week.

- What has really touched you during your prayer times? Why?
- How has the grace for which you have been asking impacted you these past few days?
- What has surprised you during your prayer times this past week? Why?

Colloquy

Spend time expressing thanksgiving and gratitude individually to God the Father, Jesus the Son, and the Holy Spirit for their investment, sacrifice and demonstration of love to you and to the world.

⋘ SECTION 3 OF 5 ⋙

The grace you are seeking is to sorrow with Christ in sorrow, anguish with Christ in anguish, with tears and interior suffering because of the suffering that Christ endured for you.

Examen questions

- Today, did you recall to your mind Jesus' willingness to suffer physical, emotional and spiritual trauma for you? Why, or why not?
- How did the truth of Jesus' willingness to suffer and die for you and others impact the way you interacted with others with whom you came in contact today?
- How did you die to self today?

Three considerations

- What did Jesus suffer in his humanity in this narrative? Enter into Jesus' pain and suffering.
- How did Jesus hide (not use) his divinity in this narrative?
- Consider your response to Jesus' sacrifice for you in terms of how you might view life, live life and interact with others.

Start your time by slowly making the sign of the cross. Conclude with a bow, demonstrating your reverence for and honouring of God, while asking God that everything in your day may more and more lead you to divine praise and service.

Process

☐ Opening   ☐ Closing
☐ Daily exercise   ☐ Noontime examen
☐ Journalling   ☐ Evening examen

DAY 1

Read Matthew 26:57–68.

Imagine you are with Jesus. In conversational prayer (colloquy), ask God to help you experience the depth of feeling, love and compassion for Jesus and to be present with Jesus through everything that happens.

• What are you feeling as you watch Jesus being falsely accused, falsely testified against, remaining silent, speaking, getting spat upon and hit in the face?

Make your way over to Jesus and be with Jesus.

• What are you feeling?
• What do you desire to say and to do to Jesus?

Conclude this time by saying the Lord's Prayer.

DAY 2

Read Matthew 26:69–75.

Imagine you are Peter.

• What are you feeling as you once again deny Christ, hear the cock crow and recall Jesus' words, 'Before the rooster crows, you will deny me three times'?
• What are your tears about?

Now look at your own life. When do you find it difficult to make yourself known as a follower of Jesus? Why?

Ask God to show you if there are ways in which you explicitly or implicitly deny Jesus.

Conclude your time with conversation prayer (colloquy) with Jesus, sharing your feelings, discoveries and insights with him.

DAY 3

Read Luke 23:1–7.

Imagine that you are continuing to be with Jesus as they move him from place to place and take him to Pilate.

- What do you see and feel as Jesus is questioned by Pilate?
- As Jesus answers Pilate?
- As Jesus is palmed off by Pilate to Herod?
- What are you learning, discovering about Jesus as you walk this journey with him?

DAY 4

Review the past two days.

- What has really touched you during your prayer times? Why?
- How has the grace for which you have been asking impacted you these past few days?

Do something today for another, something that will cost you (time, money, comfort, security). Remember that Jesus, motivated by love, gave himself up for you.

DAY 5

Read Luke 23:8–12.

Imagine that you are continuing on with Jesus to Herod's palace.

- What are you feeling and thinking?
- As you watch Jesus remain silent before the mighty and powerful Herod, what do you think and feel?
- What do you feel as you watch Jesus ridiculed and mocked by the guards?
- What do you want to say to these guards?
- To Herod?
- To Jesus?

DAY 6

Read Luke 23:13–25.

Imagine that you are continuing on with Jesus from Herod's palace back to Pilate's.

- What are you feeling and thinking?
- When you hear Pilate desire to punish and then release Jesus, what do you feel inside?
- What do you feel as you hear a few shouts from some bystanders in the crowd saying, 'Crucify him! Crucify him!'
- What do you feel as you notice that those shouts are growing in number and intensity?
- What do you feel as Pilate gives in to the crowd's demands and agrees to have Jesus crucified?

DAY 7

Review this past week.

- What has really touched you during your prayer times? Why?
- How has the grace for which you have been asking impacted you these past few days?
- What has surprised you during your prayer times this past week? Why?

Colloquy

Spend time expressing thanksgiving and gratitude individually to God the Father, Jesus the Son, and the Holy Spirit for their investment, sacrifice and demonstration of love to you and to the world.

Conclude this time by saying the Lord's Prayer.

SECTION 4 OF 5

The grace you are seeking is to sorrow with Christ in sorrow, anguish with Christ in anguish, with tears and interior suffering because of the suffering that Christ endured for you.

Examen questions

- Today, did you recall to your mind Jesus' willingness to suffer physical, emotional and spiritual trauma for you? Why, or why not?
- How did the truth of Jesus' willingness to suffer and die for you and others impact the way you interacted with others with whom you came in contact today?
- How did you die to self today?

Three considerations

- What did Jesus suffer in his humanity in this narrative? Enter into Jesus' pain and suffering.
- How did Jesus hide (not use) his divinity in this narrative?
- Consider your response to Jesus' sacrifice for you in terms of how you might view life, live life and interact with others.

Start your time by slowly making the sign of the cross. Conclude with a bow, demonstrating your reverence for and honouring of God, while asking God that everything in your day may more and more lead you to divine praise and service.

Process

- ☐ Opening
- ☐ Daily exercise
- ☐ Journalling

- ☐ Closing
- ☐ Noontime examen
- ☐ Evening examen

DAY 1

Read Matthew 27:32–44.

Read through the narrative two different times.
First, imagine you are Simon, who is forced to carry Jesus' cross.

- What is Jesus' reaction as you take his cross?
- What do you see in his eyes?
- What goes through your mind and your heart as you take Jesus' cross on your back and walk with him?
- What do you want to say to Jesus?

Now imagine you are a devoted follower of Jesus who is following at a safe distance, seeking to go unnoticed, yet hearing and seeing all that is going on.

- What are you feeling?
- What do you want to say to Jesus?
- To God the Father?
- In which of the above characters do you most see yourself?
- Which one do you desire to be? Why?

Slowly read the following poem, 'The cross' by Lois A. Cheney, and allow yourself to linger with each stanza. Stay with the words wonder, fear, weep and rejoice.

I stand before the cross
And wonder.

I stand before the cross
And fear.

I kneel before the cross
And weep.

I pray before the cross
And rejoice.

To know the cross
Is to know Christ.

To feel the cross
Is to feel Christ.

To gaze at the cross
Is to gaze at Christ.

To carry the cross
Is to be a Christian,
And not until then.

God, forgive me.[13]

- What does each word—wonder, fear, weep and rejoice—say to you about God, yourself and the cross?
- How do they fit together?
- How does the cross help you to know Christ, feel Christ and see Christ?
- What does it mean for you to carry the cross in your life?

DAY 2

Read Luke 23:33–44.

Read the entire passage, then spend your time meditating on Jesus' words in verse 34. Afterwards, imagine you are standing with others near the cross, and you hear Jesus' words about forgiveness.

What is your reaction?

Now imagine you are standing before the cross and Jesus looks at you, calls you by name and says, 'Father, forgive [your name], for she/he did not know what she/he was doing.'

- What goes on within you as you hear Jesus' words to you?
- To what degree are you able to internally embrace Jesus' forgiveness?

Spend time thanking God/Jesus for the forgiveness Jesus has provided for you through his suffering and death on the cross.

DAY 3

Read Philippians 2:5–8.

Read through the passage three times, allowing yourself to soak in the words. After a while, read the words below, taken from the passage, asking yourself which of these words, values or mindsets you are most resistant to and why:

- made himself empty
- servant
- humbled himself
- obedient
- died on a cross

Now go back through the above list and ask God to show you how manifesting each of these mindsets and values in your life could draw you into a closer relationship with God.

DAY 4

Review the past three days.

- What has really touched you during your prayer times? Why?
- How has the grace for which you have been asking impacted you these past few days?

Colloquy

Spend time expressing thanksgiving and gratitude individually to God the Father, Jesus the Son, and the Holy Spirit for their investment, sacrifice and demonstration of love to you and to the world.

Conclude this time by saying the Lord's Prayer.

Do something today for another, something that will cost you (time, money, comfort, security). Remember that Jesus, motivated by love, gave himself up for you.

DAY 5

Read Luke 23:38–43.

Imagine you are the criminal on the cross who rebukes the other criminal and says, 'Jesus, remember me when you come into your kingdom.'

- What are you feeling when you hear the other criminal hurling insults at Jesus?
- What is it about Jesus that makes you feel the need to defend him?
- What is it about Jesus that causes you to say, 'Jesus, remember me when you come into your kingdom'?
- What goes on in your mind and heart when Jesus responds to you, 'I tell you the truth, today you will be with me in paradise'?
- What makes you believe Jesus' words?
- What is your response to Jesus?

Additional imaginative exercise

Imagine you are Peter, standing near enough to the cross to hear what is going on between Jesus and the criminals. You are still feeling shame and disgust for your triple rejection of Jesus, and now you hear one of the criminals come to Jesus' aid. You hear Jesus' promise that the criminal will join him in paradise that very day.

- What goes on in your head and heart?
- What do you want to say to Jesus? Why?

DAY 6

Read John 19:25–27.

Imagine you are John or Jesus' mother.

- What do you feel toward Jesus as you hear his words?
- What do they express to you about Jesus?
- What do they express to you about you (your value, worth, significance)? Why?

DAY 7

Review this past week.

- What has really touched you during your prayer times? Why?
- How has the grace for which you have been asking impacted you these past few days?
- What has surprised you during your prayer times this past week? Why?

Colloquy

Spend time expressing thanksgiving and gratitude individually to God the Father, Jesus the Son, and the Holy Spirit for their investment, sacrifice and demonstration of love to you and to the world.

SECTION 5 OF 5

The grace you are seeking is to sorrow with Christ in sorrow, anguish with Christ in anguish, with tears and interior suffering because of the suffering that Christ endured for you.

Examen questions

- Today, did you recall to your mind Jesus' willingness to suffer physical, emotional and spiritual trauma for you? Why, or why not?
- How did the truth of Jesus' willingness to suffer and die for you and others impact how you interacted with others with whom you came in contact today?
- How did you die to self today?

Three considerations

- What did Jesus suffer in his humanity in this narrative? Enter into Jesus' pain and suffering.
- How did Jesus hide (not use) his divinity in this narrative?
- Consider your response to Jesus' sacrifice for you in terms of how you might view life, live life and interact with others.

Start your time by slowly making the sign of the cross. Conclude with a bow, demonstrating your reverence for and honouring of God, while asking God that everything in your day may more and more lead you to divine praise and service.

Process

☐ Opening   ☐ Closing
☐ Daily exercise ☐ Noontime examen
☐ Journalling   ☐ Evening examen

DAY 1

Read Mark 15:33–36.

Sit with the words in verse 34. Imagine the anguish and pain as Jesus, who has been one with the Father, now feels separated from God. Notice that Jesus does not use the word 'Father' to address God, but rather the more distant term 'God'.

Using conversational prayer (colloquy), ask God to help you experience the depth of feeling, love and compassion for Jesus and to be present with Jesus as he experiences separation from the Father.

DAY 2

Read Isaiah 53:3–6.

Spend your time meditating on this passage, especially focusing on what Jesus went through for you—he was despised, rejected, smitten, afflicted, crushed for you—and what Jesus took on for you: your transgressions, your infirmities, your sorrows, your iniquities, your punishment.

Conclude your time with prayers of gratitude and thanksgiving, for by his wounds you have been healed.

DAY 3

Read Luke 23:44–46.

Imagine you are standing before the cross, hearing the last few words of Jesus. You just heard him cry out in an anguished voice, 'My God, my God, why have you forsaken me?' and now you hear him say, 'Father, into your hands I commit my spirit.'

- What has changed?
- Why does Jesus now address God as 'Daddy'?
- What is the invitation and the challenge for you in these two statements of Jesus?

DAY 4

Review the past three days.

- What has really touched you during your prayer times? Why?
- How has the grace for which you have been asking impacted you these past few days?
- What has surprised you during your prayer times this past week? Why?

Colloquy

Spend time expressing thanksgiving and gratitude individually to God the Father, Jesus the Son, and the Holy Spirit for their invest-ment, sacrifice and demonstration of love to you and to the world.

Do something today for another, something that will cost you (time, money, comfort, security). Remember that Jesus, motivated by love, gave himself up for you.

DAY 5

Read John 19:30.

Reflect on Jesus' words, 'It is finished.'
Imagine you are a disciple hearing this.

- What are your immediate feelings?
- What do you do?
- What do you think this means for you and the rest of the disciples?

- What do these final words of Jesus mean? What is finished?
- What do you long to say to Jesus, now departed?

DAY 6

Read Luke 23:47–49.

Imagine you are the centurion.

- What did you see in Jesus as he suffered on the cross that caused you to praise God and say, 'Surely this was a righteous man'?

As you have meditated these past several days on the seven sayings of Jesus on the cross, what stands out to you? Why?

What challenges you? Why?

Slowly read the following poem, 'The cross' by Lois Cheney, and allow yourself to linger with each stanza. Stay with the words wonder, fear, weep and rejoice.

> *I stand before the cross*
> *And wonder.*
>
> *I stand before the cross*
> *And fear.*
>
> *I kneel before the cross*
> *And weep.*
>
> *I pray before the cross*
> *And rejoice.*
>
> *To know the cross*
> *Is to know Christ.*
>
> *To feel the cross*
> *Is to feel Christ.*

To gaze at the cross
Is to gaze at Christ.

To carry the cross
Is to be a Christian,
And not until then.

God, forgive me.

- What does each word—wonder, fear, weep and rejoice—say to you about God, yourself and the cross?
- How do they fit together?
- How does the cross help you to know Christ, feel Christ and see Christ?
- What does it mean for you to carry the cross in your life?

DAY 7

Review this past week.

- What has really touched you during your prayer times? Why?
- How has the grace for which you have been asking impacted you these past few days?
- What has surprised you during your prayer times this past week? Why?

Colloquy

Spend time expressing thanksgiving and gratitude individually to God the Father, Jesus the Son, and the Holy Spirit for their investment, sacrifice and demonstration of love to you and to the world.

Conclude by saying the Lord's Prayer.

Note: If you started this section on Ash Wednesday, you will now be entering Holy Week (the week leading up to Easter) before you work your way through the section below. Go to the Ash Wednesday and Holy Week Exercises on pages 311–318. When you have completed these exercises, return here and read through the following section. If you did not start Week 3 on Ash Wednesday, or if Holy Week is not next week, then continue on with the following section.

CONCLUDING COMMENTS AND REFLECTIONS

You have completed Week 3, which can be a very dry and arduous time in the Exercises. You have spent the past several weeks walking with Jesus through the events leading up to the cross and climaxing in his crucifixion. You have been asking God for the grace of experiencing sorrow with Christ in sorrow and anguish with Christ in anguish. You have been transformed from a follower of Jesus to a companion with Jesus, seeking to see as he saw and experience what he experienced, even though painful and disheartening. You wrestled with bringing the reality of Christ crucified to the table of your everyday life and experiences. You discovered to a greater degree what it meant for Jesus to humble himself by not regarding equality with God as a thing to be grasped and by choosing to come into this world as a human and to willingly endure suffering as he refused to make use of the attributes resident in his divinity.

Now it is time to discern if you will continue into Week 4, the final section of the Exercises. There are some who get to this point and, because of weariness, decide that God does not desire them to move on to Week 4. I strongly urge you not to make your decision on that basis. If you sense that God has more for you in Week 3 or is telling you that your season in the Exercises has come to an end, then God bless you. But if that is not the case, I encourage you to enter into Week 4.

You may be caught a little off-guard by my new tone regarding entering the new Week. There are also no questions or continuums to help you discern if you should enter into Week 4. This is in part because Weeks 3 and 4 are from the same spiritual formation phase, known as the Unitive Way. So it is not a matter of if you are ready to enter into Week 4. Instead, the question is, what is your sense of God's leading and your own internal desire?

So the choice is yours, and whatever you choose is perfectly OK. But, instead of strongly cautioning you not to go forward, this time I am encouraging you to enter into Week 4 and its focus on the resurrection of Jesus.

─────── WEEK 4 ───────

RESURRECTION OF JESUS

Welcome to the fourth and final Week of the Exercises.[1] During Weeks 2 and 3, your focus has been on the life and passion of Jesus. Now you will focus on the resurrection of Christ, or, more precisely, Jesus' post-resurrection experiences and interactions. You have moved out of a time of meditating on the suffering, agony and death of Christ to enter into a period of embracing the joy and consolation that flow out of the reality of his resurrection. Additionally, Week 4 has a component known as Contemplation to Attain Love of God,[2] which is the final piece of your journey through the Exercises and encourages you to engage with the world as an active contemplative.

As you begin your time in Week 4, your sole focus will be on the resurrection, which is the linchpin of the Christian faith. The apostle Paul rightly reminds us:

If Christ has not been raised, our preaching is useless and so is your faith… And if Christ has not been raised, your faith is futile; you are still in your sins… If only for this life we have hope in Christ, we are to be pitied more than all men. But Christ has indeed been raised from the dead. (1 Corinthians 15:14, 17, 19–20)

He appeared to Peter, and then to the Twelve. After that, he appeared to more than five hundred of the brothers at the same time, most of whom are still living, though some have fallen asleep. Then he appeared to James, then to all the apostles, and last of all he appeared to me also, as to one abnormally born. (1 Corinthians 15:5–8)

Jesus' resurrection did occur within time and space, and in Week 4 this resurrection takes centre stage. We move away from the agonised suffering of Jesus in Week 3 and into the glorious light of an empty tomb and our resurrected Lord and Saviour. The goal of Week 4 is to enter into the joy of the resurrection while also affirming the reality of the crucifixion, for there is no resurrection of Jesus without the crucifixion of Jesus. Week 4 and Week 3 are two sides of the same coin, linked and inseparable from one another.

Week 4 does not proclaim that you are for ever safe within the protective bubble of the resurrected Christ but that there will be ultimate victory in and through Christ. You who journey with the resurrected Christ will experience evil, heartache and possibly even agonising death, but these will no longer have the final word in your life. Week 4 is all about freedom—freedom to be, freedom to become the person God has created you to be and freedom from paralysing fears and doubts. Jesus' resurrection removes the constricting boundary of death from your life and allows the expanse of life everlasting to cascade on you, filling your heart and spirit with the joy of Jesus.

As you make your way through the exercises of Week 4, you will discover that there are two pivotal points found in it: the resurrection appearances of Jesus, and Jesus' consoling presence. The post-resurrection Jesus brings consolation to those who are hurting and struggling in their faith.[3] Jesus frees Mary Magdalene from despair, those on the road to Emmaus from their spiritual pessimism, Thomas from his doubts and Peter from his remorse and guilt. Week 4 is a time of consolation, a time for entering into the joy of Jesus, a joy that becomes an inner strength for proactively living and dealing with life.

The desired grace of Week 4 is the ability to rejoice and be intensely glad because of the great glory and joy of Jesus, your risen Lord.[4] In Week 4 you move from weeping with Jesus as he wept (Week 3) to rejoicing with Jesus as he rejoiced (Romans 12:15).

You have moved from enduring the cross with Jesus to entering into the joy of Jesus (Hebrews 12:2).

The joy of Jesus brings life-giving freedom to those who follow him. This is the consolation of Jesus, namely, Jesus resurrected. This Week you are called to be present to and embrace the triumph of love and life in Jesus, broadcast throughout the universe by his resurrection. Week 4 is a time to celebrate, to sing and dance—so do it! Be happy! Christ is risen; he was dead but now he is alive! It is time to celebrate!

ADDITIONS TO EXERCISES

Conclude your opening prayer time by saying the following: 'Jesus is risen. Jesus is risen indeed. Alleluia. Amen.'

As you get up each morning during this Week, recall Ephesians 5:14: 'Wake up, O sleeper, rise from the dead, and Christ will shine on you.'

QUESTIONS FOR SECTIONS 1–3

These questions are to be used after you have entered the daily passage using imaginative prayer.

- How does Jesus now manifest his divine attributes, his true self, following his resurrection?
- How does Jesus console those he encounters?
- What do you experience as you encounter the resurrected Christ?

Create an ambiance that is conducive to entering into the happiness and spiritual joy that flow from the resurrection of Jesus. Allow the sunshine to fill your room, and place potted plants or cut flowers or other things around the room that communicate beauty, joy and hope to you.

Do your best to enter into the narrative as if you do not know the whole story. Try to imagine what you would be feeling, knowing that Jesus, whom you had watched, listened to and followed for three years, was dead. Seek to allow yourself to experience the confusion, wonder, joy and delight as he begins to appear and interact with you and the others. Ask God to help you to do this.

The above could feel overwhelming to you, but do not worry. You will be prompted below when to make use of those components listed above. They are provided here so that you are not caught off-guard when they make their appearance during the daily exercises and to provide additional information regarding these components without interrupting the flow of the Exercises.

REMINDER AND ENCOURAGEMENT

It is very helpful to journal through these exercises. It allows you to see patterns in your prayer times and to recall what God has spoken to you. Often, as you journal, God expands on what you have discovered or been made aware of. I strongly encourage you to journal. It will deepen your experience with the Exercises.

Please continue to strive to make the noontime and evening examen a part of your time in the Exercises, and remain faithful to showing up each day and presenting yourself to God as a living and holy sacrifice. You have almost completed your season in the Exercises.

As you enter into and journey through Week 4, my prayer for you is this:

God, bless and honour these ones as they have faithfully journeyed with you all these weeks. Help them to sense your presence with them and your delight in them. Grant them wisdom and insight, that they may come to know something of the power and joy associated with the glorious resurrection of Jesus. I pray that they may come to experience the power that is theirs, the power that raised Christ from the dead, and that the joy associated with the resurrection would become itself a strength that would enable them to live a life worthy of their calling, a life of love, a life that pleases and honours you their God. (Adapted from Philippians 3:10; Ephesians 1:19–20; Nehemiah 8:10; Ephesians 5:1)

EXERCISES FOR WEEK 4

SECTION 1 OF 4

The grace you are seeking this week is the ability to rejoice and be intensely glad because of the great glory and joy of Jesus, your risen Lord.

Examen questions

- How did the joy and power of Jesus' resurrection impact the way you viewed your life, your self and your circumstances today?
- How did it impact the way you dealt with others today?
- How did the truth of Jesus' resurrection bring consolation and the ability to experience the reality of Jesus in the happenings of your life today?

Come to prayer, conscious of the reverence God deserves, while asking God that everything in your day may more and more lead you to divine praise and service.

Process

- ❏ Opening: Conclude your opening prayer time by saying the following: 'Jesus is risen. Jesus is risen indeed. Alleluia. Amen.'
- ❏ Daily exercise
- ❏ Journalling
- ❏ Closing
- ❏ Noontime examen
- ❏ Evening examen

Questions for Sections 1–3

- How does Jesus now manifest his divine attributes, his true self, following his resurrection?
- How does Jesus console those he encounters?
- What do you experience as you encounter the resurrected Christ?

These questions can be used after you have worked through the daily passage using imaginative prayer and the suggested questions for the day.

DAY 1

Read Mark 16:1–16.

Read slowly through this passage two to three times.

- To what aspects of the story are you drawn? Why?
- With which of the participants do you readily identify? Why?
- What feelings are stirred within you as the narrative unfolds?

DAY 2

Read Luke 24:1–9.

Imagine you are one of the women going to the tomb.

- What is going on in your mind and heart as you travel to the tomb to prepare Jesus' body?
- When you discover the stone is rolled away and the body of Jesus missing?
- When you see the angels, and when you hear the angels speak to you?
- What is it like to interact with the angel and hear the angel say to you, 'Do not be so surprised. You're looking for Jesus the Nazarene, who was crucified. He is not here! He has been raised from the dead!'
- What are you thinking and feeling? Why?

....

Setting the stage
Create an ambiance that is conducive to entering into the happiness and spiritual joy that flow from the resurrection of Jesus. Allow the sunshine to fill your room, and place potted plants or cut flowers or other things around the room that communicate beauty, joy and hope to you.

....

DAY 3

Read Luke 24:10–11.

Imagine you are one of the women who went to the tomb.

- As you head back to tell the disciples about the empty tomb and the message of the angels, what is going on in your head and heart?
- What happens within you, especially as a woman who is looked down on in your society, as the disciples say your story is nonsense and they laugh in your face?
- What do you think Jesus felt about this exchange between the women who went to the tomb and the disciples? Why?

DAY 4

Review your past three days.

- What has really touched you during your prayer times? Why?
- How has the grace for which you have been asking impacted you these past few days?

DAY 5

Read Luke 24:1; John 20:3–10.

Imagine you are Peter. Although you do not believe the story told by the women, you are drawn to visit the tomb.

- Why are you drawn to the tomb?
- What is going on in your mind and heart as you travel to the tomb?
- What do you feel or think as you notice the stone has been rolled away and as you peer into the tomb and discover that Jesus' body is gone while the linens remain?
- Now, as belief slowly rises within you, what emotions also arise as you realise that this is all in harmony with scripture?

DAY 6

Read John 20:11–18.

Imagine you are Mary.

- What are you feeling as you interact with the angel and the gardener?
- Why do you have such a strong desire to attend to Jesus' body?
- Now listen for Jesus to call you by name. What do you feel as you hear Jesus call your name?

- As you hold on to Jesus, and he says to you, 'Don't cling to me, for I haven't yet returned to the Father,' what are you feeling? Why?
- What do you think Jesus was feeling about the above exchange with Mary? Why?

DAY 7

Review this past week.

- What has really touched you during your prayer times? Why?
- How has the grace for which you have been asking impacted you these past few days?
- What has surprised you during your prayer times this past week? Why?

Colloquy

Spend time expressing thanksgiving and gratitude individually to God the Father, Jesus the Son, and the Holy Spirit for their investment, sacrifice and demonstration of love to you and to the world.

SECTION 2 OF 4

The grace you are seeking this week is the ability to rejoice and be intensely glad because of the great glory and joy of Jesus, your risen Lord.

Examen questions

- How did the joy and power of Jesus' resurrection impact the way you viewed your life, your self and your circumstances today?

- How did it impact the way you dealt with others today?
- How did the truth of Jesus' resurrection bring consolation and the ability to experience the reality of Jesus in the happenings of your life today?

Come to prayer, conscious of the reverence God deserves, while asking God that everything in your day may more and more lead you to divine praise and service.

Process

- ❏ Opening: Conclude your opening prayer time by saying the following: 'Jesus is risen. Jesus is risen indeed. Alleluia. Amen.'
- ❏ Daily exercise
- ❏ Journalling
- ❏ Closing
- ❏ Noontime examen
- ❏ Evening examen

Questions for Section 1–3

These questions are to be used after you have entered the daily passage using imaginative prayer.

- How does Jesus now manifest his divine attributes, his true self, following his resurrection?
- How does Jesus console those he encounters?
- What do you experience as you encounter the resurrected Christ?

DAY 1

Luke 24:13–24.

Imagine you are one of the two people walking to Emmaus.

- What are you feeling as you are walking down the road?
- What are you thinking about?
- As another joins you, what goes through your mind? Are you glad another has joined you and is walking with you, or do you feel that this is an unwelcome intrusion? Why?
- What are you thinking and feeling as you speak with this person and as you share the events and reports of the past few days? Why?

DAY 2

Read Luke 24:25–32.

Imagine you are one of the two people walking to Emmaus.

- As you hear the other person (Jesus) reply to you, what is going on inside you?
- As he goes through the scriptures, highlighting truths about the Messiah, what is stirring within you?
- What do you feel the moment you realise it is Jesus speaking to you and he disappears from your presence?
- What do you think Jesus was feeling about the above exchange with these two individuals? Why?

DAY 3

Read John 20:19–23.

Imagine you are with the disciples, hiding behind locked doors, afraid and confused.

- What do you feel as Jesus appears before you and as he shows you his hands and feet?
- What do you think Jesus was feeling about the above exchange with the disciples? Why?

DAY 4

Review the past three days.

- What has really touched you during your prayer times? Why?
- How has the grace for which you have been asking impacted you these past few days?

DAY 5

Read John 20:24–25.

Imagine you are Thomas.

- What are you feeling when you return to hear the story of Jesus' appearance while you were gone?
- How does it make you feel that Jesus possibly showed himself to the others but not you?
- Why have you decided not to believe their reports?
- What are your feelings toward Jesus, who has not shown himself to you? Why do you feel this way?

DAY 6

Read John 20:26–29.

Imagine you are Thomas.

- What have you been feeling during this past week as you have heard over and over again about Jesus' appearance but have not seen Jesus yourself?
- What are your feelings toward the disciples?
- Toward Jesus?
- Why is it so hard for you to believe?

Now Jesus appears before you and the others.

- What are you feeling as you see Jesus alive?
- What are you feeling when Jesus walks toward you, saying, 'Put your finger here; see my hands. Reach out your hand and put it into my side. Stop doubting and believe'?
- What are you feeling when you hear Jesus say, 'Because you have seen me, you have believed; blessed are those who have not seen and yet have believed.' Why?
- What do you think Jesus was feeling about the above exchange with Thomas? Why?

DAY 7

Review this past week.

- What has really touched you during your prayer times? Why?
- How has the grace for which you have been asking impacted you these the past few days?
- What has surprised you during your prayer times this past week? Why?

Colloquy

Spend time expressing thanksgiving and gratitude individually to God the Father, Jesus the Son, and the Holy Spirit for their investment, sacrifice and demonstration of love to you and to the world.

SECTION 3 OF 4

The grace you are seeking this week is the ability to rejoice and be intensely glad because of the great glory and joy of Jesus, your risen Lord.

Examen questions

- How did the joy and power of Jesus' resurrection impact the way you viewed your life, your self and your circumstances today?
- How did it impact the way you dealt with others today?
- How did the truth of Jesus' resurrection bring consolation and the ability to experience the reality of Jesus in the happenings of your life today?

Come to prayer, conscious of the reverence God deserves, while asking God that everything in your day may more and more lead you to divine praise and service.

Process

- ❏ Opening: Conclude your opening prayer time by saying the following: 'Jesus is risen. Jesus is risen indeed. Alleluia. Amen.'
- ❏ Daily exercise
- ❏ Journalling
- ❏ Closing
- ❏ Noontime examen
- ❏ Evening examen

Questions for Sections 1–3

These questions are to be used after you have entered the daily passage using imaginative prayer.

- How does Jesus now manifest his divine attributes, his true self, following his resurrection?
- How does Jesus console those he encounters?
- What do you experience as you encounter the resurrected Christ?

DAY 1

Read John 21:1–14.

Imagine you are one of the disciples who were fishing. You have been fishing all night and have caught nothing.

- What are you feeling as the sun rises in the morning?
- What are you feeling as you hear a stranger yell out from the shore to cast your net on the other side?
- What are you feeling as you make such a huge catch of fish?
- As John recognises that it is Jesus on the shore?
- As you watch Peter jump out of the boat and start to swim ashore?
- What do you want to do and to say?

Now imagine you are back on shore, and Jesus is walking toward you. He is bringing you some bread and fish. As he stands before you, he looks deep into your eyes and you into his.

- What do you want to say and to do?
- What does Jesus say to you?

Sit in this scene for a few minutes.

DAY 2

Read John 21:15–19.

Imagine you are Peter. You are eating with the others, and Jesus walks over to you and says, 'Peter, we need to talk.' As you get up, you are well aware of the three times you denied him, even after you swore you would never do such a thing.

- As you and Jesus walk away from the others, what are you feeling about yourself and about Jesus?
- What do you long to say to Jesus?

As you move away from the others, Jesus turns to you and asks you three different times, 'Do you love me?'

- What are you thinking and feeling as Jesus repeatedly asks you if you truly love him? Why?
- What do you feel when Jesus tells you to 'Follow me'? Why?

DAY 3

Read Matthew 28:16–20.

Imagine you are one of the disciples. As you stand there, worshipping Jesus, you can see in the eyes of some of the others that they still doubt.

- What do you think about those who still doubt?
- What do you feel toward them?
- How do you think Jesus feels toward them?
- As you hear the words, the commission of Jesus, what do you feel?
- When you hear Jesus' promise, 'I am with you always, to the very end of the age,' how does that make you feel about him?

DAY 4

Review the past three days.

- What has really touched you during your prayer times? Why?
- How has the grace for which you have been asking impacted you these past few days?

DAY 5

Read Luke 24:44–53.

Imagine you are one of the disciples.

- What are you thinking and feeling as you hear Jesus explain to you from the scriptures how all this (his death and resurrection) has been foretold by Moses, the prophets and himself?
- What does his promise of sending the Holy Spirit with power upon you mean to you?
- What do you feel as you watch Jesus ascend into heaven? Why?

DAY 6

Read Acts 1:3; 1 Corinthians 15:3–9.

Even at the end, there were those who doubted.

- Do you believe that Jesus died and rose again? Why?
- What difference does your belief make to the way you live your life, spend your time and money, and interact with others?
- How is your life different because you believe Jesus died and rose again?

DAY 7

Review this past week.

- What has really touched you during your prayer times? Why?
- How has the grace for which you have been asking impacted you these past few days?
- What has surprised you during your prayer times this past week? Why?

Colloquy

Spend time expressing thanksgiving and gratitude individually to God the Father, Jesus the Son, and the Holy Spirit for their investment, sacrifice and demonstration of love to you and to the world.

CONTEMPLATION OF DIVINE LOVE

You have arrived at the final days of Week 4. The focus of this final week will be on contemplating the love of God.[5] You will be focusing on God's gift to you, God's self-giving to you, God's labour for you and God's unceasing giving and gifting.

The goal of this small section is to plunge you into the love of God, which will in turn teach and empower you to love and serve God in all things: 'to be a contemplative in action, finding God in all things: to be able always to recognise the Love that surrounds us, the Love in which we are immersed, the Love from which everything comes and to which everything goes.'[6]

Ignatius stated at the beginning of this section that 'love ought to be more in deeds than words'. This is reminiscent of the words of the apostle John, 'Dear children, let us not love with words or tongue but with actions and in truth' (1 John 3:18). Here Ignatius made it clear that this journey through the Exercises does not result in a privatised faith but in a life of loving service, of active contemplation.

◄ SECTION 4 OF 4 ►

The grace you are seeking is an intimate knowledge of all the goods that God lovingly shares with you so that, filled with gratitude, you may be empowered to respond just as totally in your love and service to God.[7]

Examen questions

- How has your awareness of God's unceasing giving to you and God's continual labouring for you impacted the way you view your life, your self and your circumstances today?

- How did it impact the way you dealt with others today?
- How did it enable you to enter more fully into and manifest the fullness of God in your life?

Process

- ☐ Opening
- ☐ Daily exercise
- ☐ Journalling

- ☐ Closing
- ☐ Noontime examen
- ☐ Evening examen

DAY 1

Today spend time with the two prayers below. One is taken from Ignatius' Exercises and the other is from John Wesley's writings. Both of these prayers are an expression of the indifference communicated in the Principle and Foundation, which marked the beginning of Week 1.[8] Read the prayers three times, paying attention to what you are drawn to in the prayers, as well as what you are resistant toward. Then work through the questions that follow the prayers.

Take, Lord, and receive all my liberty, my memory, my understanding, my entire will—all is yours; do with it what you will. Give me only your love and your grace. That is enough for me.[9]

I am no longer my own, but thine. Put me to what thou wilt, rank me with whom thou wilt; put me to doing, put me to suffering; let me be employed for thee or laid aside for thee, exalted for thee or brought low for thee; let me be full, let me be empty; let me have all things, let me have nothing; I freely and heartily yield all things to thy pleasure and disposal.[10]
JOHN WESLEY'S COVENANT PRAYER

- What were you drawn to and resistant toward in these prayers? Why?

- Is God's love and grace enough for you? Why, or why not?

Conclude your time by reading Psalm 73:25–28 and talking to God about why God is or is not enough for you.

DAY 2

His divine power has given us everything we need for life and godliness through our knowledge of him who called us by his own glory and goodness. Through these he has given us his very great and precious promises, so that through them you may participate in the divine nature and escape the corruption in the world caused by evil desires. (2 Peter 1:3–4)

For no matter how many promises God has made, they are 'Yes' in Christ. And so through him the 'Amen' is spoken by us to the glory of God. (2 Corinthians 1:20)

God made him who had no sin to be sin for us, so that in him we might become the righteousness of God. (2 Corinthians 5:21)

Make a list of all that God has done, is doing and will do for you (God's gifts to you).

Spend time resting in God's love for you and presence with you.

Colloquy

(This colloquy will be used on days 2, 3, 5 and 6.) Spend time expressing thanksgiving and gratitude individually to God the Father, Jesus the Son and the Holy Spirit for rooting you and establishing you in love. Thank them also for all that they have done, are doing and will do on your behalf, which communicates their investment, sacrifice and demonstration of love to you.

Consider what you have to give to the Divine Majesty (God). Conclude by praying the following: 'Take, Lord, and receive all my liberty, my memory, my understanding, my entire will—all is yours; do with it what you will. Give me only your love and your grace. That is enough for me.'

DAY 3

Read Acts 17:28.

'For in him [God], we live, move and have our being.' And I might add, 'And in you, God lives and has his being.'

Spend your time pondering how God dwells in creation, giving and sustaining life, making you his temple (dwelling place), creating you in God's own image and God's self-giving to you.

Spend time resting in God's love for you and presence with you.

Colloquy

Spend time expressing thanksgiving and gratitude individually to God the Father, Jesus the Son and the Holy Spirit for rooting you and establishing you in love. Thank them also for all that they have done, are doing and will do on your behalf, which communicates their investment, sacrifice and demonstration of love to you.

Consider what you have to give to the Divine Majesty (God). Conclude by praying the following: 'Take, Lord, and receive all my liberty, my memory, my understanding, my entire will—all is yours; do with it what you will. Give me only your love and your grace. That is enough for me.'

DAY 4

Spend your time resting in God's love, thanking God for God's goodness to you and adoring God for who God is, not for what God has done. You might want to take a walk as you do this.

DAY 5

Read Isaiah 64:4.

'Since ancient times no one has heard, no ear has perceived, no eye has seen any God beside you, who acts on behalf of those who wait for him.' Spend time pondering how God works and labours for you in all created things on the face of the earth.

Spend time resting in God's love for you and presence with you.

Colloquy

Spend time expressing thanksgiving and gratitude individually to God the Father, Jesus the Son and the Holy Spirit for rooting you and establishing you in love. Thank them also for all that they have done, are doing and will do on your behalf, which communicates their investment, sacrifice and demonstration of love to you.

Consider what you have to give to the Divine Majesty (God). Conclude by praying the following: 'Take, Lord, and receive all my liberty, my memory, my understanding, my entire will—all is yours; do with it what you will. Give me only your love and your grace. That is enough for me.'

DAY 6

Read James 1:17.

'Every good and perfect gift is from above, coming down from the Father of the heavenly lights, who does not change like shifting shadows.' Spend time pondering how all good things and gifts descend from above.

Spend time resting in God's love for you and presence with you.

Colloquy

Spend time expressing thanksgiving and gratitude individually to God the Father, Jesus the Son and the Holy Spirit for rooting you and establishing you in love. Thank them also for all that they have done, are doing and will do on your behalf, which communicates their investment, sacrifice and demonstration of love to you.

Consider what you have to give to the Divine Majesty (God). Conclude by praying the following: 'Take, Lord, and receive all my liberty, my memory, my understanding, my entire will—all is yours; do with it what you will. Give me only your love and your grace. That is enough for me.'

DAY 7

Reflect on and review your week.

- What has really touched you during your prayer times? Why?
- How has the grace for which you have been asking impacted you these past few days?
- What has surprised you during your prayer times this past week? Why?

Spend your time today resting in God's love for you and presence with you.

Colloquy

Spend some time expressing thanksgiving and gratitude individually to God the Father, Jesus the Son and the Holy Spirit for rooting you and establishing you in love. Thank them also for all that they have done, are doing and will do on your behalf, which communicates their investment, sacrifice and demonstration of love to you.

FINAL WORDS

You have made it to the end of this journey, but your adventure of faith will continue. At this point you cannot yet fully know how God has used, is using and will use your experience in these exercises in your life and the lives of others. As a result of the time you have spent in the Spiritual Exercises of St Ignatius of Loyola, God was and is at work in you and will continue to bring fruit into your life and the lives of those with whom you journey.

You have used many different prayer methods throughout your time in the Exercises, methods you can continue to draw from and make use of in the days, weeks and years ahead. At some time it would be beneficial for you to review the journal you kept as you journeyed through these exercises. This can bring to mind prayer practices you may want to make use of, or specific days or experiences in the Exercises that you want to ponder or re-enter. To help you in your review process, there is a series of questions provided in Appendix 5.

Finally, as you move on in your journey, I encourage you to continue to employ some of the tools you have used and attitudes you have fostered during your time in the Exercises. The examen, imaginative prayer and the practice of intentionally presenting yourself to God are powerful tools to help you as you embrace a new chapter in your adventure of faith. The attitudes of indifference, being the beloved of God and finding God in all things can give you the focus and the strength needed to fight the good fight of faith. Seek to carry with you those things that God has used in your life as you have journeyed through the Exercises. The value of these various practices and attitudes extends far beyond the Exercises, and they are profitable to you who continue to partner intentionally with God in being conformed to the image of Christ.

PART 4

RESOURCES

BIOGRAPHY OF ST IGNATIUS OF LOYOLA

The Exercises were born out of Ignatius' own adventure of faith. As he walked with God, read about Jesus and interacted with others who shared their spiritual experiences, he incorporated this learning into what was to become the Exercises. Thus it is important to have at least a snapshot of his life and times.

Ignatius was born and baptised Íñigo López de Loyola in 1491, one year before Columbus set sail from Spain. He was the youngest of seven sons and one of 13 children. He was in his mid-20s when the Protestant Reformation began and would become a major figure in the Counter-Reformation.

Ignatius was raised in nobility and at an early age began to serve in the court of Don Juan Velázquez de Cuéllar, during which time he learned poetry, Christian devotion and the use of weaponry. On his departure he was given a horse, weapons and a sack of gold, and he set off to pursue a life of fame and fortune as well as gambling, womanising and general mischief.

Ignatius' conversion did not result from hearing the Gospels read or experiencing a crucifix speaking to him. God used a French cannon ball. The shattering of Ignatius' leg by a cannon ball at the Battle of Pamplona marked the beginning of his conversion process.

During an extended time of convalescence, Ignatius became overwhelmed with boredom and asked that books on chivalry be brought to him. Instead, he was given two religious books: Ludolph the Carthusian's *Life of Christ* and Jacobus de Voragine's *The Book of the Lives of the Saints*. For the next several months, these two books became his constant companions and the means that God would use to woo and draw him. *Life of Christ* in particular was formational for Ignatius; he spent close to a year reading it, meditating on it and journalling what he discovered within its pages.

This was the beginning of an inner purging for Ignatius. The focus of his loyalty and desire to serve was gradually changing from loyalty to an earthly kingdom, with its fame and glory, to Christ the King and the fame and glory that might be his through that avenue of service. Ignatius was still externally focused, but things within were slowly beginning to change. His life was on the verge of launching on a new trajectory, one firmly fixed on the person of Jesus.

In 1522, Ignatius left Loyola physically healed but very much spiritually a work in progress. He was still Íñigo, seeking after fame and fortune but now seeking to serve Christ the King, desiring to perform severe penances and do great and glorious works as the saints before him had done. He was becoming a knight of Christ—a theme seen in the meditations he designed for those going through the Exercises.

Ignatius arrived in Montserrat, where he accepted the hospitality of Benedictine monks and secured a confessor. His written confession took three days to complete. After his confession, he slipped away at night for a vigil of arms, which was traditionally done by new knights as they entered into the service of an earthly lord or king. On 24 March 1522, Ignatius gave his fine clothes to a beggar, put on a pilgrim's tunic and spent the whole night in prayer at the altar. When he was finished, he left his sword and dagger at the altar. Ignatius was now a knight of Christ.

From there Ignatius journeyed to Manresa, a league (three and a half miles) away, where he was planning to stay for a few days and write some notes about what had been taking place. Instead he stayed in Manresa for about eleven months, and it was there that God met him powerfully, shaping and moulding him into a true knight of Christ.

Upon arriving in Manresa, Ignatius began wholeheartedly to

embrace the ascetic lifestyle. He begged for alms, ate no meat, drank no wine, did not comb or cut his hair, and allowed his fingernails and toenails to grow. Ignatius was fighting against the vainglory that had directed so much of his life and consumed so much of his thinking. During this time, he prayed for seven hours a day.

As his stay in Manresa lengthened, Ignatius endured many physical, mental, emotional and spiritual hardships. Some of his hardships were self-generated through his ascetic practices, especially of fasting, while others were results of battles with the world, the flesh and the devil. This practice did much physical damage to him, which he battled throughout his life. Ignatius' own struggles with temptations, his scruples and his practices of spiritual disciplines during this time gave shape to various components within his Exercises.

For Ignatius, the time in Manresa was one of deep, profound and lasting consolation and agonising despair. It was also a time of great devotion and supreme testing. Manresa was a refining crucible for Ignatius, purifying him from the inside out, bringing clarity and insight and helping to put flesh on the skeletal pieces of the Exercises that had begun with his reading and note-taking while at Loyola.

From Manresa, Ignatius journeyed to Barcelona and then on to Jerusalem, where he arrived destitute. He planned on praying at the holy sites and helping souls, but he was ordered to leave by the Franciscans, who feared for his life. Ignatius eventually returned to Barcelona and began a ten-year period of study, teaching others using the Exercises, having spiritual conversations with people and numerous run-ins with those of the Inquisition (a dozen times he was arrested, and he ended up in jail on a couple of those occasions). Although Ignatius was confronted by those of the Inquisition for teaching the Exercises, the material he taught was never called into question. The problem was that he had not been officially trained and sanctioned by the church to teach such things—true or otherwise.

Ignatius began preparation for his formal theological education by studying Latin grammar alongside schoolboys in Barcelona while continuing to teach the Exercises. After learning the basics of Latin grammar, he began taking classes at Alcalá (during this time he was jailed for 42 days) and then Salamanca (where he was jailed for 22 days) and eventually ended up in Paris, first at Montaigu and then in Sainte Barbe, where he concluded his studies in 1535. His room mates at Sainte Barbe were Pierre Favre and Francis Xavier, who would become his first permanent companions. In 1528, Ignatius started giving the Exercises to non-Spanish-speaking people and was forced to begin to translate the Exercises into a rudimentary Latin.

On 15 August 1534, Ignatius and six followers gathered at Montmartre and swore a vow of poverty and chastity and to embrace a life of missionary work in Jerusalem (Ignatius still desiring to return to Jerusalem), and if that did not work out, to journey to Rome and offer their service to the Pope in whatever way he deemed best.

They all gathered in 1537 in Venice as ordained priests and began giving the Exercises as they awaited the opportunity to journey to Jerusalem. They were unable to secure passage that year and spent their time giving the Exercises, teaching in churches and helping the sick and poor. When the year was up, true to their vow, they went to Rome to have an audience with the Pope and pledge their service to him.

On his way to Rome, Ignatius stopped at a church at La Storta. There Ignatius experienced himself as intimately united with Christ. This experience affirmed his desire to found an order dedicated to Christ, bearing the name of Christ and being about the work of Christ for the service and glory of God and the spiritual well-being of others.

On 3 September 1539, Ignatius presented the materials to the Pope for the forming of a religious order, and on 27 September 1540 he and his ten followers were officially sanctioned as an order:

the Society of Jesus, known as the Jesuits. The Spiritual Exercises of St Ignatius received official approval from the church in 1548. Ignatius died on 31 July 1556.

There is much more that can be said about Ignatius' life. The Exercises arose from the laboratory of life and not the hallowed halls of academia, and thus have a down-to-earth, honest feel to them. They reflect the insights of Ignatius' own spiritual saga with God, beginning with a cannon ball and culminating in the acceptance and publishing of the Exercises and the founding of the Society of Jesus.

RESOURCES

Ganss, George E. (ed.), *Ignatius of Loyola: Spiritual Exercises and Selected Works*, Classics of Western Spirituality (Paulist Press, 1991).

Tylenda, Joseph N., *A Pilgrim's Journey: The Autobiography of St Ignatius of Loyola* (Ignatius Press, 2001).

ASH WEDNESDAY AND HOLY WEEK EXERCISES

ASH WEDNESDAY

These exercises are for you if you begin Week 3 on Ash Wednesday or start on the first Monday of the Lenten season following Ash Wednesday. If you are starting Week 3 on Ash Wednesday, please start with the exercises designated 'Ash Wednesday' below and continue through to Sunday. When you have completed these five days of exercises, go to Week 3, Section 1, and continue on in Week 3.

Process

☐ Opening   ☐ Closing
☐ Daily exercise   ☐ Noontime examen
☐ Journalling   ☐ Evening examen

Start your time by slowly making the sign of the cross. Conclude with a bow, demonstrating your reverence for and honouring of God, while asking God that everything in your day may more and more lead you to divine praise and service.

The grace you are seeking this week is to sorrow with Christ in sorrow, anguish with Christ in anguish, with tears and interior suffering because of the suffering that Christ endured for you.

Examen questions

- Today did you recall to your mind Jesus' willingness to suffer physical, emotional and spiritual trauma for you? Why, or why not?
- How did the truth of Jesus' willingness to suffer and die for you and others impact the way you interacted with others with whom you came in contact today?
- How did you die to self today?

Three considerations

- What did Jesus suffer in his humanity in this narrative? Enter into Jesus' pain and suffering.
- How did Jesus hide (not use) his divinity in this narrative?
- Consider your response to Jesus' sacrifice for you in terms of how you might view life, live life and interact with others.

ASH WEDNESDAY

Read Isaiah 53:3–5.

THURSDAY

Read Philippians 3:10.

FRIDAY

Read 1 Peter 2:22–24.

SATURDAY

Read 1 John 4:9–10.

SUNDAY

Review this past week.

- What has really touched you during your prayer times? Why?
- How has the grace for which you have been asking impacted you these past few days?
- What has surprised you during your prayer times this past week? Why?

Colloquy

Spend time expressing thanksgiving and gratitude individually to God the Father, Jesus the Son and the Holy Spirit for their investment, sacrifice and demonstration of love to you and to the world.

Conclude by saying the Lord's Prayer.

Now go to Section 1 of Week 3 (page 255) and continue through the Exercises. When you get to the end of Section 5, return and begin the section below. This will take you up to Easter (Resurrection) Sunday.

FINAL DAYS OF WEEK 3 (HOLY WEEK)

This section is for those who started Week 3 on the first Monday of Lent. When you have finished these exercises, return to Week 3 and read through the final section of Week 3, entitled 'Concluding comments and reflections' (pages 279–280).

FINAL DAYS OF WEEK 3

This begins the Monday after Palm Sunday. If you did not begin Week 3 either on Ash Wednesday or the following Monday, these exercises are not for you. Just journey through Week 3 as found in the earlier part of this book.

Spend your time during the next few days sitting in the Gospel narratives of the crucifixion of Christ. Use the colloquy, asking God to help you experience the depth of feeling, love and compassion for Jesus and to be present with Jesus through everything that happens. Use your imagination to enter more fully into what is happening. As you explore the scripture passage for each day, choose whose perspective you will take: try being a different individual (such as a criminal, a disciple, a centurion, Jesus' mother, John).

- How does your experience change with the different role you take in the story?
- To which of the Gospel depictions are you most drawn? Why?
- What are your feelings as you watch Jesus being nailed to the cross, being insulted, being pierced by the spear?
- What are you feeling as you hear his words?
- Which of his words from the cross do you find most challenging? Why?
- Which of his words from the cross do you find most hope-producing? Why?

I encourage you to:

- fast on Good Friday
- attend a Maundy Thursday service
- attend a Good Friday service
- attend an Easter Vigil service, which is on Saturday night
- celebrate Easter!

PART 6 (HOLY WEEK)

Start your time by slowly making the sign of the cross. Conclude with a bow, demonstrating your reverence for and honouring of God, while asking God that everything in your day may more and more lead you to divine praise and service.

Process

☐ Opening
☐ Daily exercise
☐ Journalling
☐ Closing
☐ Noontime examen
☐ Evening examen

The grace you are seeking this week is to sorrow with Christ in sorrow, anguish with Christ in anguish, with tears and interior suffering because of the suffering that Christ endured for you.

Examen questions

- Today did you recall to your mind Jesus' willingness to suffer physical, emotional and spiritual trauma for you? Why, or why not?
- How did the truth of Jesus' willingness to suffer and die for you and others impact the way you interacted with others with whom you came in contact today?
- How did you die to self today?

Three considerations

- What did Jesus suffer in his humanity in this narrative? Enter into Jesus' pain and suffering.
- How did Jesus hide (not use) his divinity in this narrative?
- Consider your response to Jesus' sacrifice for you in terms of how you might view life, live life and interact with others.

MONDAY

Slowly read the following poem, allowing yourself to linger with each stanza. Stay with the words wonder, fear, weep and rejoice.

The cross

*I stand before the cross
And wonder.*

*I stand before the cross
And fear.*

*I kneel before the cross
And weep.*

*I pray before the cross
And rejoice.*

*To know the cross
Is to know Christ.*

*To feel the cross
Is to feel Christ.*

*To gaze at the cross
Is to gaze at Christ.*

*To carry the cross
Is to be a Christian,
And not until then.*

God, forgive me. [1]

- What does each word—wonder, fear, weep and rejoice—say to you about God, yourself and the cross?
- How do they fit together?

- How does the cross help you to know Christ, feel Christ and see Christ?
- What does it mean for you to carry the cross in your life?

TUESDAY OR WEDNESDAY

Stations of the Cross

You can visit a local Catholic church to go through the stations, or go online, where you will find a pictorial Stations of the Cross with text at www.metamorpha.com.

Now begins what is referred to as the Triduum: Holy Thursday, Good Friday and Holy Saturday.

THURSDAY

Lord's Supper: John 13:1–38

Put yourself in the story.

- Where are you sitting, and who are you sitting next to?
- What is your sense or experience of Jesus?
- What is your experience of the meal?
- The foot washing?
- Jesus' words?
- What is your internal reaction when Jesus says that one of you will betray him?

GOOD FRIDAY

Crucifixion: John 19:28–42

Put yourself at the foot of the cross, seeking truly to be with Jesus in his pain and agony—physical, emotional and spiritual.

- What are you feeling for Jesus?
- What are you feeling as you help take the body down from the cross?
- As you hold his lifeless body?

Spend some time thanking Jesus for his willingness to die for you.
Conclude your time with the Lord's Prayer.

HOLY SATURDAY

Put yourself in the place of the disciples. You have been following Jesus for three years. You have watched as he performed miracles. You have been stirred by his teachings. You have come to believe that God was with Jesus in a special way, so much so that when others ceased to follow him, you continued believing he had the words of eternal life. Now you sit with the other disciples. Jesus has been crucified and buried. Your hopes, dreams and beliefs are as dead as Jesus.

- What are you feeling? What is going on in your heart and head?

Spend time journalling.

RESURRECTION SUNDAY

He is risen. He is risen indeed! Rejoice and be glad! Return to the end of Week 3, and read through 'Concluding comments and reflections' on pages 279–280.

SHORTER OPTIONS FOR JOURNEYING THROUGH THE EXERCISES

I have designed three formats of varying durations that you may choose from in order to interact with the Exercises in an abbreviated way. Ignatius originally designed the Exercises to be entered into for a period of 30 days or about nine months. The nine-month format is the one used in this book and is often referred to as the 19th Annotation, or the retreat in everyday life. The shorter retreats (seven and 17 weeks) outlined below do not incorporate the intensity of the 30-day retreat or the longevity of the nine-month retreat, which are each key components in bringing profound depth and transforming power to your experience in the Exercises.

If you are leaning toward choosing an option with a shorter time frame (seven and 17 weeks), I urge you to explore the reasons for your decision. As you process through the following questions, remember that these Exercises are not for everyone.

- Why are you willing or desiring to enter into a journey through the Exercises that will be somewhat limited in what it can accomplish in your life?
- Why are you unable to make the longer commitment to the Exercises at this time?
- Why not wait for a time when the 19th Annotation format (a nine-month journey, as presented in this book) might work for you?

- What has convinced you that now is the time to go through the Exercises and that the shorter option is the best for you?

If you are convinced that God would have you enter the Exercises at this time and that a shorter version of the Exercises would be the best fit for you, I have designed a seven-week and a 17-week option, as well as a third option (which I consider to be the most viable) for you to choose from. As far as choosing between the seven-week and 17-week options is concerned, I would suggest the 17 weeks, because there is something that happens in terms of the spiritual breadth and depth of the journey that results from an extended time in the Exercises.

Before you choose, consider the third option, which I believe is a much better choice than either of the first two choices. This third option incorporates all the Exercises as laid out in this book, but broken into bite-sized pieces, which will give you the opportunity eventually to enjoy the whole banquet contained in each of the sections rather than just getting a taste. This method affords you the ability to take breaks between each of the Weeks while still allowing you to journey through the Exercises in their entirety.

THE ALTERNATIVE JOURNEYS

SEVEN-WEEK EXERCISES

Please read the introduction to each of the sections below before you enter into them. When you are finished, please read the final portion of the section you have just completed. The beginning and ending portions of each section contain valuable information that will help you, and, although not everything will pertain to those who choose to use the shorter format, it still has value for you.

Preparatory Exercises

1. Section 1—Day 1 and 2 combined
2. Section 1—Day 5
3. Section 1—Day 6
4. Section 2—Day 1 and/or optional exercise
5. Section 2—Day 2
6. Section 2—Day 5
7. Section 3—Day 6

Principle and Foundation

1. Section 1—Day 1 and 2 combined
2. Section 2—Day 2
3. Section 3—Day 1
4. Section 4—Day 5
5. Section 5—Day 1 (Read special introduction to Section 5.)
6. Section 5—Day 3
7. Section 5—Day 7

Week 1

1. Section 1—Day 2
2. Section 1—Day 5
3. Section 2—Day 2
4. Section 2—Day 3
5. Section 2—Day 4
6. Section 2—Day 5
7. Section 3—Day 6

Week 2

1. Section 4—Day 3
2. Section 5—Day 5

3. Section 6—Day 1
4. Section 6—Day 3
5. Section 6—Day 5
6. Section 6—Day 7
7. Section 7—Day 1
8. Section 7—Day 3
9. Section 7—Day 5
10. Section 8—Day 2
11. Section 8—Day 5
12. Section 9—Day 1
13. Section 9—Day 2
14. Section 9—Day 7
15. Section 10—Day 5
16. Section 10—Day 6
17. Section 11—Day 1 and 2
18. Section 11—Day 5
19. Section 12—Day 1 and 2
20. Section 13 and 14 (Read beginning section of 13 and then choose one of the 'I am' statements of Jesus from Section 13 or 14 to spend your prayer time with.)
21. Section 15—Day 7

Week 3

1. Section 1—Day 1 and 2
2. Section 1—Day 6; Section 2—Day 2
3. Section 4—Day 1
4. Section 4—Day 2
5. Section 5—Day 1 and 3
6. Section 5—Day 2
7. Section 5—Day 7

Week 4 is not included. If you would like to extend your time by seven days, feel free to use Week 4, Section 2—All (seven days).

SEVENTEEN-WEEK EXERCISES

Please read the introduction to each of the sections below before you enter into them. When you are finished, please read the final portion of the section you have just completed. The beginning and ending portions of each section contain valuable information that will help you, and, although not everything will pertain to those who choose to use the shorter format, it still has value for you.

Preparatory Exercises

Section 1—All (seven days)
Section 2—All (seven days)

Principle and Foundation

1. Section 1—Day 1 and 2
2. Section 2—Day 2
3. Section 3—Day 1
4. Section 3—Day 6
5. Section 4—Day 2
6. Section 4—Day 5
7. Section 4—Day 7
8. Section 5—All (seven days)

Week 1

Section 2—All (seven days)
Section 3—All (seven days)
Section 4—All (seven days)

Week 2

Section 1—All (seven days)
Section 2—All (seven days)
Section 5—All (seven days)

Section 6—All (seven days)
Section 9—All (seven days)
Section 10—All (seven days)
Section 11—All (seven days)

Week 3

Section 2—All (seven days)
Section 4—All (seven days)
Section 5—All (seven days)

Week 4

Section 2—All (seven days)

THIRD OPTION

The third option uses the full expression of the 19th Annotation found in this book. This format allows you to journey through the entire experience in the Exercises while taking breaks between each section. After completing your break, I encourage you to review your journal, covering the previous section before re-entering the Exercises in the new section. During your review, be open to God inviting you to sit with something or even to go back through one or more of the exercises from the previous section.

Before entering into the next section, work through the questions and continuums at the end of the section you are finishing. This will help you discern if it is a good time for you to move on. Remember, the point is not to finish the Exercises but to encounter God through the Exercises as God leads you. This third option provides you the opportunity to journey through the Exercises, yet incorporates a more manageable time frame and flexibility for doing so.

Please read the introduction to each of the sections below before you enter into them. When you are finished, please read the final portion of the section you have just completed. The beginning and ending portions of each section contain valuable information that will help you.

- Preparatory Exercises (21 days)
- Principle and Foundation (35 days)
- Week 1 (35 days)
- Week 2 (105 days)
- Week 3 (35 days)
- Week 4 (28 days)

FOR SPIRITUAL DIRECTORS AND LISTENERS

You have had a great honour bestowed upon you. You have been offered a front-row seat to witness first-hand the spiritual journey of another. This person has chosen you because she feels you can be trusted with her heart, because she believes you have the spiritual maturity and deepening relationship with God needed for this endeavour.

However, before you say yes, please consider if you are truly up to the challenge. Read through all that follows and see if this is something you are willing to commit to. This journey, though quite amazing and satisfying, will not be a walk in the park for the person going through the Exercises or for you. Besides meeting with the person two to four times a month (as you mutually decide) for about an hour, you will also need to prepare before each session. So as you read through this section prayerfully, consider if this is a journey God is inviting you on.

As you start meeting, it is important for you to read through the section the retreatant will be entering. Also familiarise yourself with the Rules of Discernment that apply to that section and be aware of the 'grace' and the examen questions the retreatant will be asking God for and interacting with.

The information that follows will help you as you prepare to meet with your retreatant. It includes insights gathered from people who have taken others through the Exercises. Many of the insights are taken from a section in the Exercises known as the 'Annotations', which was written for spiritual directors. As you make your way

through this section, if you come across a term or concept you are
not familiar with, please check the glossary.

NOTES FROM IGNATIUS' EXERCISES 1–20

It is important for you to discern if the retreatant possesses great
courage and generosity toward God. This is the focus of the
Preparatory Exercises as well as the Principle and Foundation. If
the retreatant does not possess these requisite qualities in his walk
with God, he may not be ready to proceed into Week 1.

There will be an ebb and flow to the retreatant's experiences
in the Exercises. There will be times of consolation, desolation,
dryness and nothingness. This is how it should be, and if the ebb
and flow is not there, make sure the retreatant is spending the
specified time in prayer each day and is doing the examens, as well
as journalling.

When the retreatant is struggling, be gentle, giving her courage
and strength, helping her to process the whys of her desolation (see
'Rules of Discernment' in the introduction to Week 1).

If you perceive that your retreatant is struggling with evil
taking on the appearance of good, take him through the Rules of
Discernment for Week 2.

If the retreatant is going through times of extreme consolation,
caution her against making a hasty promise or vow to God or
another.

Help your retreatant see if there is any disordered attachment
that is keeping him from coming fully before God.

Note to spiritual directors: I am well aware that some of you
reading this are trained spiritual directors who have developed
a level of expertise when it comes to accompanying others. The
following sections are not designed to teach you; rather, they will
expose you to the type of questions that are important as you

journey with someone going through the spiritual Exercises—and they will provide you with an overall feel regarding what the Exercises entail (see 'Brief overview of weeks' on pages 331–334). So even if you are trained in the art of spiritual direction, I would strongly encourage you to keep reading through the following sections and even visit the website www.b-ing.org.

GENERAL QUESTIONS TO ASK A RETREATANT

- How have your prayer times with God been since we last met? Why?
- What are you feeling during your prayer times regarding God, Jesus and yourself? Why?
- What stands out to you regarding your time spent in the Exercises since the last time we met?

If something is shared, take time to process this with your retreatant. Ask questions such as: What feeling(s) did this stir within you? How did this make you feel toward God, Jesus and/or yourself? What has been the impact of this time on your heart? In your life?

- What might be God's current invitation or challenge for you? How do you feel about that invitation or challenge?
- How are the examens going for you—the noontime one, the evening one? Which is easier for you? Why? What difference do these times seem to be making in your life?
- How is your journalling going? Why? Have you tried different approaches to journalling? Why, or why not? What are you noticing during your journalling times?
- Are your times in the Exercises beginning to impact the rest of your day? If yes, how? If no, why not? How do you feel about this?

- During this period of your journey, do you feel that it is pre-dominantly a time of desolation or of consolation? Why? What is the source of your desolation or consolation? What is the suggested response to your current situation in the Rules of Discernment?
- Is there any one overall theme, invitation or life/heart change that you have noticed rising within you since the last time we met?
- How can I pray for you until our next time together?

HELPING A RETREATANT UNPACK AN EXPERIENCE WITH GOD

- How would you describe this experience with God? How did you feel during the experience? What was God like? What were you like? What seem to be the results of your experience?
- As you are now reflecting on that previous experience: What are you feeling? What, if any, new insights or feelings are arising? As you continue to reflect on your experience, what feelings concerning God arise within you? How does that make you feel about God, about you and God?

HINDRANCES TO LISTENING TO OTHERS

- If you 'know' what the person will say, you stop paying close attention.
- If you share your own story (so that you feel important, interesting, helpful, experienced), this brings the focus off the retreatant and on to you.
- A drive to fix the situation keeps you from listening and instead occupies your mind with seeking solutions or similarities to the person you are listening to.

- If you 'know' what a person means, you stop seeking to under-stand. For example, if a retreatant tells you about a painful situation, and you automatically assume that would make her feel sad, you stop seeking to understand and you move forward in the conversation instead of taking time to ask her how that situation made her feel.
- Your own woundedness, fear of or discomfort with pain, struggle and feelings can lead to non-listening and therefore not being fully present to the journey of the retreatant.

GOOD QUESTIONS

Good questions:

- are open ended.
- cause one to reflect, ponder, explore, and get in touch with self, God and feelings.
- focus attention on feelings (movement), God and self-discovery.
- focus on resistance, places the retreatant is not willing to ex-plore. This may be a conscious or unconscious choice on the part of the retreatant, but if you notice resistance, gently invite the retreatant to enter into it. Resistance can be a place of great divine and self-discovery when it is entered into.
- help the person pay attention to her internal movements.
- help the person deepen, explore and sink into his experience.
- help the person move from head to heart.
- invite raw honesty and unhindered exploration of God and self.
- help the retreatant get in touch consciously and/or subcon-sciously with internal feelings, energy and movements that lead her in divine and self-discovery.

BAD QUESTIONS

Bad questions:

- are closed-ended questions, needing only a yes or no answer.
- focus on circumstances alone.
- lead the person in the way you want him to go.
- move the person from heart to head.
- have one right answer.
- are born out of curiosity.
- stop reflection.
- are asked too quickly without the proper time given for reflection.
- flow from your own discomfort and/or desire to control, fix, correct or make the retreatant think a certain way about something.

Listening is a gift you are giving to the retreatant. As you journey together, you will become a better listener. Remember that the person's growth is God's responsibility, not yours. You are to show up, create a safe, caring place, and let the retreatant share his heart while you listen to what is said and not said. Yours is not an easy task, but with God's help you will be able to do beyond all you ask, think or even imagine. Trust God and trust the process, and seek to do no harm.

BRIEF OVERVIEW OF WEEKS

It would be very beneficial for you as a spiritual director or listener to read through each section, from beginning to end, before your retreatant enters them, paying attention to the grace(s) she will be asking for and the examen questions she will be considering each day.

As the retreatant nears the end of a section, become familiar with the materials he will make use of to decide whether to move forward into the next section of the Exercises or not. It is important for you to assist him in discerning his readiness to enter into a new part of the Exercises. As you help him, it is key for you to remember, and to remind him, that the important thing is not to get through the Exercises but to use the Exercises to present himself before God as a living and holy sacrifice.

PREPARATORY EXERCISES: SECTION 1

During this week, the retreatant will be seeking to embrace and internalise the unconditional love God has for her. The grace she is seeking from God is a deeper awareness of God's love. This can be a difficult section for those who realise they do not believe, at a deep level, that God loves them, or who come face to face with situations where they did not experience God's love and care. It is important for them to process these issues honestly. It is also very important that they do not leave this section until they have a deep and abiding sense of God's love.

PRINCIPLE AND FOUNDATION: SECTION 2

In this section, the retreatant will focus on God as creator and spend time pondering, reverencing and praising God. Then he will seek to understand and embrace the role of indifference in his spiritual life. The grace he is seeking will change weekly, but the emphasis of this section is on developing a healthy concept of God.

THE WEEKS

Please note that 'Week' does not refer to a seven-day period but is a section possibly lasting many weeks.

Week 1

This can be a difficult section of the Exercises for the retreatant. Pay special attention to her feelings in terms of her own worth and value. Be alert to signs that she is struggling with self-condemnation or shame. The focus of this section is on sin: the sin of Adam and Eve, the sin of the angels, the sin of the world and our own sin. The grace the retreatant is asking for is the ability to experience sorrow, tears and confusion over her choices to sin in light of God's limitless love, grace, mercy and faithfulness.

It is important that the retreatant keeps the truths of his own sinfulness and God's unlimited love and grace tightly tethered together. If things get difficult for him, consider having him revisit some of the Preparatory Exercises. Making a confession is an optional exercise during this week.

Week 2

This section focuses on Jesus, from birth to Palm Sunday. It is a time of discovering one's willingness to follow Jesus. The grace the retreatant is asking for in Week 2 is the ability to know Jesus intimately, to love him more intensely and to follow him more closely. The retreatant will be asked again and again to ponder the depth and level of her desires. This section can be a place where she begins to experience dryness and discouragement and may struggle to do the daily exercises. She may begin to realise that there are days when God feels far away. Remind her that the key to the Exercises is 'showing up' and presenting herself as a living and holy sacrifice to God. This is what is important, not what does or does not happen during these times. Also, encourage her to continue the practice of the examen at noontime and night.

There are four meditations especially designed by Ignatius for this Week, and there are three cautions listed on pages 168–169. Please take a look at the meditations and the cautions. There are many retreatants for whom Week 2 will mark the end of their journey through the Exercises, and that is as it should be. They are not ready to continue to the greater level of commitment required for Week 3.

Week 3

This section follows Jesus through Holy Week, ending with his crucifixion. Those entering this Week are choosing not merely to follow Jesus but also to be with Jesus in his pain and suffering. The Week is not for everyone. The grace that is asked for is sorrow with Christ in sorrow, anguish with Christ in anguish, with tears and interior suffering because of the suffering that Christ endured for them. The discipline of fasting is encouraged during this Week, as well as instructions regarding eating food contemplatively. The experience of retreatants in the section varies greatly.

Week 4

The post-resurrection encounters of Jesus are the focus of this section. The grace sought during Week 4 is the ability to rejoice and be intensely glad because of the great glory and joy of Jesus, their risen Lord. For many, it is difficult to enter fully into the joy of Week 4. The 'Contemplation to Attain Love of God' serves as an encouragement to put faith into action. The retreatant is encouraged to become an active contemplative who loves God and others in word, deed and truth.

FINAL THOUGHTS

It is an honour to be chosen to journey with another as a spiritual director or listener, but it is also a good bit of work. If you can be patient with yourself, give yourself grace, trust in God and take one leg of the journey at a time, you will do well. This will be an incredible journey for you too.

USING THE EXERCISES WITH A GROUP

Going through the Exercises as a group could be a very beneficial experience. A group of three to five people (no bigger) can provide accountability, encouragement, insight and support to each other as you journey through the Exercises. The group does not necessarily take the place of an individual spiritual director or listener but certainly augments that resource. What follows are some general insights regarding forming a group and some ideas regarding the format of a group meeting.

MEMBERS OF THE GROUP

Besides being actively involved as participants in the Exercises, it would be important for the members to:

- be open and honest with God, themselves and each other
- be trusted by each other, keeping confidences, speaking from a place of love
- know Jesus and have a deep desire for God and the things of God
- fully participate in the group through prayerful listening, sharing and attendance

FORMAT FOR MEETINGS

- **Time frame**: about two hours.
- **Prayer**: committing time to God, asking for an openness to God and to each other.
- **Sharing**: each person takes a turn sharing about his experience in the Exercises (about ten minutes), and everyone else prayerfully listens.
- **Silence (about three minutes)**: everyone sits together in silence listening for God's still small voice on behalf of the person who just shared.
- **Response (about ten minutes)**: the group shares responses (questions, comments, images, senses received) with the person who shared. These are not 'thus says the Lord' statements but merely offerings.
- **Prayer (about five minutes)**: the group prays silently for the person who has shared.
- **The process**: sharing, silence, response and prayer are completed by each person in the group. It helps the sharing to flow if you designate a leader and the group members become familiar with the insights in the section 'For Spiritual Directors and Listeners'.

Finally, because this is a group that is journeying through the Exercises together, it would be helpful to check in with each other about whether you are putting the time in each day, practising the examen at noontime and evening, and seeing a listener or spiritual director. The point is not condemnation but positive accountability. Check to see if anyone feels he is in a period of desolation or consolation, so that you may remind each other what Ignatius encourages you to do during those times.

Going through the Exercises with a group can be a very meaningful and beneficial journey. Just choose your companions wisely.

REVIEWING YOUR JOURNEY THROUGH THE EXERCISES

Once you have finished your journey through the Exercises, it can be very beneficial to revisit what took place during your sojourn. This is akin to looking at your pictures after you return from a trip. I suggest you take a month or so after completing your time with the Exercises, and then set aside time to begin to revisit your time in the Exercises. I have suggested two methods of doing so. Please feel free to adapt, modify and tweak them as you see fit. The goal is to help you reconnect with your experience in hope that God may reinforce and deepen your learning while encouraging you regarding what God has formed and shaped in you.

PLAN 1

DAY 1

Review your journal for the Preparatory Exercises (God's love). As you begin your review, remind yourself of the grace you asked for during that section.

- What stands out to you from that time?
- What was the invitation, challenge, reminder or encouragement from God that flowed out of that section to you?

Conclude your day with a colloquy with Jesus, sharing your insights, thoughts and feelings about your experience in the Preparatory Exercises.

DAY 2

Go back and review your journal for the Principle and Foundation exercises, which dealt with praising, honouring and serving God, as well as indifference. As you begin your review, remind yourself of the grace you asked for during that section.

- What stands out to you from that time?
- What was the invitation, challenge, reminder or encouragement from God that flowed out of that section to you?

Conclude your day with a colloquy with Jesus, sharing your insights, thoughts and feelings about your experience in the Principle and Foundation.

DAYS 3 AND 4

Review your journal for Week 1 of the Exercises, which dealt with sin. As you begin your review, remind yourself of the grace you asked for during that Week.

- What stands out to you from that time?
- What was the invitation, challenge, reminder or encouragement from God that flowed out of that Week to you?

Conclude your day with a colloquy with Jesus, sharing your insights, thoughts and feelings about your experience from Week 1.

DAYS 5 AND 6

Review your journal for Week 2 of the Exercises, which dealt with Jesus' life. As you begin your review, remind yourself of the grace you asked for during that Week.

- What stands out to you from that time?
- What was the invitation, challenge, reminder or encouragement from God that flowed out of that Week to you?

Conclude your day with a colloquy with Jesus, sharing your insights, thoughts and feelings about your experience from Week 2.

DAYS 7 AND 8

Review your journal for Week 3, which dealt with Jesus' death. As you begin your review, remind yourself of the grace you asked for during that Week.

- What stands out to you from that time?
- What was the invitation, challenge, reminder or encouragement from God that flowed out of that Week to you?

Conclude your day with a colloquy with Jesus, sharing your insights, thoughts and feelings about your experience from Week 3.

DAYS 9 AND 10

Review your journal for Week 4, which dealt with Jesus' resurrection. As you begin your review, remind yourself of the grace you asked for during that Week.

- What stands out to you from that time?
- What was the invitation, challenge, reminder or encouragement from God that flowed out of that Week to you?

Conclude your day with a colloquy with Jesus, sharing your insights, thoughts and feelings about your experience from Week 4.

PLAN 2

Instead of a daily focus as in Plan 1, this plan employs a week-long focus (feel free to take longer), which encourages you to sit once again with the material of a given section while reviewing your journal entries that cover that section. This plan also has an artistic expression aspect to it.

Spend a week on each of the sections you went through (Preparatory Exercises, Principle and Foundation, Week 1 and so on), reflecting on the grace(s) asked for, the examen questions and your journal entries. During your review, make a note of feelings that arise within you regarding God. Also make a note of insights you received and words that seem to grab hold of you.

When you have completed your review of a specific section, use what you have gathered to create a collage, or use another artistic expression to capture the essence of your time in that section.

This can be a powerful way to revisit your experience in the Exercises and can be stretched over an extended period.

ABOUT THE WEBSITE

www.b-ing.org

An additional tool to assist you on your journey through the Exercises is this website, which has a designated area designed to be a resource for you and your spiritual director or listener as you journey through the Exercises. The website, though comprised of many static pieces, also has a dynamic component through which new material will be added, such as frequently asked questions.

GLOSSARY

This glossary contains a list of terms and concepts employed in this book, along with explanations for each, all of which are uniquely pertinent to the Exercises. Additionally, if these terms and concepts are covered more fully in other sections of the book, directions on where to find this information will be given after the word's explanation.

19th Annotation: The annotation that allows the Exercises to be administered in a format other than the traditional 30-day format. Those who are journeying through the Exercises outside the 30-day format often refer to their experience as the '19th Annotation', or the retreat in everyday life.

All is gift: An important attitude for retreatants to bring with them into the Exercises. It is the awareness that it is not our effort but God's grace that is the determining factor in our experience in a given prayer time or on a given day.

Annotation(s): Notes written by Ignatius to aid those taking others through the Exercises. There are 20 annotations that precede the material the retreatant will be journeying through.

Colloquy: 'Little conversation', a type of prayer that is one of simply conversing with God, Jesus and the Holy Spirit as directed. It flows from the heart and is somewhat informal.

Consolation: A deep connection with God that does not necessarily have anything to do with emotions (see 'Rules of Discernment: Week 1', page 123).

Desolation: A disconnection with God that does not necessarily have anything to do with emotions (see 'Rules of Discernment: Week 1', page 124).

Discernment of spirits: Discovering which spirit is behind the inner movements you are feeling.

Disordered attachment: Anything that you become attached to in a way that takes away your freedom to respond freely to God.

Evil spirits: Primarily used for spirits from Satan or Satan, but, for the purposes of this book, 'the evil spirit', 'evil one' and so on refer to that which seeks to take a person away from following God's call or invitation.

Examen: Exercises used to help people to review and explore their life, seeking to discern what God has been up to and how well they are able to cooperate with God (see 'Prayer of Examen' on pages 29–32).

Exercises: When the word 'Exercise(s)' appears with an upper case E, it refers to the Spiritual Exercises of St Ignatius of Loyola. When the word 'exercise(s)' appears with a lower case e, it refers to the daily prayer times spent in the Exercises.

Finding God in all things: A five-word summary of Ignatian spirituality and a natural outcome as a person journeys through the Exercises.

Good spirits: Spirits from God, angels.

Grace: The gift for which the retreatant is asking God during prayer time. Each Week has a unique grace that is tied to that Week, something the retreatant asks God for.

Imaginative prayer: A way of entering into the scriptures with Jesus. This style of prayer is a components unique to the Exercises (see 'Imaginative Prayer' in chapter 1).

Indifference: An attitude that does not desire one thing over the next but seeks to be open to whatever comes, discerning God's invitation or challenge in each event and circumstance of life (see pages 102–107).

Lectio divina: 'Sacred reading'; refers to a fourfold approach to entering into the scriptures (see '*Lectio Divina*' in chapter 1).

Listener: One who has agreed to accompany the retreatant on the journey through the Exercises (see also 'Spiritual director').

Optional exercises: Exercises that are not a part of the original Exercises but are added by the author as aids in helping the retreatant experience a truth more fully. These exercises are what they say—optional.

Preparatory prayer: The ways in which retreatants ready themselves holistically to enter intentionally into the presence of God.

Repetition: Days that occur weekly and give the retreatant the opportunity to revisit something that was stirred within them on the prior days. It gives space for the retreatant to go deeper with God in a particular experience.

Retreat in everyday life: Another name for a 19th Annotation retreat.

Retreatant: A person who is journeying through the Exercises.

Rules of Discernment: Rules that Ignatius developed to help people discern what is going on within them and which spirit is behind it. There are two sets of these rules: those written for those in Week 1 of the Exercises and those written for those in Week 2. These rules have much to say on the topic of consolation and desolation.

Slowdown: A method designed to help retreatants release the internal stuff they carry in order to be better able to enter into the daily prayer time. It is not a part of the original Exercises (see 'Slowing Down' in chapter 1).

Spiritual director: One who is mature and trained in the art of spiritually companioning another.

Week(s): When the word 'Week(s)' appears with an upper case W, it refers to the fourfold division of the Exercises. It does not refer to our traditional week of seven days. When the word 'week(s)' appears with a lower case w, it refers to the daily prayer times spent in the Exercises.

NOTES

Introduction

1   Dallas Willard, *The Divine Conspiracy* (HarperCollins, 1998), p. 370.
2   David L. Fleming, SJ, *Draw Me into Your Friendship* (Institute of Jesuit Sources, 1996).
3   George E. Ganss, SJ, *The Spiritual Exercises of Saint Ignatius* (Institute of Jesuit Sources, 1992).
4   This phrase is not only a goal of the Exercises but also a succinct articulation of Ignatian spirituality.

Part One: Chapter 1: The Daily Elements of the Exercises

1   Fleming, *Draw Me*, no. 46.
2   Fleming, *Draw Me*, no. 49.
3   This prayer is often attributed to St Ignatius but was written the previous century. It has become a part of the Exercises.
4   Fleming, *Draw Me*, nos. 32–43.
5   Though originally referred to as Examen of Conscience by Ignatius, today many refer to it as the examen of consciousness—both are correct.
6   Particular Examen of Conscience: Fleming, *Draw Me*, nos. 24–31.
7   Morton T. Kelsey, *Adventure Inward: Christian Growth through Personal Journal Writing* (Augsburg Fortress, 1991), p. 23.
8   Quoted in James L. Wakefield, *Sacred Listening* (Barker Books, 2006), p. 22.
9   Richard J. Foster, *Prayer* (HarperCollins, 1992), p. 147.
10   Eugene H. Peterson, *Under the Unpredictable Plant* (Eerdmans, 1992), pp. 169, 171.

Part Two: Chapter 1: The History of Preparatory Exercises

1   Fleming, *Draw Me*, no. 23.
2   Fleming, *Draw Me*, no. 5.
3   Fleming, *Draw Me*, nos. 313–327.

Part Two: Chapter 2: God's Love

1   David G. Benner, *The Gift of Being Yourself* (InterVarsity Press, 2004), p. 49.
2   David G. Benner, *Surrender to Love* (InterVarsity Press, 2003), p. 76.
3   Benner, *The Gift*, p. 48.
4   Evelyn Underhill, *The Spiritual Life* (Morehouse, 1996), p. 59.
5   Benner, *The Gift*, p. 49.
6   Benner, *The Gift*, p. 49.

Part Two: Chapter 3: Principle and Foundation

1   Joseph A. Tetlow, SJ, *Choosing Christ in the World* (Institute of Jesuit Sources, 1989), p. 128.
2   Fleming, *Draw Me*, p. 26 (emphasis added).
3   Fleming, *Draw Me*, no. 23 (emphasis added).
4   Quoted in Gerald G. May, *Addiction and Grace* (HarperCollins, 1988), p. 15.
5   May, *Addiction and Grace* , p. 144.
6   Fleming, *Draw Me*, no. 21.
7   Thomas Merton, *Thoughts in Solitude* (Shambhala, 1993), p. 4.

Part Three: Week 1: Sin, Me and God's Love

1   Fleming, *Draw Me*, nos. 23–90.
2   Fleming, *Draw Me*, nos. 48, 55.
3   Fleming, *Draw Me*, nos. 53–54, 61, 63, 71.
4   Fleming, *Draw Me*, nos. 239–243.
5   Fleming, *Draw Me*, nos. 48, 62.
6   Fleming, *Draw Me*, no. 54.
7   Fleming, *Draw Me*, nos. 328–336.
8   Timothy M. Gallagher OMV, *The Discernment of Spirits* (Crossroads, 2005), pp. 16–25.
9   Gallagher, *Discernment of Spirits*, p. 33.
10   Thomas Green, *Weeds Among the Wheat* (Ave Maria Press, 2000), p. 104.
11   Ignatius, in his writing, uses 'evil spirit' or 'enemy' to refer to the legions of Satan, while the good spirits refer to the emissaries of God.
12   The spoiled child imagery is not found in the original Exercises but in Fleming, *Draw Me*, p. 257.
13   Fleming, *Draw Me*, no. 60.

14   Fleming, *Draw Me*, no. 61.

15   Fleming, *Draw Me*, no. 60.

Part Three: Week 2: Walking with Jesus

1   Fleming, *Draw Me*, no. 112.

2   Fleming, *Draw Me*, nos. 122–125.

3   Fleming, *Draw Me*, nos. 91–100.

4   Fleming, *Draw Me*, nos. 136–148.

5   Fleming, *Draw Me*, nos. 149–157.

6   Fleming, *Draw Me*, no. 91.

7   Fleming, *Draw Me*, no. 104.

8   Fleming, *Draw Me*, no. 98.

9   To download an audio version of *The Imitation of Christ*, go to http://christianaudio.com/advanced_search_result.php?keywords=kempis.

10   Fleming, *Draw Me*, no. 130.

11   Fleming, *Draw Me*, nos. 326–336.

12   Gallagher, *Discernment of Spirits*, pp. 16–25.

13   Fleming, *Draw Me*, no. 329.

14   Fleming, *Draw Me*, no. 330.

15   Fleming, *Draw Me*, no. 332.

16   Fleming, *Draw Me*, no. 91.

17   Fleming, *Draw Me*, no. 55.

18   This section is an adaptation of the meditation entitled 'The Two Kingdoms', Fleming, *Draw Me*, nos. 91–100.

19   Fleming, *Draw Me*, no. 130.

20   Fleming, *Draw Me*, no. 117.

21   Fleming, *Draw Me*, no. 91.

22   This is an adaptation of the Two Standards; exercises 136–146.

23   Fleming, *Draw Me*, nos. 149–155.

24   Fleming, *Draw Me*, nos. 165–168.

Part Three: Week 3: Journey to the Cross

1   Fleming, *Draw Me*, nos. 190–218.

2   Fleming, *Draw Me*, no. 95.

3   Fleming, *Draw Me*, no. 193.

4   Marian Cowan CSJ, and John C. Futrell SJ, *Companions in Grace* (Institute of Jesuit Sources, 2000), p. 124.

5   Quoted in Calvin Miller, *The Book of Jesus* (Simon & Schuster, 1996), p. 417.

6   Fleming, *Draw Me*, nos. 195–197.

7   Fleming, *Draw Me*, no. 229.

8   Fleming, *Draw Me*, no. 79.

9   Fleming, *Draw Me*, no. 206.

10   Fleming, *Draw Me*, nos. 210–217.

11   Fleming, *Draw Me*, no. 203.

12   Fleming, *Draw Me*, nos. 195–197.

13   'The Cross': Lois A. Cheney, *God Is No Fool* (Abingdon, 1969), p. 105. Reprinted by permission.

Part Three: Week 4: Resurrection of Jesus

1   Fleming, *Draw Me*, nos. 218–229.

2   Fleming, *Draw Me*, nos. 230–237.

3   Fleming, *Draw Me*, no. 306.

4   Fleming, *Draw Me*, no. 221.

5   Fleming, *Draw Me*, nos. 230–237.

6   Cowan and Futrell, *Companions in Grace*, p. 133.

7   Fleming, *Draw Me*, no. 233.

8   Fleming, *Draw Me*, no. 23.

9   Fleming, *Draw Me*, no. 234.

10   John Wesley's covenant prayer

Part Four: Ash Wednesday and Holy Week Exercises

1   'The Cross': Lois A. Cheney. Reprinted by permission.

Helga Trumpet's Bestseller

Published under licence by Brown Dog Books and
The Self-Publishing Partnership, 7 Green Park Station, Bath BA1 1JB

www.selfpublishingpartnership.co.uk

ISBN printed book: 978-1-83952-273-4
ISBN e-book: 978-1-83952-274-1

Cover design by Patrick Knowles
Internal design by Andrew Easton

Printed and bound in the UK

This book is printed on FSC certified paper

Helga Trumpet's Bestseller

Lisa Stewart

BROWN
DOG
BOOKS

Chapter 1

Helga felt a prod on her shoulder. She whirled round to see two giggling teenage girls, one dressed as a tiger the other a lion. She didn't like to ask the reason.

'Can you do us a photo?' The tiger waved her mobile phone in a furry paw.

'Of course!' Helga beamed. She snatched the bobble hat off her head and tugged her fingers through her wilful brown hair. 'I think I've even got a spare copy of *Candy Martini* if you'd like me to hold it up?'

'A copy of what?'

'My novel – *Candy Martini Reaches Out*.' Helga moved towards the boot of her car.

'Och, we don't have time for that! Are you going to take our photo or not?'

'Daft old bag,' the lion muttered.

'Oh … you mean a photo of you two?'

'Aye! Me and my cousin.' The teenagers hugged each other, their fuzzy cheeks pressed together.

'Right,' Helga sighed, capturing the blurry image before handing back the phone.

Hastening to zip up her jacket, Helga caught the skin under her chin. 'Aya!' she yelped. A sharp gust chased a swirl of crisp packets down the street. She pulled the bobble hat back on and picked her way up the rough path to the bleached front door. Remembering from previous visits that the bell had long since stopped working, she rapped on the splintered wood. Shouts came from beyond the flimsy door, which sprang open. Helga was met with the scowl of a shapeless woman in stretched, stained cottons and matted sheepskin slippers. As she spoke, the cigarette – gripped between tight lips – flicked ash down her front. 'He's out the back. *Again.* You'll have to do something about it or he can't stay here much longer. I've got enough problems with my prolapse without having to look after him.' Helga made for the back door, mindful not to breathe in the stale cooking smells from the morning's fried sausages, the remains of which languished in a frying pan of gritty white lard. A tangle of wild grass and shrubbery led to the railway track at the foot of the garden. Several years ago the street had clubbed together to give the outdoor space a much-needed makeover – the results of which were long forgotten. Helga followed the tyre marks through the rutted terrain. Stumbling over a corpsed gnome, she twisted her ankle. 'Dennis!' she shouted irritably. He ignored her clamouring. She approached the mobility scooter that he'd propelled to the land's perimeter a few feet from the industrial train tracks. A raw wind blasted across the deserted route. Helga checked in both directions before stepping into his eyeline. The old man shook with cold as he gripped a tousled mutt with stiff hands.

'Come on inside, Dennis. It's flipping Baltic out here.'

'Never going back,' he mumbled into the dog's fur. 'They hate me.'

'No, they don't.' Helga sighed. 'Come on, Dennis – you'll freeze to death.'

'This time I'm going over. I mean it.' He revved the scooter, inching it towards the railway line.

'At least give me Pepper,' Helga reasoned. The dog's ears pricked up hopefully.

'If I go, I'm taking him with me. Wouldn't give them the satisfaction. They care more about this damn dog than me.' Pepper gave her an imploring look.

'Now you know that's not true.'

'Tis! They keep me locked up in my room all day without so much as a snifter.'

Helga chanced a step closer. 'Give me Pepper.'

His grip tightened. 'I'm nearly eighty-five you know.'

'Dennis, you just had your eighty-fourth birthday last week.'

'And what did I get for it? An Asda sponge cake and a pair of bloody new pyjamas! Not even a bottle of whisky for the old man. What do I want with new pyjamas? Who do they think I'm trying to impress?' He raised his hands in frustration. Pepper seized the opportunity and made a dash for the back door.

'Pepper!' he cried. 'See, even the dog can't bear to be near me. No one will miss me!'

'Well, *I'd* miss you, Dennis – you know how concerned I am about you,' Helga said in soothing tones. She glanced at her watch. 'Let's get you inside before both of us end up with the flu.'

'If I did, no one would come and visit me.'

'Dennis, we've had this conversation before. If it's company you're looking for, we'd be delighted for you to join us at the Tuesday Chatters.'

'Load of old women moaning on, I expect?' he grumbled, blowing his nose on a soiled hankie. 'What do you lot get up to anyway? I bet it's all jigsaw puzzles and Happy Clappy singing.'

Helga took this as consent to retreat into the house as she moved the scooter into reverse.

'Not at all. We have a real mix of folks. Peter's in his thirties and Kamal's only twenty-two.'

'Then what do they know about getting thrown on the scrap heap?'

'Well you can ask them yourself next week.' She followed Dennis as he navigated the scooter through the kitchen and into his bedroom, which appeared to be doubling up as a laundry facility. His daughter emerged at the doorway, blocking the exit. 'You should stop wasting everyone's time,' she barked at her father.

'Oh, it's no trouble,' Helga said, squeezing through the narrow gap into the hall. 'Your dad's agreed to come to our wee social group on Tuesday.'

'Has he?' she grunted. 'Will you give him a bath?'

'That's not really what he's there for,' Helga answered, thinking the entire family would benefit from a good soaking. 'He's there to make new friends. The minibus will pick him up about one thirty if you can have him ready and dressed.'

'Dressed?' She snorted, stubbing out the cigarette on the doorframe. 'He's so lazy he sleeps in his clothes.'

'Then why buy me bloody new pyjamas?' Dennis hurled back.

Helga took a hurried left into the staff car park and, checking all the nooks and crannies for an empty space, abandoned the car on double yellow lines. She was locking the vehicle when Vanda exited the building. 'Ah, Helga, I'm just going out for a sandwich – want one?'

'No, thanks, I've brought my lunch today. Leftover mac cheese,' she replied, patting her bag. 'At least I hope I've remembered it.'

She rummaged around in her crammed shoulder bag but came up with nothing. Dumping the holdall on to the pavement she reached in and handed Vanda items one by one: scarf, gloves, purse, umbrella, a paperback. 'What – not yours?' asked Vanda, with her arms full.

'Hang on.' Helga raked around the bottom of her bag.

'You *do* know we only get thirty minutes for lunch?'

'Looks like I will need a sandwich,' Helga nodded, repacking her bag.

'What kind do you want?'

'I'll just have what you're having.'

'Tuna mayonnaise?'

'Oh no, I don't want that.'

'What about ham salad?"

'Och, it's a bit cold for that. See if they have cheese savoury but if the savoury is red onion forget it. I'd rather go for something else.'

'Chicken?'

'I had chicken yesterday.'

'Helga!'

'Oh alright, just get me anything.'

Chapter 2

Vanda strode off as Helga entered the health centre. She took the stairs to the first-floor corridor and tapped in the security code. She pressed a further code to enter the office that she shared with the other members of the Harrison Intervention Team: Vanda, Bobbie, Aiden and Molly. Molly was alone in the office, sitting at her PC when Helga entered. 'Oh, hi, Helga,' Molly said without turning round. 'You just missed Chan. She was in here looking for money from you. Says you sponsored her son to do the school's sponsored silence.'

'How much?'

'A pound for every hour. So that's eight pounds.'

'Gosh – he's not a Tibetan monk, is he? I thought teachers were always complaining they can't control the kids.'

'Seemingly it's not so hard when they're raising money for a school trip.'

'I don't remember offering to fund a world cruise.'

Molly handed Helga a pink sticky Post-it note. 'And someone called Kate Crosbie left a message.'

'Oh, that's my agent,' Helga said breezily. 'Did she say what she wanted?'

'Something about plans for a bog tour?'

'A *blog* tour, Molly!'

'Oh, I don't know about these things. And she mentioned a "Writers' Block"?'

'Ah yes,' Helga nodded. 'Did I mention that I've been asked to participate as one of four local authors?'

'Hmm, I think you did say something about that.'

'Are you coming? It's on the fifteenth of March at Musselburgh Town Hall. Seven thirty.'

'What day of the week is that?'

'Wednesday.'

'Ah well, Wednesday's always a bloody nightmare in our house. Caz is still doing her shift at Morrisons to pay back what she owes and I need to run Mandy to Brownies.'

'Can't she go herself?'

'It's way over at Gilmerton.'

'So?'

'She's *seven*,' Molly tutted. 'And I can't risk leaving Connor unsupervised for any length of time. Last week when I nipped to the supermarket he attempted the Heimlich manoeuvre on our dog and I came home to find vomit all over the stairs.'

The door code sounded and Vanda returned with the sandwiches. She dropped a cellophane pack on to Helga's desk.

'What about you, Vanda?'

'What about me?' she asked, flicking on the kettle and taking a large bite from a baguette. She glanced into the mirror above the sink and ran a hand through her spiky blonde hair.

'Did you say you wanted a ticket for my Writers' Block evening in March?'

'Did I? Don't think so. What night?'

'Wednesday.'

'Can't. Meeting my pal at the Black Horse. It's steak night.' She stirred her coffee, winking at Molly, who turned back to her PC.

The door code punched again and Aiden swept in, chucking

his rucksack on the floor and collapsing on to his chair. 'That Mrs McGowan is doing my nut in!'

'What's she done now?' Vanda queried, booting up her PC.

'We've spent the last six weeks practising getting in and out of the bath, which she can manage fine. And now she says she wants the bath taken out and a shower put in. Says her son is insisting. "But you can manage the bath fine," I said. But no, she says she's putting her foot down.'

'Isn't that what got her leg broken in the first place?' Vanda quipped, not taking her eyes off the screen.

'Aiden, are you coming to my Writers' Block evening next month?' Helga asked the back of his head.

'What's that when it's at home?' He filled up his sports bottle from the water container.

'Remember I told you? It's an evening when myself and three other female authors talk about our writing and discuss what themes are emerging out of our novels?'

'Why would I be interested in that?' He took a long swig.

'It might enlighten you to understand more about the female psyche.'

'Helga, I'm surrounded by women. If I don't understand what makes you lot tick by now, I never will.'

'There are veiled influences that you can't imagine,' Helga insisted. 'We've been misunderstood and maligned for centuries. We'll be exposing our inner ruminations.'

'Well, why didn't you say so?' Aiden asked.

'So you'll come?'

'No chance.'

'Will J.K. Rowling be there?' said Molly.

'Don't be daft!' Vanda scoffed. 'She probably *owns* Musselburgh and she certainly doesn't need to plug her books.'

'Oh, we're not there to plug our books!'

'Really?' challenged Vanda with her mouth full. 'So you won't have a pull-along suitcase of *Candy Martini*?'

'I might have a few to hand for signing.' Helga sniffed.

'Anyway, you lot better get a move on with your lunch. Quinn's starting the meeting in ten minutes,' Molly advised, picking up her notepad and pen. 'I'm going to set up the room downstairs. 'Can someone bring him a mug of coffee? He takes it with milk. Where's Bobbie?'

Quinn Adamson commandeered the head of the table. He wore a fitted grey waistcoat with starched white shirt and pink tie, his sleeves rolled up and held in place with chrome armbands. His fingers tapped the table with impatience, as though giving a speedy rendition of 'Chopsticks'. 'Where's the other one?' he asked.

'What other one?' Vanda replied.

'You know!' he snapped. 'The ... you know – the older lady?'

'Bobbie?' Vanda frowned. 'She should be on her way.'

Quinn checked his watch again. 'I'm giving her one more minute then we're starting.'

'Has everyone signed the sheet?' Molly asked, skimming a piece of paper across the table. Vanda, Aiden, Helga and Molly sat facing six other representatives from the building's teams. Opposite Quinn a twenty-something-year-old sat solidly with her arms folded and face blank. 'Sorry, I don't think we've been introduced?' Molly said. 'I'm Molly – admin worker from upstairs. I don't think I know you?'

'Probably not,' the girl mumbled. 'I'm on placement with the community health project.'

'Lovely! How are you enjoying it?'

'I only started yesterday. It was mostly giving out condoms.'

'Lovely,' Molly repeated, scribbling 'student' on her sheet.

'Right, let's get moving,' Quinn barked. 'I haven't got all day.' He swiped at his iPad. 'Any other business anyone wants to add?'

'Shouldn't we do a round of introductions first?' Molly suggested, nodding towards the student.

He sighed. 'Mr Adamson, general manager.'

'Vanda, staff nurse, Health Intervention Team.'

'Aiden, occupational therapist – same.'

'Helga, link worker – also based in that team.'

'You all know me – I'm Molly.'

'Chan – Chinese health.'

'Angie – Smoke Free.'

'Danny – CPN.'

'Linda – student nurse.'

'Cameron – podiatrist.'

'Audrey – social worker.'

'Lance – community health.'

'Happy now?' Quinn grumped.

'Can I add something to AOB?' Audrey asked. 'The Easter Fundraiser dinner.'

'What you get up to after hours is not my concern,' said Quinn. 'Let's stick to core business. The main purpose for today's meeting is to update you on the building's closure. One of the—'

The door flew open and Bobbie waddled in, grey hair escaping a bun and full-length winter coat flapping. In one hand she held an open brown paper bag and, in the other, a floppy chip. The room was filled with the aroma of a sausage supper, salt and sauce. She bustled to the furthest end of the table and squeezed herself next to Linda, who reluctantly shifted her chair.

'That's Bobbie,' Molly whispered for the benefit of the student.

'Is that absolutely necessary?' Quinn complained.

'You mean lunch?' asked Bobbie, all innocent. 'I'd say so. Can't work all day and survive on coffee alone. Chip, anyone?' She held out the bag as chips were plucked like raffle tickets. 'Ooh, greasy!' Molly smiled.

'Can we get on?' Quinn said, through gritted teeth. 'Now where was I?'

'Shutting us down?' Molly supplied helpfully.

'It's not me that's shutting you down. The building is deteriorating week by week. It's only a matter of time before the whole thing collapses.'

'When *are* we getting moved?' Cameron asked. 'The podiatry centre has been ready for ages but we haven't heard anything. We'll need at least six weeks' notice to pack everything up and rearrange all our patient appointments.'

Quinn sighed. 'As far as I know it's still the same issue with procuring the sterilisation equipment. The new-build is way over budget so we're having to make efficiencies where we can.'

'Maybe we could save money by throwing all the equipment into the dishwasher along with the dirty plates?' Cameron scowled, crossing his arms. 'The staff are getting really fed up with the conditions here. Only last week a patient got stuck in the toilet for two hours because the lock jammed.'

'Well, certainly the fabric of the building is forcing us to focus,' Quinn conceded.

'So perhaps the building needs a little push?'

'Which brings me to the rest of you lot,' Quinn said. He swiped at his iPad again. 'So last time we met I informed you that all the teams will be relocated on separate premises. Well,' he coughed nervously, 'there's been a bit of an update on that scenario. It's looking like there is some risk we might have adjusted requirements going forward. As you are aware, when the building closes, some teams will be merged, resulting in duplication of roles.'

'Which teams?' Aiden probed.

'I can't exactly say.'

'Why not?' Vanda demanded.

'It's complicated.'

'Try us,' said Aiden. 'I know we're pretty remote out here and operate under some fairly revolutionary practices but we do speak English.'

'If you must know,' said Quinn, irritated. 'It's the Intervention team at risk.'

'What?' the team chorused.

'Why?' Helga asked.

'As you know, you will be merged with the larger South Team and there are not sufficient referrals to justify the workforce.'

'Have you seen our waiting list?' Aiden said hotly. 'We're not exactly short of work.'

'Ah, but some would say you could work smarter and get that list right down.'

'*Who* would say?' said Aiden.

'I'm not at liberty to divulge.'

'But surely you'll back us up?' Vanda persisted. 'You know the range of work we cover.'

'I will do what I can but we have to consider other options too.'

'For example?'

'There may be some natural wastage. Perhaps some people

are thinking of retirement?' Quinn glared at Bobbie, who was chomping on a battered sausage. 'Wha...?' she said with her mouthful.

'Bobbie's not going anywhere.'

'Then you better start getting your numbers up.'

'And how can we possibly do that?' Helga asked in amazement. 'All our referrals come from the GPs and district nurses.'

'Well, I suggest you get out there and sell yourselves.'

'We're not hookers,' Vanda objected.

'I'm merely suggesting—'

'That we prostitute ourselves?' said Helga.

'Am I minuting that?' asked Molly. 'Mr Adamson recommends we don a red cocktail dress and parade around the GP practice in the hope that we get more business.'

'I didn't say that!' Quinn snapped.

'So Bobbie's an OAP and Vanda's a tart?' Aiden fumed.

'Thanks, Aiden,' Vanda said. 'Why can't Helga be a tart? Helga, you're multitalented.'

'Look, this is getting out of hand,' Quinn growled.

'Is that how you like it?' Vanda jibed. 'I have heard that rumour.'

'Enough!' he blustered, gathering up his iPad and shoving it into a briefcase. 'I don't have time for this ridiculous nonsense. I've tried to be fair with you – I've shared our concerns and given you a positive steer.'

'Thanks,' Aiden muttered.

Quinn pushed his chair back and slammed the door behind him.

'So, what about the fundraiser?' Vanda grinned.

'I've had this flyer up on the noticeboard since last week,' Chan said, passing round the sheet of paper. 'So far we have twelve names. No one from podiatry – Cameron?'

'We've got another night out that evening – Keir's stag do,' he answered, leaving the table.

'But who's going to massage our feet after we've been dancing all night?' Vanda called out to him.

'Oh, ha ha!'

'*I'm* not dancing,' said Bobbie, popping the last bite of sausage into her mouth. 'I'll come for the meal, though.'

'Never!' laughed Vanda. 'And what about you, Helga – are you coming dancing? The Castle High is a great place to pick up talent.'

'No, thanks, Vanda. I think I'll pass on that. I've had enough of men to last quite a while.'

'Oh? Something you'd like to share with us?'

'She was jilted by her fiancé at the church last year,' whispered Bobbie.

'Thanks, Bobbie!' cried Helga. 'I don't think everyone needs to know every detail.'

'Harsh,' Aiden sympathised. 'You must have been broken-hearted, Helga?'

'Oooh – good name for a book,' Bobbie grinned. '*Broken-hearted Helga*.'

'*Broken-hearted Helga and her Fucked-up Fiancé,*' Vanda added.

'Anyway … I'm quite happy to fly solo for a while,' Helga proclaimed, gathering up her belongings as the meeting drew to a close. Chan tapped her arm. 'Hi, Helga, did Molly mention my son's sponsor money?'

'Oh yes.' Helga nodded. 'But I'm in a bit of a hurry right now. I'll get it to you soon.'

Returning to the office, Aiden browsed the whiteboard. 'So what's on the menu for this afternoon?'

'What?' groaned Helga. 'Who put *two* appointments up for me for this afternoon? I've got a blog to write and upload by four o'clock today!'

Molly swivelled round in her chair. 'Helga, you specifically asked me to book Miss Trench in for her shopping trip today.'

'Did I?'

'Yes – and the other is a new patient referred by Dr Syme. She said it was urgent so I popped him in for just now.'

'Anyway,' said Aiden, stuffing a Helping Hand into his rucksack, 'you're not supposed to be writing during the day.'

'Aiden,' Helga replied in a calm voice, while she cleaned her glasses with the edge of her jumper. 'What time did you leave work yesterday?'

'Four thirty.'

'No doubt on the dot? Whereas I was still sitting here writing up notes till after six. I have nothing on my conscience.'

'Just saying – Quinn is looking for any excuse to jettison folk.'

'I'm not worried about his browbeating tactics,' Helga said.

'Oh no?'

'No.' Helga loaded her MacBook into her shoulder bag and picked up the case notes. 'Well, I better be off. Can't keep my patients waiting, can I?'

Chapter 3

Mr McAllistair's flat was on the fifteenth floor of a high-rise block in Dumbryden, necessitating a series of lifts, corridors and security doors to access. By the time Helga reached his flat, the door was open and Mr McAllistair was already shuffling back to the living room, his braces hanging off his shoulders. The TV had been paused mid-scene – a young couple stared wide-eyed as a suited gent held up a polished silver gravy boat for inspection.

'Good afternoon,' she announced, waiting until he had dropped down on to his armchair with a plop. 'I'm Helga Trumpet – Harrison Intervention Team's link worker.' She smiled. 'Can I sit here?' Despite the stifling heat of the room, she kept her fleece on.

'Aye. That's a bit of a mouthful,' he commented. His face had a worried look as he ran his hand over his balding head, smoothing over the remaining three strands.

'Yes, that's why some people call us the HIT Squad,' she confided. 'So, Mr McAllistair, Dr Syme asked me to come and see you?'

'Just call me Jimmy.' He scooped his braces up over his shoulders.

'Righty-oh, Jimmy. Now, if you don't mind, I'm just going to make a few notes here on my computer.'

'Carry on.'

Helga opened up her MacBook, found what she was looking for and began typing away. After a couple of minutes she glanced up. 'Perhaps you could tell me a bit about yourself, Jimmy? Start at the beginning. Where did you go to primary school?'

'Eh? Is that really relevant?'

'It helps me form a picture,' Helga said, not looking up from her screen. She touch-typed rapidly as he cleared his throat. 'Well, my first school would have been Clovenstone Primary. I quite enjoyed those school days as my best chum, Sandy, from over the road, sat next to me and we did everything together. Walked to school, sat in class, played after school. Even attended the same Boys' Brigade club on the corner.'

'Mmm, hmm. Keep going.'

Jimmy shrugged. 'Oh, well then I went to high school and I found that an entirely different matter. Full of school bullies and break-time fights. I was a lanky kid back then and used to get called "Skinny Jimmy" but, of course, it could have been much worse. Poor Sandy had a stutter and got beaten up so often his parents eventually moved away and he changed schools, so I ... do you really want me to go on?'

'Yes, yes. All very interesting. Oh, can you think of another word for *difficult*?'

'Difficult?'

'Yes?'

'Oh, I don't know. Let me think ... problematic? Challenging? Burdensome?'

'Burdensome! Good word. Carry on. What about your first job?' Helga prompted.

'Ah, well I landed on my feet with that one. My father knew someone from the bowling club who was looking for an electrician's apprentice. In those days you just turned up, they took a note of your name and that was it. I did that for a few years, during which time I met my wife, Elsie. We were both only eighteen and we met at the Palace. It wasn't love at first sight, but that didn't bother either of us. And then of course wee David came along soon after and … I'm really not sure why you're interested in all this?' Jimmy wondered out loud. He gazed at the top of Helga's head, bent in concentration. 'Miss?'

'Hmm? You were saying about getting bullied? That must have been awful for you. Which do you think sounds better: "I hate having to face a blank screen," or "I try to avoid staring at a blank screen"?'

'Sorry?'

'You're right. The second one *is* rather confusing. Although I never like to use the word *hate* – it's a very strong emotion and should be used sparingly.'

'I hate having to shave every day.'

'Quite.'

'So do you think you can help me at all?' Jimmy asked, leaning forward in his chair. 'Dr Syme says you can help people get out and about more. It's just that I never see anyone way up here. I got given this flat two years ago in exchange for my big house, which I didn't need any more. But I never see anyone for weeks. I don't even see the postie, as he's gone before I can get to the door. My son has my shopping delivered but the chap's always in such a hurry.'

Helga glanced up. 'Yes – good point. It's all about connecting with people. Now, I have a social group I run in the health centre – called the Tuesday Chatters.'

'Oh yes?'

'Have you ever thought it might be good for you to meet some other folk?'

'Well, that's what I've been saying!'

'Look,' she said, checking her watch. 'That's been really helpful for me today. Perhaps when I come back next time you can tell me a bit more about yourself. Is that okay?'

'I suppose so. What about this group, then?'

'I'll get our admin worker to give you a wee ring with all the details. It's just that I'm rather pushed today.' She snapped her MacBook shut, throwing it into her bag. 'Don't worry about getting up, Jimmy. I'll see myself out.'

'Bye, then!' he called to her retreating back.

Helga hared across town in the pool car, cursing every red light and roadwork hold-up. She dodged along the bus lane, screeching to a halt outside a plush Victorian mansion on Murrayfield Avenue. Entry into and out of the property was regulated through a set of imposing iron gates welded on to a stone wall that surrounded the exclusive property. Helga stretched out of the car window and jabbed the buzzer, announcing, 'Helga Trumpet,' into the intercom. The gates released with a mechanical creak. She parked under a large oak and traversed the gravel pathway, stepping up to the covered stone porch. Lex Trench glared at her from the open front door – a nineteen-year-old rebel with long green hair, Emo eyes and purple lipstick. She wore a multi-zipped black hoodie and ripped skinny jeans with tatty black Converse boots. Her left hand was covered with an intricate tattooed spider's web.

'Afternoon!' Helga greeted her with a wave.

'What time do you fucking call this?' Lex sniped.

'Now, Lex – I refuse to proceed with our session if you insist on using language like that,' warned Helga. 'Remind me what your counsellor suggested?'

Lex sighed, pulling the door closed behind her. 'To be more

creative with my communication.'

'Good.' Helga smiled, holding open the passenger door.

'So what time do you *trucking* call this?'

Helga winced. 'Better,' she acknowledged. 'Yes, sorry about that. Molly put me in for an extra session with an urgent new patient.' She pulled out on to Corstorphine Road and sped towards Haymarket.

'Whoa, lady. What's the hurry?'

'Oh well, we don't want to get caught in the rush hour.'

'You're the one that's rushing.'

'So we agreed we'd start with Debenhams, then?' Helga asked.

'S'pose.'

'Good-oh. And how are your parents doing?'

'Still breathing.' Lex snorted. 'Getting on my case twenty-four hours a trucking day.'

'Oh, that's surely an exaggeration,' Helga said, slamming on her brakes and squeezing into a parking space, much to the annoyance of the car behind, which tooted in anger.

'Feels like it,' Lex grumbled, getting out of the car. Helga stuck a parking permit on the dashboard and grabbed her bag. They entered the department store and were pounced upon by a sales assistant who sprayed the air above them with perfume. 'Just walk through it and you'll smell like heaven!' she declared.

'Truck's sake,' Lex said under her breath.

'Now,' said Helga, facing her patient. 'As we agreed, this is your first opportunity to test some of the strategies we've discussed. I want you to browse the whole shop, going on to several of the floors. If you do want to buy anything, that's fine – just keep a receipt.'

'What are you going to do?' Lex asked. 'I hope you're not going to follow me around like some sad nanny?'

'Not at all! I know you need your own space. I've got work to do so I'm going to take the lift to the café on the top floor. When you've finished, come up and find me there. Okay, how do you feel?'

'Alright.' The girl's fists were tucked into her sleeves.

'Not too anxious? Not angry?'

'Let's just get on with it,' Lex said, scowling at the perfume sales assistant who had armed herself with another spray.

'Right, then. See you in a wee while. Good luck!' Helga summoned the lift, leaving Lex fingering the Italian leather handbags.

Helga ordered a latte and a buttered teacake and settled herself in a corner table near the window. Down below, buses ambled along Princes Street, weaving in and out of the sliding trams. She flipped open her MacBook and found her blog. 'Now, where was I?' she pondered. *People are always asking me where I get my ideas from. Life! I say. The people I meet and the snatches of conversation I hear ...*

'Trying to work, are you?'

Helga concentrated on her words, reading them back to herself.

'I said, *Trying to work, are you?*' the voice repeated. Helga glanced up to see an elderly lady, folded almost double, peering across at her from the neighbouring table.

'Sorry, yes.' Helga nodded, getting back to her writing.

'Only, in the old days when I used to come up here for my afternoon cuppa, people always chatted to each other much more. You know? Complain about the weather, or the price of fish, or how you can never find a winter coat your size. But now all I see are people stabbing at gadgets for hours. I've no idea what they're doing. They all say they're working but how can they be working and eating a scone at the same time? I *said—*'

'Yes, I heard you,' Helga interrupted. 'But I have a deadline, you see. Must get this finished.'

'But that's what I don't understand,' the lady said, topping up from a chipped teapot. 'Finish what?'

'It's a blog I'm writing.'

'A what?'

'A blog – a web log? For my readers. I'm a writer, you see.'

'Ah well, I know what a writer does. Just not sure what you're doing sitting in a café drinking coffee. Have I heard of you?'

'Helga Trumpet? I *am* local to Edinburgh. You might have seen a generous article on me the other week in the *Edinburgh Evening News*?'

'Oh, I don't bother buying that any more. I'm not interested in football and if I hear one more mention of the trams I swear I'll throw myself under one.'

'*Candy Martini Reaches Out*?' Helga prompted.

'Are you talking to me?' The lady frowned.

'My debut novel *Candy Martini Reaches Out* is at one hundred and fourteen on the bestseller list,' Helga announced rather too loudly.

'Nope. Never heard of it. Was it any good? Did it have lots of sex in it? Only I don't go in for that sort of thing. Everything on the telly is sex, sex, sex. You'd think it had only just been invented.'

'Well, I really must be getting on,' Helga said, her hands hovering over the keyboard.

'Don't let me keep you!' The lady sniffed. 'You're the one bragging about being a hotshot writer. I'm just trying to have a quiet cup of tea here.'

Helga focused on her words, rereading her last sentence for the third time. Her thoughts were interrupted yet again by a commotion at the café entrance. Stepping off the escalator a young woman hurried into the café, scanning the faces. She wore a black top hat, a full-length scarlet woollen coat and six-inch heeled black leather boots. Two designer handbags – one silver and one gold – were hooked over each shoulder. She strode with purpose towards Helga as a crimson-faced, rugby-playing security guard jogged in pursuit. His hand reached out and clapped the woman on the shoulder just as she drew level with Helga's table. 'Gotcha!' he declared, sweat trickling down his rosy cheeks.

Helga looked up from her writing. She sighed, 'Oh, Lex, what have you done?'

It was after six by the time Helga dropped Lex off at her gated home. Having been escorted by the security guard to the store's head office, they had a lengthy wait for the police and an even longer delay while Helga attempted to explain Lex's supervised sessions. Helga had hoped that gradual exposure to shopping would put a halt to Lex's thieving habits. But every episode antagonised her parents further and became yet another opportunity to tarnish their precious reputation. Helga and Lex were finally released into the bitter twilight, Helga forced to hand over an outwardly remorseful but inwardly triumphant Lex to her mother, who waited with arms folded and a grim expression. Any further excursions were banned. Lex's only respite from permanent grounding would be to attend the Tuesday Chatters as a last-ditch attempt to develop appropriate interactions with the community.

By the time Helga returned with the pool car, the health centre car park was in complete darkness, a handful of late-night workers remaining in the building. She scurried inside, trying to ignore the creepiness of the deserted corridors and the feeling she was being watched. Sitting in their empty office, she finally finished her blog and uploaded it to her site. 'Better late than never,' she said to herself. From the office next door she heard a movement, then the door open and close. She froze at her desk. Footsteps clicked past the door as Chan shouted, 'Bye!' to the light coming under Helga's door. 'Night!' she returned, relaxing. Helga had tried to ignore the embellished stories Molly liked to recount about the building's history of being a home for wayward girls and how the teens had been forced to earn their keep through providing a laundry service to wealthy locals. 'If you're still in the office at night you can hear a girl crying,' Molly had recounted in serious tones. 'Sobbing her heart out for her newborn baby that was taken from her.' When Molly had been challenged – after all, who would be in the building during the night? – she had conveniently glossed over the details. But Helga had already built up a backstory for the unfortunate lass and had no intention of experiencing the night-time wailing of a grief-stricken teenager. She flicked off the lights and pulled the door closed. On the stairs she passed Ray, the building's maintenance worker. His shoulder-length oily hair was pulled back into a ponytail, his hands shoved deep in the pockets of his grubby overalls. 'Night, Ray,' Helga said in passing. He ignored her and continued up the stairs. She exited the building, clenching her car keys in front of her like a switchblade as she crossed the moonless car park. Earlier that day, when she'd gratefully snatched any space, she'd given no thought to parking in the furthermost corner – the dark overflow corner by the generator that all other cars had long since left. Something rustled in the shrubbery and she paused, brandishing the key in front of her. 'Hello?' she called. Silence. Then suddenly, a cat shot from under a bush and darted under her car. 'Bloody hell, cat!' She frantically opened the car door and started the engine. Before moving off, she checked the puss had gone but there was no sign of the prowler. Or the cat.

Chapter 4

'Morning, Helga!' Molly chirped while typing at speed. 'Kettle's on.' Helga dumped her bag on the desk, hung up her coat and unwound the hand-knitted scarf. 'I don't know how you cycle in this weather,' Helga said to Aiden as he neatly folded his Lycra shorts and top, having changed into the generic therapy uniform. 'Mornings like this aren't too bad, if you watch out for the frost patches.' He rubbed his head to even out the cycle helmet lines on his buzz cut. Helga switched on her PC, announcing, 'Aiden, since you're the Punctuality Police, you might like to know I didn't leave here until after seven yesterday evening.'

'Get your blog done, then?' he remarked.

'That's not why I was late, *actually*. For your information Lex nearly got done for shoplifting.'

'Back to square one, then?' He shrugged.

Vanda threw her Puffa jacket over the back of her chair. 'Be with you in a minute, guys. Must just use the ladies.' She crossed the corridor, swinging open the door to the ladies, almost railroading a man standing at the row of basins. 'Wha …?' she blurted to the stocky character with dark skin and black, gelled hair. He wore a lilac flowery shirt, chinos and tan loafers without socks. 'Sorry, think you've got the wrong toilets,' Vanda said, holding the door open.

'Don't think so, miss.' He pointed to the cracked tiles above the basins. 'I'm here to see about the tiling.'

'Clearly.' She frowned, indicating his attire. 'Is this the new standard issue for Facilities? While I welcome any exotic diversity, it's hardly practical for your line of work. And where's your ID badge?'

The man continued to poke at the tiles with a brown finger.

'What's your name?'

'Anver. I don't suppose you have a knife, do you?'

'I'm not armed, if that's what you're worried about.'

His round face broke into a broad, toothy smile. 'A butter knife will do.'

Vanda retreated from the ladies and appeared at the office door. 'Molly, do you know there's a man in the ladies?'

'Oh sorry! Yes, I should have said. That's Anver the tiler.'

'Like Zorba the Greek?' Helga suggested.

'Apparently he's from South Africa,' Molly replied.

Vanda walked over to the cutlery tray, picking out a knife. 'He wants a knife. *What's* he doing?'

Molly swivelled round. 'He's replacing the tiles in the toilets.'

'But the whole building is falling apart. Why is Quinn worried about a few cracked tiles in our toilets?' Vanda asked.

'Seemingly a shard from the top tiles fell off while one of the Silver Singers was washing her hands – just about chopped her hand off. There was blood everywhere. The Silver Singers have put in a mega-complaint.'

'Right,' Vanda said. 'So now we're being attacked by the fabric of the bathrooms? Mental.'

She returned to the ladies where Anver was chatting into his mobile. 'Yes, a bottle of Jack Daniel's – two if you can. Gotta run.'

Vanda handed him the knife, which he used to run round the edges of the cracked tiles. He inspected each tile, nodding and prodding.

'Call me old-fashioned but *is* this what the Facilities department is wearing now? It doesn't exactly comply with health and safety.'

'You're right!' He grinned. 'No flies on you, eh?'

'And why haven't you got a toolbox or something?'

'Another very good question.' He handed her back the knife and jotted some numbers on a scrap of paper. 'I'm actually on my way to a birthday lunch for an old buddy – it's his fortieth. I was passing the health centre and thought – why not take the opportunity to scope the job and get the tiles ordered?'

'Still,' Vanda said in a doubtful voice. 'It *is* February in Scotland. Is your pal's party in Barbados by any chance?'

He grinned again. 'You're a comedian! But no, I'm heading to the jazz club.' He lifted a maroon pork-pie hat from the back of the door and placed it on his head, saluting Vanda on his way out. 'I'll be back.' He winked. 'Funny lady,' he chuckled to himself.

The Harrison Intervention Team pulled their chairs into a circle as they briefly ran through each of the patients on the caseload. 'Any new referrals?' Aiden enquired.

'This just came in this morning,' Molly said. 'I took a call from Dr Jasper at eight – sounds like a Rapid Response.'

Aiden took the referral, scanning it quickly. He sighed. 'Ian Taggart – again. How many times has he been referred?'

'At least three that I know of,' Bobbie answered, her hand in a grab bag of pickled onion crisps. She popped open a can of diet Irn Bru.

'Why do you even bother with diet drinks when you're eating crisps for breakfast?' said Aiden in exasperation.

Bobbie shrugged. 'It's fewer calories.'

'I read somewhere that diet drinks actually make you fatter,'

Helga chipped in.

'Eh? How?' Bobbie challenged. 'This can only has one calorie.' She tipped the can to one side to read the small print, pouring juice all over the case notes.

'Bobbie!' Vanda cried, grabbing handfuls of paper towels.

'Oops,' Bobbie muttered, wiping her trousers. 'Anyway, there's no point in me seeing Mr Taggart again. I'm sure I only just discharged him last month.'

'Says here he needs physio,' Aiden read.

Bobbie puffed out her cheeks. 'What's the point? He never does my exercises. What's happened to him now?'

'Got stuck in the bath.' Aiden passed her the sheet.

'Then that's *your* department.' Bobbie gave a smug smile, throwing the sheet back at him.

'Nope – according to Dr Jasper his knees locked.' Aiden dropped the referral back on her damp lap.

'Children, children!' Vanda interrupted. 'Why don't you *both* go?'

'As long as she washes her hands first,' Aiden muttered. 'I don't want pickled onion all over the pool car.'

'Now, while we've got everyone here,' Vanda began. 'What are we going to do about increasing our referrals?'

'Surely you're not going to take any notice of Quinn's rants?' said Helga, glancing at her mobile phone. Spotting nineteen Twitter notifications she tapped on the bird icon. Scottish Words had retweeted her book blog tweet – and LitMe! One of her regulars, Penny Pen, had commented on what a fab blog it was. She quickly checked the other notifications. Four new followers, plenty of favourites and retweets.

'Quinn is all about the data,' Aiden said with contempt. 'If we can get our numbers up he'll respond to that. If our referrals start to go down one iota, he'll pounce. He's ruthless. Any excuse to split us will give him great joy.'

'Well maybe he needs to hear some patient stories,' Bobbie suggested. 'You know – how we've made such a difference to people's lives?'

Aiden snorted. 'Like Mr Taggart you mean? No – he won't be interested in success stories or the personal touch. He just wants to know how many people we've kept out of hospital and how much money we might have saved in acute care.'

'Much as it pains me I tend to agree with Aiden,' Vanda nodded. Aiden threw her the V-sign.

'So – ideas, then?' Bobbie asked. 'Helga?'

'Hmm? Yes, I agree.'

'Agree with what?' Aiden demanded.

Helga blushed. 'Soz, folks! It's just I'm getting great feedback from my blog.'

'We're so pleased for you,' said Aiden drily. 'Come on, Helga – you're the creative one. How are we going to drum up more business?'

'And he doesn't mean create fictional numbers.'

Helga frowned, putting down her phone. 'Okay, I guess there are two things – firstly, we can look at which GP practice is making the fewest referrals and target them.'

'I can get your numbers for the last year?' Molly offered.

'Good,' Vanda said. 'And secondly?'

'Well, maybe we need to have a bit of a marketing campaign,' Helga suggested. 'I mean, I have a marketing strategy for my writing. I've got agreed objectives relating to the development of my marketing materials, personal appearances, the blog tour, my blogs, tweeting etc. I have a whole Helga Trumpet brand. Maybe it's time this team had a makeover and we relaunch ourselves?'

'Makeover?' Aiden repeated. 'I don't think the NHS is going to pay for Bobbie to have her teeth straightened and for Vanda to get a boob job just to boost our referrals.'

'What's wrong with my teeth?' Bobbie asked, getting up to peer in the mirror. 'As long as they chew food I'm perfectly happy.'

'I wouldn't say no to a cosmetic enhancement,' said Vanda, pushing out her chest.

Helga shook her head. 'I just meant – what if we got a new photo taken and made up a flyer and went round all the practices to remind them what we've got to offer?'

'Is this before or after my boob job?' Vanda asked.

'That's not a bad idea,' Aiden mused. 'We haven't had any referrals from Westside Practice for months.'

'And Baberton has apparently got two new GPs since Christmas.'

'I could take your team photo and mock up a flyer, if you like?' Molly volunteered.

'Oh, but you should be in it too,' Helga said. 'You're most definitely part of this team. I've only been here eight months.'

'And that's only two months less than me,' Aiden added. 'Molly, you've been here the longest!'

Molly blushed. 'Well, if you insist. Just wait till after Wednesday, when I'm getting my hair done.'

'Yeah, you can stand in front of me – block my buck teeth,' Bobbie said, punching Aiden's arm.

'Right,' said Vanda, standing up. 'Let's get going. Molly, are you happy to take charge of the marketing, then?'

'Of course! I've got desktop publisher installed, which will be perfect for it.'

'Ooh! Have you?' Helga swooped. 'Only I'm planning to do a wee newsletter about my writing – so that would be dead handy.'

'Aye – just let me know what you need.'

Chapter 5

Helga washed out her plastic lunchbox at the sink, balancing it on the pile of mugs and cutlery on the draining board. 'Molly, did you say you'd give me a hand setting up my group this afternoon?'

'Surely,' Molly said, springing up from her chair.

'If you could take a tray downstairs with the mugs, tea and coffee etc.? And fill the kettle? Only I've got a couple of tweets I need to respond to.'

'You tweet away!' Molly chirped. 'Whatever that is!'

'Come in,' Helga welcomed. The slim Asian lad hovered at the door. From behind a floppy, black fringe his dark eyes flitted around the room. Helga pulled out the chair beside her, giving it a pat. 'Have a seat.'

'What's *your* name?' Peter shouted from across the table. Peter, although in his thirties, had a boyish, chubby face and a pudding-bowl haircut. He wore a red sweatshirt boasting, *big is best* and baggy tracksuit bottoms. Not that he'd ever been to a track of any description in his life. He waited for a response. His pale complexion and expansive girth gave the impression of one never far from a TV dinner. 'What's your name?' he repeated in a loud voice, staring at the newcomer, who slipped on to the chair, head bent.

'This is Kamal, everyone. Welcome to our Tuesday Chatters

group. Would you like to introduce yourselves to him?'

'I'm Peter,' he grinned, several teeth missing. 'I live with my mum but she likes to go out with her friend Ishbel once a week so I've been coming here, haven't I, Helga?'

'That's right. And it's been so nice having you. Who's next?'

'Harry,' drawled an elegant woman in her sixties; dressed in a smart tweed suit, her bluish-grey hair cut in a sharp pixie-style. She peered over her tinted glasses at Kamal. In her right hand she held a cigarette holder, the cigarette unlit. 'Delighted, I'm sure.'

'My name's Princess!' the girl next to Harry exclaimed. She bounced up and down on her seat, her blonde curls bobbing and pale blue eyes glistening. Her pink, glittery dress rucked over her plumpness. 'Hiya, Kamal, that's a lovely name. Where are you from?'

Kamal continued to gaze at his delicate hands, his shoulders hunched.

'That's grand! And I'm Helga,' she beamed. 'Everyone is welcome at our Tuesday Chatters. What we normally do,' she addressed Kamal, 'is help ourselves to a cup of tea or coffee then we have a wee chat. Sometimes we play board games or do an activity – or even invite a speaker. Today, Sharon – one of the podiatrists – is going to join us.'

'I like cola,' Peter announced. 'I bring my own.' He waved a can for the group to see. As he tugged the ring pull, cola erupted over the table. 'Oh, look what I've done!' he cried, dropping the can as it sprayed over Harry's suit. 'You idiot!' she cursed. 'This is Harris Tweed you know.'

'But I thought *you* were Harry,' he said, bewildered.

Helga leapt up to mop the spilt juice. Twice in one day! Peter peered into the can forlornly. 'Now there's hardly any left.'

'That's God's way of telling you you've had enough sugar for one day,' Harry grumbled. She patted at her sleeve. 'Any chance of a wee brandy for my coffee?' she asked Helga. 'It's been quite a shock for me.'

'No chance.'

'How much is enough sugar?' Princess wondered out loud, scooping three spoons into her tea.

'Kamal, would you like a drink?' Helga offered, to which he shook his head.

'Have you got any cola?' Peter asked.

'Okay, so just to recap,' Helga began. 'Last week we brought in the newspapers and had a bit of a chinwag about what was going on in the world, didn't we?'

'Yes, Helga, it was exciting!' Princess clapped her hands. 'I liked hearing about the famous people, didn't I?'

'We should never have got on to politics,' Harry commented.

'Yes, that man got very angry, didn't he?' Princess frowned. 'What was his name?'

'That was Albert,' Helga replied.

'Why did he throw a chair, miss?' Peter asked. 'Was it not very comfy?'

'I hope he's not coming today,' said Princess, checking the door fearfully.

'No, Albert won't be coming today,' said Helga. 'But the good news is that next week we have *three* new members.'

'Oh goody! Will there be a handsome prince?' Princess giggled.

'Oh lord!' Harry rolled her eyes.

'We will be joined by two gentlemen and a young lady: Jimmy, Dennis and Lex,' Helga announced, sipping her coffee.

'Lex?' Harry echoed. 'Hasn't she been before? The young lass with blue hair?' *Pot, kettle, black*, thought Helga. 'That's right, although it's green now.'

'Hasn't she got a bit of a potty mouth?' Harry asked. 'Thought she was banned too?'

'No one is *banned*.'

'What about Albert?' Peter suggested.

They were interrupted by a polite knock at the door. Sharon popped her head in. 'Am I too early?'

'No – come in. Everyone, this is Sharon.'

'Hi, guys!' Sharon trilled. She had a round, smiley face and choppy, auburn hair. Her blue tunic and thin cotton trousers stretched over her portly frame.

She dumped an armful of products on to the table. 'My name's Sharon and I'm a podiatrist. Helga has invited me along today to talk about foot care.'

Peter snatched up a foot file. 'What's this for?' he asked.

'That's for filing off dead skin.'

'How gross!' Harry tutted.

'Now, what would be really great is if one of you could volunteer to have me assess your feet then we can all have a lovely chat about the dos and don'ts of foot care.'

'Didn't realise there were laws about it,' Harry remarked.

'Pick me!' Peter shouted, waving his hand in the air.

'Fabulous,' Sharon gushed. 'What's your name?'

'I'm Peter.'

'We'd never have guessed,' Harry muttered.

'So if you don't mind slipping off your shoes and socks?' Sharon suggested. 'And perhaps everyone might like to move their seats so they can all see.'

'Oooh, this is like on the telly,' Princess said.

Harry scowled. 'God knows what programmes you watch!'

Peter whipped off his old trainers and mismatched holey socks, which he threw on the table.

'Eugh!' Harry recoiled. She removed an eau de cologne from her bag and scooshed the air in front of her.

'You've got *smelly* feet,' Princess giggled.

'Have I?' Peter asked, not the least bit offended. 'Thought all feet smelt like that?'

'Do you mind me asking how often you wash your feet, Peter?' Sharon asked.

'I have a bath every week,' Peter answered proudly. 'My mum makes me.'

Sharon frowned. 'So the first lesson of today is that we should all wash our feet every day and make sure they are dried properly before putting on our socks.' She slipped on a pair of rubber gloves and pulled out a reel of antibacterial wipes from an industrial-sized tub. Kneeling on the floor in front of him she proceeded to rub his feet.

'Tickles!' he guffawed, wriggling in his chair. He couldn't help but gawp down her tunic where her breasts bumped together with each firm scrub.

'Now,' Sharon said, poking at his thick brown toenails. 'How often should we cut our toenails?'

'Every day?' Princess offered.

'Hmm, not quite.' Sharon selected a pair of clippers from the table and began to trim Peter's dense nails. The first piece shot off, hitting Harry on the cheek. 'Jesus!' she ducked. 'Some warning, please!'

'So, I'm just trimming back Peter's nails like this. Straight across. Tidying up your nails every few weeks should be fine.' She picked up a large file. 'And you may want to file down any thickness.' She made sawing motions, her chest dancing playfully.

'I can't reach my feet so my mum cuts them,' Peter confided. 'Only she's not so keen. Says she'll cut them if I buy her a packet of fags.'

Sharon lifted up his foot and inspected his heel. 'Now, what do any of you do about dry skin?'

'Nail clippers?' Peter suggested.

'My feet are all soft and pink because my mum says to rub them every night with baby lotion. She says a prince won't want a princess with feet covered in corns and cowliss.'

'Calluses,' Sharon nodded, filing away at Peter's heel. He began yelping and flapping his arms. 'Stop!' he begged. 'Stop – it tickles too much!' His hand flew out, catapulting Helga's mug of coffee against a wall. The mug shattered as coffee dripped down the white wall.

'What a klutz!' Harry sighed. Helga wiped down the wall with paper towels – third spilt drink of the day – and carefully gathered up the pieces of her fractured mug. Ironic really as it was a promotional freebie from a calcium drugs rep.

'Oh my!' Sharon exclaimed. 'Maybe we should stop for today.'

'Please,' Harry urged. 'Some of us have chronic lung damage as it is without clogging it up with his dead skin.'

'Well, Peter,' Sharon pointed to a pumice stone sitting on the table. 'You might find that helps with your problem.'

'Really? Social isolation?'

'Actually, I meant ...' Sharon slumped on to her bottom. 'Ooh, my knees have gone numb.' She held up both hands from the floor. 'Any chance someone can pull me up?'

Helga took one hand and began to strain as Peter grabbed Sharon round her wide girth and heaved mightily. As Sharon clambered to her feet, Peter was left hugging her as though enjoying the last slow dance.

'Think I'm fine now,' Sharon's voice came muffled from his jumper. Red-faced, she gathered up her tools and scrambled for the exit. Kamal stared wide-eyed as the door closed behind her.

'Oh, Helga, that was super!' Princess applauded.

'And hopefully we've all learnt something today?' Helga said. 'I'm sure we're all going to go home today and give our feet some loving!'

'Can't wait,' Harry replied.

'Okay, we'll see you next Tuesday,' Helga said. 'And be ready to welcome our new friends!'

Helga returned to the office and sank into her chair, a headache beginning to form.

'Your phone's been going mad!' Molly said. 'Pinging all afternoon!'

Helga snatched it eagerly – three missed calls, four emails, fifteen Twitter notifications, Instagram alerts, thirteen What's App messages and two texts. She made a cup of coffee and settled down at her desk.

'Anything exciting?' Molly enquired.

'Mmm?' Helga answered, distracted.

'I was just asking—' The door entry intercom buzzed sharply, sending Molly into the air. 'That gets me every time!' She pressed the button, 'Harrison Intervention Team. How may I help you?' A man's voice crackled 'Delivery!' She allowed him access to the corridor, jumping up from her seat to open their office door. Returning with a lavish bouquet of red roses, tied with a cream bow, she presented it to Helga. 'For me?' Helga cried, blushing.

'*Someone's* popular,' Molly smiled. 'A bit late for Valentine's Day, though, aren't they? That was last week. Who are they from?'

Helga glimpsed the card, her face clouding, then scrunched it up, dropping it into the wastepaper bin. 'Oh, it's just a fan getting a bit carried away.'

'I could do with some of that. This year I spent Valentine's Day scrubbing down my cream living-room walls after my Connor and his pals had the bright idea of replacing potato with beetroot so their spud gun would make more realistic wounds – it was like Culloden on a bad day.'

'Oh dear,' Helga said. 'Look, why don't you take them home? I have to go somewhere after work and they really need to get into some water.'

'What? No, I couldn't!'

'Go on,' Helga insisted, placing the cellophane-wrapped roses on Molly's desk. 'You'd be doing me a favour.'

'Oh well, in that case …'

'Tell your kids you got them from a secret admirer!'

'LOL,' Molly replied, making air quotations.

'Actually, I could do with heading off about now,' said Helga, gathering up her belongings.

'Oh?' Molly glanced at her watch.

'Do you mind letting the others know? Just tell them I had an appointment or something.'

'O-kay,' Molly faltered. 'Well, see you tomorrow?'

'Yes, must dash.'

Helga scanned the parked vehicles as she wound her way towards her car, still with the nagging feeling of being watched. She fumbled with her key as she felt a hand thump down on her shoulder. 'Wah!' she cried, dropping the key.

'Didn't mean to scare you,' Bobbie apologised. 'Here – have a toffee.'

'No, thanks.' Helga shook her head.

'Quite right – they ruin your teeth. It's just that I had a poppy seed bagel for lunch and a patient told me I'd got seeds stuck in my teeth. I hoped the toffee might pull them out. Skiving off home, are you?'

'Er …'

'Only joking!' Bobbie punched her arm playfully. 'I don't give a fig what you do. I'm only grumpy because I've got Weight Watchers after work and I know Linda will bite my head off. Still – at least I won't weigh as much if she does!' She ambled off, laughing at her own joke.

Helga sped off home, ran up the two flights of stairs and double-locked the flat door behind her. She peered down from the lounge window but spotted nothing unusual in the handful of folk making their way home. Dumping her bag, she retrieved her MacBook and set it on the coffee table. The clock on the wall drummed out each second. With a sigh, she opened the manuscript and clicked on 'Go to … Page 50.' This called for another cup of coffee. She filled the kettle and reread the last paragraph. The words blurred into a scramble. She woke up, her neck stiff, and glanced at the clock – 7.30 p.m. *Shit!* She was going to have to pull another all-nighter.

Chapter 6

Cameron attached an additional lens on to his camera as he peered through the viewer again and made a few adjustments. 'We need better lighting,' he grumbled.

'I don't know why Cheryl always cuts my hair too short!' Molly wailed, tugging at her fringe. 'I ask for a trim and, to anyone else in the salon, a trim means taking a smidgeon off my ends.'

'Oo-er, I should be so lucky!' Bobbie grinned. 'Anyway, your hair looks fine. Give someone else a shot at the mirror.'

'No, it doesn't,' Molly protested, pushing back in front of the mirror. 'I look like when I was a kid and my mum cut my hair.'

'My mum *still* cuts my hair,' Aiden remarked. 'I just hand her the Number Two guard and away she goes.'

'I wish mine was that easy.'

'I can ask her if you like? Sure she won't mind an extra customer.'

'At least you haven't got a plook right on your nose,' Bobbie complained. 'I can't believe I'm fifty-five and still getting spots. Has anyone got any concealer?'

'I've got a bag that will just about go over your head, if that helps?' Aiden laughed.

'Come on, guys – get a move on. I've got patients arriving in ten minutes,' Cameron moaned. 'Where's Vanda?'

'She's in the ladies,' said Molly. 'Will I shout for her?'

46

'Yes!'

'Right, I told her to get a shifty.'

Vanda burst into the office wearing her uniform but tarted up in evening make-up, lipstick and full-volume false eyelashes. The high-definition eyebrows gave her a look of surprised anxiety. She sprayed her hair with silver glitter as she hurried in.

'Nice,' Aiden commented with sarcasm. 'I hope you're planning to include a list of your hourly rates on the flyer.'

'I'm just adding a bit of glamour to the team photo.'

'Thanks,' Helga said, dragging a brush through her thick brown hair.

'Right – perhaps we could have Vanda and Aiden sitting in the front and Molly, Helga and Bobbie standing behind?'

'Oi!' Aiden protested. 'Bobbie, your stomach is pushing into the back of my head. I don't want it to look like I've got a massive growth. Stand back a bit.'

'Oh, charming! Maybe I should stand in the office next door. Would that suit you better?'

'In more ways than you can ever imagine,' he snipped.

'Smile,' Cameron instructed. They broke into a cheesy team grin. *Click!*

There was a knock at the door and Chan entered the office. 'Sponsor money!' Helga remembered, grabbing her purse. She counted out the eight pounds. 'Going somewhere special, are they?' she asked pointedly.

'Not really – Almond Valley Farm, I think.'

Helga muttered under her breath. 'Could probably treat the whole class to lunch.'

'Sorry?'

'Nothing. Your son must be very strong-willed.'

'Meaning?'

'To stay quiet for eight hours – that takes some determination.'

'Oh, they're allowed to do it over a week, so it's not so hard.'

'Bloody hell!' Vanda laughed. 'That's as bad as the MeMarathon that you're allowed to run – or even walk – over a year. Jesus, that's like saying I'm going on a diet and I'll forego dessert once a month.'

'The class is trying to be inclusive,' Chan said defensively.

'I bet. Might as well fundraise by saying we'll charge sponsors a pound every time the pupils pause for breath!'

'Anyway – that's not why I'm here,' Chan grumped. 'Have you seen the pool cars?'

'Nope,' Vanda replied. 'Someone mislaid them? I get the bus in so I'm nowhere near the car park.'

'I cycle,' said Aiden.

'Bus,' Molly added.

'I drive but I can't say I noticed anything,' said Helga.

'I hardly know the day of the week,' Bobbie puffed. 'Don't ask me to take notes.'

'Why, what's up with the pool cars?' Aiden asked.

'Nothing *per se*,' said Chan. 'It's just that someone has put a picture of Pingu under the wipers of all the pool cars.'

'So?' Vanda challenged. 'We're always getting flyers for stuff.'

'Maybe,' Chan mused. She held out a piece of paper. 'But it's just a picture of Pingu. No details of a show or an appearance anywhere. Not much of a flyer?'

'I don't have kids.' Vanda shrugged. 'Means nothing to me.'

'Well, I have four and I can tell you that none of them were ever into Pingu,' Molly offered.

'Not even Callum?' Aiden joked.

'Not unless Pingu is a buffed six-foot firefighter.'

'Ah well, that would be Fireman Sam. Now him, I've heard of,' said Vanda.

'So what's the problem, Chan?' Bobbie asked, making herself a coffee.

Chan blew out her cheeks. 'Well, it's not really a *problem*. Just a bit weird. Why would someone come into the car park at night and leave lots of pictures of Pingu? Seems a bit of a wasted effort. Anyway, we've collected them all in now.'

'So seems like something over nothing?'

'Maybe,' Chan acknowledged, leaving the office. 'Thanks for the money.'

'Any time,' Helga replied.

'You don't mean that?' Molly whispered.

'Gosh no!' Helga exhaled. 'I'm steering well clear next time.'

That evening Helga glared at her closed MacBook. She knew she should open it, 'Go to … Page 75' and draft the next paragraph, but she was obsessed with missing anything on Twitter. She scrolled through the day's tweets, pausing briefly to scan what other authors had posted, noting two new book covers. Anyway, how could she concentrate on the next chapter when her Twitter followers were waiting for a titbit of her life? She had already tweeted that week about her upcoming blog tour, and that the follow-up to *Candy Martini Reaches Out* is well underway. If *only*. So she dashed something off about *#ThursdayThoughts* – how book sales were making her spirits soar. Good. Now she could settle down to drafting the next scene. She found her place and reread the last few pages. That's right, following the advice of her manager, Candy had moved to London. The deposits flowing into her account were obscene. She'd been advised to invest in a townhouse and settled on Ilchester Place – frightening how many zeros were included in the sales price. Helga gazed out of the window into the darkness for inspiration. She knew she'd be able to focus better with a hot drink. Yes – she'd make herself yet another cup of coffee. But no point having that instant rubbish – she retrieved a bag of beans and raked out her stone grinder …

'No offence, Helga, but you look like hell,' Molly said, watering the office's neglected plants.

'Didn't sleep too well,' Helga murmured.

'Ah well – bet you're glad it's Friday?'

'Spot on!' Aiden agreed. He wetted a cloth and wiped down his bare legs. 'Those bloody taxis deliberately swerve into the puddles just to spray us cyclists. I feel like I'm in a log flume ride half the time.' He grabbed his uniform and went to get changed. Helga concentrated on her mobile, tweeting *Looking forward to seeing how Candy explores London life this weekend #FridayFeeling*. Ping – two retweets already.

After the morning's run-through Molly held up a trifold leaflet. 'Hot off the press – what do you think of the HIT Squad leaflet I've put together?'

'Jings, that was quick,' Bobbie smiled, munching on a croissant. 'Let me see?'

'I, er,' Molly hesitated.

'Bobbie, she's not going to let you get your greasy paws all over it,' said Aiden, taking it from Molly. 'Wow! Looks great! Cameron has done a good job of the photo.'

'What!' Vanda exclaimed, peering over his shoulder. 'I look like a tranny!'

'I did try to warn you,' Aiden grinned.

'But has he used some kind of filter on me or something?' Vanda protested. 'Why am I so orange?'

'You're not,' Bobbie replied. 'It's just that we're all a slightly whiter shade of pale. If we'd had any warning we could all have done with a wee blast under the tanner.'

'Anyway, we're just in time with the leaflets as Westside is having a Health and Well-being day on Monday,' Molly announced. 'I've spoken to the practice manager and she's going to let us have a table in the main foyer.'

'But we don't just want to speak to any old randoms,' Vanda said.

'I know but apparently all the GPs will be around at lunchtime – that would be the best time to catch them.'

'Okay – so maybe we can do shifts? Helga and Bobbie, do you want to cover the morning and Aiden and I will come along at lunchtime?'

'I can't do Monday afternoon – I'm seeing Mr Wooler.'

'Okay, then take the morning with Bobbie. Helga – you alright for the afternoon?'

'Sure,' she nodded.

'And in the meantime I'll print off loads of leaflets,' Molly offered. 'Helga, there's a letter for you – here you go.'

'Ta.'

'Oh, and Aiden, there's also one for you somewhere.' She rummaged under the notes, passing him an envelope.

'Who's writing me a letter?' he frowned.

'Maybe it contains a nice surprise?'

Aiden shook the letter. 'Nope, there are no twenties in there.'

'Could be a thank-you note?'

He snorted, ripping open the envelope. 'Shit, that's all we need!

It's a complaint from Mrs McGowan's son,' Aiden cursed. 'Says he's unhappy with my decision not to put a shower in – says he's going to take it further.'

'Then let him.' Vanda shrugged. 'You've got nothing to worry about. After all, it's the council's criteria not ours.'

'I know but …'

'What?'

'It's just he's not particularly pleasant to deal with and I need to go back to see Mrs McGowan. I'm just hoping he's not waiting for me with a baseball bat.'

'Hardly!'

'Right, I'm away out,' Helga announced. 'If I don't see you later, hope you all have a good weekend!' Helga crossed the car park, her head bent over her mobile. Message from Mum: `Are you coming for lunch on Sunday? She messaged back: Yes, but got lots of writing to do` ☺

'Naturally you must have lots of writing to do!' her mother said, clearing the table. 'Bestsellers don't write themselves. That's what I've been telling Mags. Oh, by the way, is it still okay for her to come along to the authors' evening?'

'Of course,' Helga replied, scrolling through her notifications. She must remember to tweet something later about it being World Imagination Day. 'Who's Mags again?'

'From my creative writing class, silly!'

'Oh yes.'

'Sometimes she's a bit too intense – goes on about plot twists and gripping protagonists but I just let it all wash over me. I can't get over involved in what *she's* writing – not when I've got my *own* novel on the go. Coffee?'

'Yes, please,' Helga said, distracted. Another rude Direct Message from that awful so-called writer from Skye.

Her mother returned from the kitchen with a tray of coffee and biscuits. Perched on top was a sheaf of papers. She waved it in front of Helga's face. 'The first fifty pages!' she cried triumphantly. 'You must tell me what you think! It's about my tenth rewrite so go easy on me – my nerves won't take too much criticism.'

'But you'll have to get used to that – the world of professional creative writing is cruel. People will say horrid things about your innermost thoughts.'

'I know, darling – but perhaps not from my own daughter?'

Helga took the document and put it in her bag.

'Aren't you going to read it now?'

'Mum, you know I need to get back – I told you. Anyway – here are the two tickets. I best be going.'

'But you've hardly touched your coffee!'

'Sorry, Mum – I have to crack on.'

'Oh well … but before you go. What book title do you think sounds better: *Rose-Marie Gala's Brush With Romance* or *Rose-Marie Gala Touches Love*?'

'Er … Do you have to decide right now?'

'I just think I'd bond with the novel better if I could imagine the book sitting on a shelf at Waterstones.'

'Okay then, I'd go with the second one.'

'Super!'

'Right, I really must be off.'

'Bye, darling – see you at Musselburgh!'

Chapter 7

'How was your weekend?' Aiden asked Bobbie as they loaded up the car.

'Oh, the usual,' Bobbie replied, shoving a bright pink therapeutic ball into the boot.

'What's that for?' Aiden demanded. 'Where am I supposed to put all *my* equipment?'

'Stick it on the back seat and stop your whining. And get a move on – I'm getting soaked here.'

They pulled out of the car park and headed along Gorgie Road, the wipers squeaking against the windscreen.

'What's the usual?'

'Huh?'

'For your weekend?'

'Oh! Well, me pretending to do the housework and shopping and Bob spending most of it down the allotment, making no more effort with his appearance than a hobo.'

'Your husband's called Bob?'

'Yes, what of it?' Bobbie bit into an apple and chewed with her mouth open.

'Isn't that a bit confusing?'

'How do you mean?'

'Well, with you called Bobbie and him Bob?'

'Two completely different names. It's not like we're both called

Tanya or something.'

'Still.'

'So were we supposed to change our names just because we got married? Take a left here cos there are roadworks up ahead and there's a four-way thingy. Anyway, are you telling me there isn't a gay couple in the world both called Daniel? Or Tracey, for that matter?'

'I suppose.'

'Or maybe you'd have them get a tattoo with *Lesbian One* and *Lesbian Two* on their foreheads just to make life easier for you? Life's not all about you, Aiden.'

'Look, I'm just making conversation,' he replied tetchily.

'And you wonder why you're single,' Bobbie tutted, throwing the apple core out of the window.

They arrived at the slick glass and timber healthy living centre sited in the middle of a crumbling council estate. The new-build was an attempt to combine health, social work and community living under one roof, the Open Day providing an opportunity for all departments to promote their services to the public and the centre staff. Gail the practice manager, dressed in a smart black suit, stalked across the foyer to address them. 'Service?' she snapped, clipboard in hand.

'We're the Harrison Intervention Team,' Aiden replied as Gail eyed Bobbie with suspicion. Bobbie smiled, craning her head round the large therapeutic ball that she embraced with podgy hands.

'Table nine.'

Aiden and Bobbie made several trips back and forth from the car park as they set up their stall. 'You can't leave your ball there,' Aiden objected. 'It's blocking our table.'

'Fair enough. I'll stick it behind us and bring it out if someone wants a go. Do you mind if I have a wee nosy at the other stuff?'

'Be my guest.' Aiden reclined in a plastic chair, retrieving his mobile. 'I'll guard the fort.'

Bobbie started at one end and made her way round. All the tables had pop-up banners to sell their services: dementia clubs, benefits advice, physical activity, energy conservation, housing, heart disease support. One corner had been cleared to allow a small group of unemployed, in matching tabards, to demonstrate tai chi. In another recess a dummy lay on the ground, the ambulance service advising a pensioner how to resuscitate his wife. Bobbie's eye was drawn to the dietitians' stall, which was offering healthy snacks. 'Can I help myself?' Bobbie asked boldly.

'Please do,' a teenage student with braces nodded. 'They're health bars.'

'Nice.' Bobbie smiled, shoving three in her pocket. 'What's that?' She pointed to a plastic plate, divided into sections.

'Oh, it's an Eating Well plate. It's to guide people as to how much of each food group they should be having; you know – dairy, protein, fat?'

'But why are the sections so teensy?'

'To control portion size,' the student answered knowledgeably.

'But why are the sections so *teensy*? You know what – forget it.' Bobbie grabbed another two bars and moved on to the next stall.

'Community Food – this is more like it!' She nodded in appreciation at the spread of fruit and veg piled high. A scruffy man with half a beard and muddy hands shifted turnips from one side to the next.

'Come straight from the farm, have you? Bobbie asked.

'Sorry?'

'Been working the land this morning?'

'Not really – just got the bus from Ravelston; why?'

'Oh, no reason. Any freebies?'

'Are you staff or patient?'

'*Der!*' Bobbie pointed at her uniform. 'I'm a physiotherapist!'

'How am I supposed to know?' he grumbled. 'Everyone wears pyjamas out these days. Anyway, staff are allowed two pieces of fruit. The patients can take a mixed bag.'

'Cheers,' Bobbie said, picking up an orange and a banana.

'You've been away for ages,' Aiden griped. 'I'm going to the café to get a coffee.'

'Bring me one back?'

'What do you want?'

'A scone if they've got one. Or a muffin.'

'I meant coffee.'

'Oh – just a skinny latte. I'm watching my weight this week.'

Bobbie turned to her neighbouring table. The attractive woman placed next to her was kitted out in a sterile white tunic and trousers, her platinum hair immaculate. She relaxed with her eyes closed, her hands resting flat on the table, nails beautifully manicured and polished silver. An assortment of oils and lotions were lined up neatly in two rows, a ceramic pot sitting on a small heater. Bobbie couldn't help but pick up the nearest bottle for inspection. '*Essential Lavender Sleep-Easy,*' she read. One of the woman's eyes popped open. 'I was meditating,' she said in a crisp tone.

'Sorry,' Bobbie whispered, replacing the bottle.

'Never mind.'

'What's your thing?' Bobbie asked, peeling her banana.

'My thing?'

'Yes – your service. What do you do?'

'I provide an aromatherapy service for patients. It's incredibly beneficial in relieving stress and pain and facilitating sleep.'

'I thought *you'd* dropped off for a minute!' Bobbie chortled. 'What are you cooking?'

The woman gave a tight smile. 'That's my paraffin hand wax. Again – a lovely experience if you've never had a hand spa before.'

'Can I have a recce?'

'If you must.' The therapist lifted the lid off the pot and Bobbie breathed in the warm waxy smell. 'Yum,' she said. 'I used to love dripping candle wax on to my hand and peeling it off.'

'Quite.'

'Used to be free in my day. Uh-oh – got a customer!'

A pensioner with a wide face and a rigid grey perm leant on Bobbie's table. She was dressed in layers of scarves, jumpers and winter coat, a walking stick hooked over her arm. 'What are you selling?' she croaked.

'We're the Harrison Intervention Team,' Bobbie answered. 'We provide assessment and rehabilitation for people living in this area.'

'Oh, do you now. Got any freebies?'

'Well, I see you have a walking stick there.' Bobbie moved round to the other side of the table, finishing up her banana.

'So?'

'Do you mind if I take a look?'

'Please yourself.' The woman leant on the table again while Bobbie turned the stick upside down. She gave a sharp intake of breath. 'Looky-see! Your ferrule has worn right through.' Bobbie pulled off the worn rubber stop. 'If you carry on using this stick, it'll be like walking on ice. No grip whatsoever!' She dropped her banana skin on the floor and moved it back and forth with her shoe. 'It will be like stepping on this. No matter – I have the very solution for you.' She selected a new ferrule from her collection and pushed it on. Handing back the stick, Bobbie smiled. 'Good as new!'

The woman grunted and continued on her way.

'You're welcome!' Bobbie addressed the back of the coat.

Aiden returned carrying two coffees in paper cups.

'No scones?'

'I'm doing you a favour. Oh, fuck! Don't look now but have you seen who's just coming in?'

'How can I look if I'm not allowed to look?'

The automatic doors opened and a hulking man with bushy black beard, football top and faded jeans pushed a wheelchair through the foyer. A bird of a woman huddled in the chair, gripping the armrests as the man strode past the stalls. Without warning, he jolted to a standstill in front of Bobbie, almost catapulting the woman out of the chair.

'Well, well,' he growled. 'If it isn't Mr Obliging. No speaking today?'

Aiden half looked up. 'Oh, er, good morning, Mr McGowan. And how are *you* Mrs McGowan?'

Mrs McGowan's eyes bulged in panic. 'Oh, I'm—'

'She's very upset,' her son said. He scratched his bald head, where a football stadium had been tattooed across one side.

'Sorry to hear that,' Aiden muttered.

'Yes, apparently you have mandated that she doesn't qualify for a shower.'

'Well, it's not really …'

Mr McGowan held up his hand. 'Listen, sonny. You've had your chance to make it right. Now, we're on our way to see Dr Christie and I'm quite sure he will see things very differently. You seem to think she can manage the bath, no problem.'

'But you *can* manage, can't you, Mrs McGowan? Remember we practised it last week?'

'Oh, I don't know anything,' she warbled. 'My memory is terrible.'

'And you seem to think it's acceptable for her to get in and out of the bath using a plank of wood?' spat her son. 'She's eighty, you know. *And* she has dizzy spells. Did you tell him that, Ma?'

'I, er …'

'Well then, standing in a shower wouldn't be a safe option, either,' Aiden replied.

'Oh, so you're a smartarse now? I wonder how clever you'll feel when Mr Adamson receives a letter of complaint about *you*?' He jabbed Aiden in the chest before wheeling his mother towards the lift.

'*Tosser!*' Aiden coughed into his hand.

One of the tai chi unemployed broke off from the pack and sidled up to the table. 'Do you mind me asking? What's with the pink ball?'

'Oh, that's mine,' Bobbie gushed, trotting round the table again. 'Have you ever tried it?'

'No, but my neighbour swears it's marvellous for alleviating back pain.'

'It most certainly is!' Bobbie agreed. 'What's your name?'

'Gordon.'

'Okay, Gordon, well let's give you a wee shot of Mr Happy – that's what I like to call my Swiss ball.'

'Oh,' he replied nervously.

'Now before we start, we must always do a couple of warm-up

exercises. What must we always do?'

'Warm-up exercises?'

'Very good, Gordon. I can see we're going to get on like a house on fire. So let's see you do a couple of stretches – follow my lead.' Bobbie stretched up, and then to the side, then down, keeping a watchful eye on Gordon, who was stiff as a board.

'Very good,' she encouraged. 'Now have a wee seat on Mr Happy. Don't be shy.'

Gordon lowered himself on to the pink rubber ball as Bobbie held his arm. She placed one hand on his stomach and the other at his back. 'Keep your feet flat on the ground,' she instructed. Now, can you feel your core muscles at work? I want you to roll your bottom forward and back on Mr Happy and make those muscles work.'

'God help us!' Aiden sighed.

'How does that feel?' Bobbie enquired.

'Nice.' He nodded. 'Yeah – good.'

'Okay, we're going to try a couple of exercises now.'

'Shit! Here comes Quinn,' Aiden muttered. Mr Adamson had left his office on the first floor and was leaning over the balcony, surveying his empire below. He gave a smug smile to his audience, descending the stairs towards the stalls.

'*He's* going for gold,' Aiden remarked, taking in Quinn's fitted navy suit, pale yellow shirt and navy polka-dot tie. Bobbie glanced up. 'I expect he's getting his photo taken – any opportunity to have his mug over the front page.' Sure enough, an anoraked photographer was snapping away at the crowd impressed by the revived dummy. Quinn made a pretence of being interested in each of the stalls as he neared.

'That's smashing, Gordon, you're really getting the hang of it. Now, can I let go of you?'

'I'll give it a shot,' he said, hands gripping the ball.

At that point Gail, the practice manager, spied Quinn and hurtled across the foyer to be by his side. Just as she approached Aiden, she skidded, colliding with Mr Happy. Gordon's legs flew upwards, kicking the aromatherapy table with a *whack!* The ceramic pot hurtled into the air, landing squarely on Quinn's chest, the paraffin wax plastering his entire torso and pooling down his trousers. He stood as rigidly as one of Madame Tussauds' celebrity figures. Gordon had landed on Gail and the two grappled on the slippery, waxy floor, as Bobbie hurried to their assistance. 'Ow! I think I've done my back in,' Gordon complained, limping across to the first aid stall. The St Andrews's crew were ill-prepared for such emergencies, with only a few bandages to hand – and offered a caramel wafer as compensation. Gail hauled herself up as though on ice, one stiletto shorn off, her black suit crumpled like a bag of crisps. Grease dripped from her matted hair. Aiden stared open-mouthed.

Gail stumbled towards Quinn. 'Oh my God – Mr Adamson, I am *so* sorry! I don't know what happened. Are you alright?' He remained steadfast in shock. She frantically scanned the area for some plausible explanation for her clumsiness. And she found it. Hobbling towards Bobbie she bent and scooped up the banana skin. 'Who in God's name left a banana skin on the floor?' She wheeled around in anger to blank faces. 'I *mean* it – if I find out who did this I'll … I'll …' She carried the offending item at arm's length as she retreated to her office, sobbing.

Quinn seemed to come to as though slapped in the face. He stared down at his ruined suit. 'How …? What …?' he garbled.

Bobbie stroked his arm. 'Now Mr Adamson, you've had a traumatic experience. Can I suggest you have a wee seat?' She pulled up Mr Happy. 'Here, sit down.'

'I'm not sitting on that!' he cried but was powerless as Bobbie pressed down on his shoulder.

'Now, while I've got your attention,' Bobbie continued. 'You might like to have first sight of our new leaflet? It tells you *all about* the great work we're doing in the Harrison Intervention Team.' She clocked his baffled expression. 'Not to worry,' she said cheerfully, folding the leaflet and tucking it into the breast pocket of his jacket. 'Read it at your leisure!' It was then that the photographer appeared and captured the moment.

'Oh, I just can't wait for the headline!' Vanda laughed as the morning's events were shared. '"Quinn Bounces Back"?'

'"Mr Adamson is on the Ball"?' Aiden suggested.

'What do you think, Helga?' Vanda asked.

'Oh, I don't know. What about "General Manager Waxes Lyrical"?'

'Good one!' Bobbie smiled. 'Anyway, we're heading off now – enjoy your afternoon!' She left, dragging Mr Happy behind her.

Vanda and Helga settled at their table, preparing for the rush, as the centre staff were unleashed on their lunch break. 'Oh, here comes Dr Williamson.' Vanda nudged Helga as a gangling academic in suit and glasses blundered up to their table. He picked up a sock aid, frowned and replaced it. 'Are you the lot that arrange wheelchairs?' he asked.

'Well, that's certainly one of the referrals we can make on behalf of our patients,' Helga answered. 'I'm Helga Trumpet, link worker in the Harrison Intervention Team.'

'Ah – the HIT squad!' he said, sniggering at his own joke. 'Hang on a mo … Helga Trumpet? Are you the writer?'

'Oh yes, you could say that's the other string to my bow!' She glowed.

'Think my wife read one of your books – about a lifestyle guru or some such?'

'*Candy Martini Reaches Out.*'

'Sorry?'

'The title of my debut novel – it's one hundred and fourteen on the bestseller list.'

'Right.'

'If you're interested – the best way to follow me is on Twitter.'

'Hmm, I don't really ...'

Helga rummaged in her bag, retrieving a glossy business card. 'Here you go – it's got all my details: Facebook, Twitter, Instagram, email, website. All you need is there!'

'As I say, I don't really go in for ...'

She held out the card until he relented, accepting it with reluctance. 'Gosh, is that the time?' he murmured, hurrying off.

Vanda gave Helga a dig in the ribs. 'Helga! We're supposed to be handing out team leaflets not flipping business cards!'

'I can't help it if my public wants to interact with me. Don't worry – there's enough of me to go round.'

'Anyway, how do you fancy getting some coffee while I wait here? At least that way we might get rid of some of these damn leaflets.'

'Fair enough,' Helga agreed.

When she returned with the coffees Vanda was already packing up the table, shoving Aiden's gadgets into a rucksack.

'I thought we were here until three?' Helga queried.

'Molly's just called. Miss Lampard's on the floor – her neighbour heard a bump and she went to check it out. Come on, we need to get her up.' She grabbed one of the coffees, hitching the rucksack over her shoulder.

'But wouldn't Bobbie or Aiden be more help?' Helga protested. 'I'm not exactly hands-on.'

Vanda strode out to the car. 'Look, Helga, she just lives over the road. I'm not leaving her on the floor while those two get here – anyway, Aiden's with Mr Wooler this afternoon and he's way over Morningside direction.'

Vanda drew car up outside a row of single-storey box-like flats. Each property looked on to an uninspiring square patch of grass split by a concrete path leading up to the front door. Miss Lampard's lawn was cheered marginally by an ornamental wishing well, moss creeping over the peeling roof. Her neighbour had left the front door unlocked. 'Apparently, she had to rush off to pick up the grandkids,' Vanda explained, opening the door. They crossed the tiny hall into the living room, where the closed curtains left the room in semi-darkness. Vanda flipped on the light.

'Who's there?' Miss Lampard called in a feeble voice from the floor. She lay in a crumpled heap by the coffee table, the TV blaring a rerun of *Escape To The Country*.

'Switch that off, would you?' Vanda instructed. She knelt next to her patient. 'Oh dear, Miss Lampard, what happened to you?'

'Just let me die here,' she whispered.

'Can't let that happen,' Vanda replied cheerfully. 'Now, have you hurt yourself anywhere in particular? Did you bang your head?'

'I'm ready to go.'

'No, you're not.'

'What's that *smell*?' Helga said, wafting a hand in front of her face.

'What do you *think* it is?' Vanda said, through gritted teeth. 'Look, here's a pinny and gloves. Put them on.' She pulled them out of her bag, shoving the thin plastic over her head.

'But I haven't even done any manual handling course yet,' Helga protested. 'Surely I'll do more harm than good.'

'*I'll* do you harm if you don't get off your high horse.'

'Who's on a horse?' Miss Lampard asked. 'Has someone been riding in my garden?'

'Hardly,' Vanda muttered. 'So, you're not sore anywhere?'

'Well, I have a little problem with my rear passage but I don't expect you can help with that. Or can you?'

'I probably can,' Vanda nodded. 'But let's get you back on your chair first, shall we?'

'No – it's my time. I'm going to lie here until the good Lord takes me.'

Helga's phone trilled.

'Helga Trumpet, how may I help you? Oh, hi – yes, now's a good time.'

Vanda held up her two hands. '*What?*'

'Yes, yes, Kate did mention something about that. Oh, wow! That would be amazing! When do you think? This week sometime? Tomorrow? Ah, but I have another commitment tomorrow afternoon. Really? Oh, that would be too bad. Look, I'm sure I can fit it in. Perhaps if you could come to my place of work then I can give you some time? Ah-ha. Yes, yes. And a photo too? I'm sure that will be fine. I—'

'*Helga!*' Vanda hissed.

'Right. Okay, I better go. How exciting! See you tomoz! That was *Scottish Writing* ...' Helga began.

'I don't care if it was the First Minister, we have a problem here.'

'I know I'm a problem,' Miss Lampard lamented. 'I'm a burden to everyone. Just let me slip away.'

Vanda sighed. 'Look, how would you like a nice cup of tea?'

'Oh, that would be lovely. Milk and two sugars.'

'Right, well, you can't drink tea on the floor. How about we sit you in your chair? The good Lord will have to wait for another day. He's got plenty of time on his hands.'

'S'pose.'

'Okay, we're going to help you get on to your hands and knees. I'll pop this cushion under your knees. Very good. Helga – bring that footstool over here. *Helga!* Put your bloody phone away!'

'Sorry, just tweeting while it's fresh in my mind.'

'Now, Miss Lampard, do you think you can get on to this wee stool? Great. Now, we'll help you on to your chair. There! Well done!'

'Ooh, something feels a bit squishy.'

'Yes, perhaps we should go through to the bathroom. Do you think you can manage a short walk? Here's your Zimmer frame.'

'Where's my tea?'

'Helga – stick the kettle on,' Vanda ordered. 'We'll be back in a minute.'

Helga shot into the kitchen, closing the door behind her.

'Can't I have my tea first?' Miss Lampard grumbled.

'By the time we've got you cleaned up, your tea will be ready.'

'What are you like?' Vanda demanded as they drove back to the office.

'I'm a link worker – not a care assistant,' Helga answered scornfully.

'And sometimes that's part of the job.'

'Hmm, I prefer to communicate with words, rather than physical contact.'

'Jesus, Helga. We'd all rather carry a bargepole around but sometimes you just need to get down and dirty.'

'That's why I'm not a nurse. Surely nursing is a calling?'

'Nursing is a *job*. I'm not a bloody nun. It pays a wage – *barely*. Anyway, when you're a famous author I expect you'll need a whole team around you. Got any use for an ex-nurse?'

'Maybe,' Helga smiled.

'Then I'm hanging on to your coat-tails.'

Chapter 8

The following morning Vanda arrived on the first floor as Anver was sticking hazard-warning tape over the door to the ladies toilets.

'Uh-oh! Has Bobbie been on the vindaloo again?' she joked.

'Oh, it's my comedian friend,' he said. 'Toilets are going to be out of use for a few days. I believe there are more downstairs.'

'There are but that involves going through two sets of coded doors. Not particularly handy for us up here.'

'Oh, so not exactly public *conveniences*, then? See, I can make funnies too.'

'Very amusing. So what's the plan?'

'Rob a bank, share the profits and move to Mexico?'

'For the toilets?'

'Oh, well, today I'll get all the tiles off and prep the walls. I'll be back next week to re-tile.'

'Next *week*?'

'You're not the only pretty lady I'm working for.' He winked.

'But why so long?'

'Not that it's any of your business, but my three cousins are coming over from South Africa and I promised to show them around Edinburgh. Perhaps I might even bring them here – it could be the highlight of the tour.'

'But surely you're not the only tiler who can finish the job?'

'Do you want the job done or do you want the job done well?'

'Jings, you could have had the job finished by now if you stopped yakking!' Vanda stormed off in exasperation.

'Have a nice day!' he saluted.

'This is just so weird,' Molly mused out loud. 'What is going on? I come into work and there's a Barney the Dinosaur sitting outside our office.'

'God, that tiler is a slow worker!' Vanda fumed, switching on her PC. 'I'll be up and down those stairs like a fell-runner. Sorry, Molly – what did you say?'

'This.' She waggled a two-foot high purple dinosaur up and down.

'What's that?' Vanda asked, getting up to make a coffee.

Molly put the soft toy in front of her face and moved its paws. 'I'm Barney the Dinosaur!' she said in a cheery voice.

'Is that off *Toy Story*?' Vanda asked.

Molly continued with the American accent. 'I'll have you know I have my *very own* TV show in the US of A. The kids love me!'

'Sorry!' Vanda apologised. 'What are you doing with it?'

'Like I said, it's so weird. I arrived this morning and it was sitting at our office door with a ribbon round its neck, like it was a present.'

'Must be for one of the girls next door?' Vanda suggested. 'Chan's kids are about that age?'

As Bobbie, Helga and Aiden tumbled into the office at the same time, Molly swivelled her chair round. 'Did anyone order a Barney?'

'Oh, so cute!' Bobbie gushed, stroking its head.

Aiden scowled. 'I'm not even going to answer that question.'

'Not guilty,' Helga answered lightly, taking off her coat.

'Oh well, I guess I'll just have to send an 'everyone email'' around. I don't see the point in sending a present unless you say who it's for.'

After lunch, Helga approached Molly. 'Do you think you can help me set up the room for my Tuesday Chatters?'

'Of course – no problem.' Molly leapt up, dropping her sandwich on to her desk.

'Oh, are you still eating?'

'It's no problem,' Molly repeated, wiping her mouth on a napkin. 'I had my lunch late as I had to pop into the school this morning. Caz had gone AWOL.'

'What, again?'

'I know,' sighed Molly. 'She's going through a really difficult time. Her acne's gone mental and she says she's getting bullied. I'm really worried that—'

'Sorry, that's my phone!' Helga interrupted. By the time she had hung up, Molly was brushing the crumbs off her keyboard. Helga lowered her voice so the others wouldn't hear. 'I'm expecting a special guest this afternoon. Someone's coming to interview me from *Scottish Writing*.'

'Ooh, how exciting!' Molly cried.

'What are you two in cahoots about?' Vanda queried. 'Found an unclaimed lottery ticket?'

'Nothing!' Helga said, patting Molly on the shoulder. 'I'll go down just now if you can bring all the tea and coffee stuff with you?'

'Sure thing!'

Chapter 9

He had kicked himself over the Pingu flyers. In hindsight the reference was too obscure – even he acknowledged that. What a waste of colour printing! He chewed his nails thoughtfully. Someone next door was learning to play the drums and it was driving him to distraction. Bang, tap, tap, crash! He needed to focus! His hopes were pinned on Barney – the lovable companion that would stir up memories not far below the surface. A bumbling, self-deprecating purple dinosaur that was big enough to hug adults but not so monstrous to terrify toddlers. He was certain Barney would strike the right chord.

Chapter 10

'Right, Dennis, perhaps if you take your scooter round to the other side, you'll have more room. Maybe if you sit next to Jimmy?' Helga advised.

'Well seeing who's boss around here,' Dennis grumbled, bumping into each of the chairs as he made his way to the other end of the table. Peter jumped up and shook hands vigorously with Dennis and Jimmy. 'My name's Peter.'

'Great. Can I get my arm back?' Dennis muttered.

Harry sucked on her cigarette holder. 'We're being overrun by men here.'

'But no princes so far!' Princess giggled, blushing suddenly when Kamal appeared at the door. 'Sit here if you like?' She offered the chair beside her. Kamal put his head down and took the seat opposite.

'We're still waiting for … oh, here she is. Come in, Lex – you remember some of the people from Tuesday Chatters before?'

She glared at the group, blowing a large blue bubble and popping it with her finger.

'My name's Peter!' he shouted. 'Do you remember me?'

'How could I *clucking* forget?' She slumped on to the chair next to Kamal, giving him a sideways look from under her green fringe.

'Super!' Helga clapped. 'Well, I think that's everyone now. So I'd like to welcome you all to our Tuesday Chatters – our wee group that gets you out of the house and making new friends. So, as a little icebreaker, we're going to go round the group and I want you to say your name and one word that describes you beginning with the same letter as your name.'

'Clucking hell,' said Lex. 'I think I'd rather be grounded.'

'I'll go first to get you all started.' Helga smiled. 'My name's Helga and I'm *helpful*.'

'Can I go next?' Peter's hand shot up. 'I'm Peter and I'm perfect!' He guffawed.

'Pervert, more like,' Lex mumbled.

'Am I next?' Jimmy asked, straightening his tie. 'Well, hello to you all. Can I cheat a bit? My name is Jimmy and I'd say I was a *gentleman*.'

'But that's not—' Peter protested.

'It's fine,' Helga said. 'Welcome, Jimmy.'

'Dennis. I wish I was *dead*!'

'Now, Dennis, I'm sure you don't mean that,' Helga patronised. 'I would say you're Dennis the delightful.'

'Any chance we can get a drink?' Harry asked.

'In a minute,' said Helga. 'Why don't you go next?'

Harry scratched her cheek with her thumb. 'My name's Harry – short for Harriet. I'm hungry.'

'Oh well, you're lucky there. I've brought chocolate fingers to share.'

'Lex,' she muttered into her hoodie. 'I'm loaded.'

'Kamal?' Helga prompted. He stared at the ground. 'Okay, well this is Kamal and I would say he's kind.'

Princess took a large breath as though about to launch into an aria. 'My name is Princess and I would describe myself as pretty!'

'Of course you are! We all think Princess is pretty, don't we?' said Helga.

'Pretty clucking lame.'

'Good-oh, now that's all the introductions done. So please help yourself to a tea or coffee – the kettle's just boiled.'

There was a tentative knock at the door and a young woman in jeans and green tartan shirt stuck her head in. 'I'm looking for Helga Trumpet?'

'That's me!' Helga leapt up.

'Gerry Aitken – *Scottish Writing*. And this is Tony.'

'Yes, come in, come in.'

Following the journalist, a photographer sauntered in, a sizeable camera slung round his neck. Helga ushered them into a corner. 'I thought we could use this space over here. Would you like a tea or coffee?'

'Tea would be lovely – just milk,' Gerry replied, taking a seat and removing a notebook from her bag.

'Yeah – black coffee for me,' Tony answered.

'Righty-oh, make yourselves at home.'

'Who are they?' Peter demanded. 'Are they in the Tuesday Chatters? Why are they sitting over there?'

Helga poured the two drinks. 'No, they're here to see me, Peter.' She handed over the mugs and returned to the group.

'Now, everyone,' she announced. 'I have a little thing I need to do, so what I thought would be a good idea is, if I divide you into pairs and you get started with some games. I've put out a selection on the table. Now, I'm going to suggest Dennis and Jimmy pair up. Harry, perhaps you could take Kamal under your wing? And Lex I'm going to pair you with Princess.'

'What about me?' Peter wailed. 'Who can I go with?'

'Well, perhaps if you take the box of dominoes that's something you can do with Dennis and Jimmy?'

'All right, Helga. And I've got my cola.'

'Smashing. I won't be long.'

'Thanks for accommodating our request.' Gerry extended her hand.

'Not at all – it's a pleasure.'

'Don't mind him,' she nodded to Tony, who was strolling around the room with a light meter, setting off flashes every few seconds.

'Ooh, that's hurting my eyes,' Peter complained.

'Then don't look at him,' Helga tutted. 'Start your game of dominoes.'

'So,' Gerry smiled. 'Your debut novel's been a fantastic success – how does that feel?'

'Well, pretty amazing, really. And totally unexpected. No one was more surprised than me when it reached one hundred and fourteen on the bestseller list.'

'And now you're on to book two?'

'That's right,' Helga nodded, pushing her glasses up the bridge of her nose.

'And are we allowed to know what this one's about?'

'Of course! It's a follow-up to *Candy Martini Reaches Out*. So, if you remember where my last one left off …'

'I haven't actually read it,' Gerry said. 'But carry on.'

'Oh, well, it's about Candy Martini, who was found on a doorstep as a baby and is raised by the Findhorn community in the north of Scotland. Over the years, the village realises she has special talents – she has insight into people's problems and even has psychic powers that she uses to guide people through life—'

'So is this the second novel?' Gerry interrupted.

'No, this is how the story starts. Anyway,' Helga rushed on, 'she helps loads of people and gets quite a reputation in Scotland.

And then this famous American film star gets to hear about her and, when she's filming in London, flies up to Findhorn to meet her. Candy gives her all this great advice and helps her with a specific health problem. And, before you know it, she's all over the newspapers as saving this celebrity's life.'

'So ...' prompted Gerry. 'Book two?'

'Yes, so now Candy is living in London in this swanky townhouse and only needs to have appointments when she feels like it because she has more money than she knows what to do with. I'm thinking I might make her move into humanitarian circles – not just saving lives but saving the world.'

'Interesting. And where do you get your inspiration from?' Gerry asked, sipping her tea.

'That's not fair!' Dennis griped in a loud voice. 'How do you get three blanks and I get none?'

'Dennis! Keep it down,' Helga scolded. 'As I was saying ...'

'Inspiration?'

'Yes, I'd say I pull my ideas from a range of—'

'Cut it out!' Peter whined. 'Give me back my dominoes!'

'Excuse me a minute.' Helga reddened. She strode over to the group. 'Will you keep your voices down!'

'But he stole my dominoes,' Peter protested.

'He's got all the blanks. How is that a fair fight? I'm boxing with one hand tied behind my back.'

'Jimmy?' Helga appealed.

'Look, I'll mix 'em up and we'll start again. Happy?' Jimmy looked at Dennis, who shrugged.

Gerry checked her watch as Helga resumed the interview. 'Perhaps you can say how your success has changed you, if at all?' Gerry queried.

'Oh, well, I like to think that I'm pretty grounded! I wouldn't say that the success has gone to my head.' At that point a domino whizzed past Helga's ear and ricocheted off the wall. She glared at Dennis.

'And now you're trying to balance your writing career with working here?' said Gerry, making a face. 'Isn't that a bit demoralising?'

'Not at all! Well, it's such a rewarding role I have in this team – I'd be loath to leave this all behind. I mean, I feel I have so much more to give.'

'Give it *back*!' Peter cried. Another domino hit the wall.

'But you must need so much patience?' Gerry insisted.

'Oh, well, you know?' Helga gave a saintly smile.

'I didn't want to play *clucking* Buckaroo in the first *clucking* place!' Lex shrieked at Princess.

'Don't shout!' Princess cried. 'I don't like it when people shout.' She covered her ears and wept.

Helga stormed over to the group. 'People, people! *Please*, will you just keep your voices down for five more minutes?'

'But I …' Peter began.

Helga held up one hand. 'Five minutes, that's all I ask. *Please?*' The group quietened. Just as she turned back to the interview, Harry squawked with delight, 'Ha! Straight flush! Get your trousers off, Kamal.'

'Harry, what on earth?'

'I'm only teasing him,' Harry drawled. 'You know I'm just kidding you, right?'

Kamal blanched as he shuffled the pack of cards.

'Look, we're a bit pushed for time,' Gerry announced. 'Any chance we can get a photo?'

'Can I be in a photo, miss?' Peter shouted, standing up.

'Actually, I meant …' stuttered Gerry.

'Have a seat, Peter.'

'Show-off!' Lex grunted.

Tony led Helga by the arm to their corner. 'If you could just stand here, facing this way. Is that how you want your hair to look?'

'Why? What's wrong with it?' she asked, smoothing it down with her hands. Helga maintained a rigid posture as Tony looked through the viewer. 'Do you think you can turn your head towards me? A wee bit more? And relax your shoulders?' Click, click. 'Perhaps if you could lower your chin and turn a wee bit more to the right?' Helga's eyes flitted to the right. '*Duck!*' she shouted at Tony as the pieces of Buckaroo flew up in the air. A stick of dynamite landed on Gerry's head.

'You can take your *clucking* game of Buckaroo and shove it …' Lex growled.

'Right,' snapped Gerry. 'I think it's time we left.'

'Oh, well, have you got everything you need?' Helga fretted.

'More than enough,' Gerry muttered, retrieving the piece of plastic from her hair.

'Call me if you have any other questions,' Helga offered to their retreating figures. She collapsed on to a chair as Harry pushed a cup of coffee in her direction.

'Will they be coming back to our group?' Peter asked. 'I liked them.'

'I very much doubt it,' Helga sighed.

Chapter 11

'So no one seems to know anything about it?' Bobbie asked, lathering butter on to a fruit scone.

'Not a jot.' Molly shrugged.

'Oh, well, what will you do with it?'

'If no one claims it after a few weeks I'll give it to Mandy – she loves soft toys.'

'Yeah, there's nothing kids love more than cuddling up to a massive-skulled carnivore,' Bobbie remarked. 'Is it me or is Arnotts getting stingy with their sultanas?'

'How was your interview?' Molly asked as Helga returned with the tray of dirty mugs. Helga gave a rehearsed smile. 'Just wonderful. I find it so creatively stimulating to interact with the world of media. All the photojournalism and press platforms. And I think the article will provide an excellent springboard to reach a broader audience.'

'That's nice,' Molly smiled. 'By the way – there's more post for you on your desk.'

'Thanks. Look, would you mind washing up the mugs for me? I've got a few things I need to pick up on.'

'Sure,' Molly said, sitting Barney on her chair.

'That's a definite improvement,' Bobbie chortled.

Vanda burst into the office, still on her mobile. '*Shite!* You're kidding me! Tomorrow? Okay, thanks for the tip-off.'

'Scone?' Bobbie offered up her plate with the remaining half.

'Maybe later,' Vanda said, distracted. 'Actually, no, I will.' She grabbed the half-scone and shoved it into her mouth all in one go. Her cheeks bulged as she tipped coffee from a jar into one of the mugs on the draining board.

'I've just washed that!' Molly protested.

'What was that all about?' Bobbie enquired.

Vanda kept chewing as she stirred in milk. 'Bloody Sheba from the South Team is coming over here tomorrow.'

'Don't tell Aiden – he hates her!' Bobbie warned.

'Don't tell me what?' Aiden asked, dumping his rucksack at his desk. 'No – let me guess. Quinn has finally been admitted to an institution and has asked for me specifically to take on his role as general manager? Am I close?'

'Sheba's coming here tomorrow,' Vanda said, swallowing the last of her scone.

'*Fuck!*' he cursed.

'Who's Sheba?' Helga enquired from her corner.

'Sheba and Aiden up a tree, K-I-S-S-I-N-G!' Bobbie sang.

'Cut it out!' Aiden threw a biro at Bobbie. It bounced off her chest on to the floor, where she scooped it up.

'Oh aye?' Vanda grinned. 'Got history with our Sheba have you?'

Aiden ran his hand through his short hair. 'It was two years ago and I still have nightmares.'

'Hilarious!' said Vanda. 'Do tell.'

'As if I'd tell you lot anything,' he groaned. 'You know what, I'm so depressed I'm going home. What time's she coming?'

'First thing, as far as I know. Maybe she wants the element of surprise?'

Aiden shook his head and stormed off.

The following morning Helga could *not* find a space in the car park. She drove around twice, hovering hopefully near people who looked like they were leaving but had just arrived. Why someone had coned off six spaces she had no idea. Reversing into a patient's disabled space, she locked her car and hurried into the building. Vanda came stomping down the stairs as they crossed halfway. 'I forgot the ladies is still out of action,' she panted.

Molly and Chan were standing at the entrance to the office as Helga squeezed between them. 'What's with the parking today?' Helga complained.

'We were just discussing that,' said Molly. 'No one seems to know why those six spaces have been coned off. It's going to create havoc today.'

'Shall I go and move them?' Chan offered.

'Better wait until I check with Quinn's office that he's not planning something we don't know about.'

'Like what?'

'Who knows?' Molly shrugged. 'Maybe he's expecting a royal visit?'

'You think?' asked Chan hopefully. 'I like Kate best. Maybe she's coming to open a building or something?'

Molly snorted. 'You do know Quinn's shutting us down? Hardly likely he's invited the Duchess of Cambridge to witness the demolition of a health centre. It doesn't exactly have the feel-good factor the royals are into.'

'S'pose. Shame, really.'

'Anyway, she's too busy churning out babies at the moment. It's a different kind of cord she's cutting.'

'Huh?'

'Never mind. Oops – here's trouble,' she muttered.

An elfish face with a dark brown helmet of hair appeared at the square of glass at the entrance to the corridor. A hand came up and rapped on the glass. Molly opened the door. 'Can I help you?' she enquired, knowing full well the reason for the visit.

'Sheba Mount – team leader from the South Team. And you are?'

'Molly Peterson, admin worker in the HIT squad.'

Sheba frowned. 'The what?'

'Sorry – the Harrison Intervention Team. It's just it's a bit of a mouthful.'

'That's as may be but you can't go round calling yourself the HIT squad.' She pushed past, her calf-length coat flapping over her uniform like a villain's cloak. Entering the office they passed Helga, who was deep in conversation on her mobile and held the phone awkwardly against her shoulder while scrawling notes on a pad at the same time. Molly hurried over to the kettle and flicked on the switch. 'Coffee?' she offered. Sheba ignored the question as she stood with her hands on her hips and carried out a 360-degree scrutiny of the office. 'It looks more like a bloody jumble sale in here than a clinical workstation!' She frowned, pointing at the raised toilet seats, gel cushions and bath boards piled in one corner. A stack of lever-arch files rattled on an unused commode as she stomped across the office. 'And what, in heaven's name, is this all about?' She jabbed a finger at a poster-sized photo of a male model, the tanned torso naked down to a pair of unzipped bulging jeans. Bobbie had cut out a photo of Aiden's head and glued it on to the body, scrawling 'OT of the Year' in red felt-tip pen over the washboard stomach. 'Och, that's just a bit of banter!' Molly laughed. 'Team spirit, if you like.'

'That sort of unprofessional and lewd behaviour will not be tolerated when you lot are absorbed into *my* team,' Sheba declared.

'Anyway, where is everyone?' She glanced at her fob watch. 'It's eight fifteen!'

'But we don't start until eight thirty,' Molly replied. 'Can I make you a coffee?' She opened the mini-fridge and brought out a pint of milk.

'What the …!" Sheba exclaimed. 'That's a medication refrigerator – its sole purpose is for the safe storage of essential medications.' She peered into the interior. 'Sandwiches! Ketchup!' She poked at a Tupperware box. 'I can't even think what might be in there.'

'Hmm, could be Bobbie's natural yoghurt. She *is* prone to a spot of thrush. Or it could be hummus. Not that she uses that for … oh, here's Vanda back!'

'I bet I'll have shed half a stone by the end of the week,' Vanda announced to the room.

'Sheba Mount,' Sheba barked, extending her hand to Vanda. Vanda dried off her damp hands on her trousers before shaking it limply. 'Vanda Craig, staff nurse.'

'Well, Vanda, I don't know what kind of ship you run here …'

'A sinking one by the looks of it.'

'… but I am very disappointed by what I've seen so far.'

'Eh? What have I missed?'

'You seem to be short of half your team for starters.'

'Sorry about that,' Helga said, hanging up. 'I'm Helga Trumpet – link worker.' She waved from behind her desk. Sheba's eyes narrowed. 'Helga Trumpet? I seem to know that name. Did you ever work in the North Team?'

'She's a famous author!' Molly blurted.

'Ah. I thought it sounded familiar. Should we be grateful you're still contributing to the public sector?'

'Sorry?'

'Thought you'd be living off your commission by now. That kind of bubblegum for the brain sells by the bucketload.'

'Oh, well I ...'

The door code sounded and Aiden appeared, looking like he'd slept on a park bench. He put his head down, strode over to his desk and dropped his rucksack on the floor. Without a word he grabbed his uniform and retreated to the changing room.

'Nice to see you again, Aiden,' Sheba smirked, taking in his Lycra-hugging rear.

'Coffee, Miss Mount?' Molly asked for the third time.

'Just black. And please make sure you wash out the mug first. These draining boards are a breeding ground for harmful bacteria. The last thing the NHS needs is staff going off with staphylococcus.'

'Right,' said Molly, making a show of squeezing washing-up liquid from a great height into a mug. Aiden returned, nodded curtly in Sheba's direction, and made himself a coffee.

'And what have you been doing with yourself these last couple of years?' Sheba enquired.

Aiden coughed, still avoiding eye contact. 'Oh, this and that.'

'I heard you've started your Master's?'

'Yeah, just into my second year.'

'I'll need to watch myself,' Sheba remarked. 'You'll be after my job next.'

'I wish,' Vanda muttered.

'Right, well, let's get down to business, shall we?' Sheba began. 'Gather round everyone – I need your full attention.'

There was a fumbling of the door code as Bobbie reversed into the office. She grasped a bulging Lidl bag-for-life in one hand; the other clutched two walking frames and a croissant was wedged between her teeth. She pushed the door open with her bottom, dragging the walking frames behind her. Molly leapt up to help.

'So,' Sheba said, checking her watch once more. 'You must be Bobbie?'

Bobbie nodded as she dropped the croissant on to her desk like a dog rewarding its master with a gift. 'That's me. Sorry, I didn't catch your name.'

'Sheba Mount.'

'Who?'

'Team leader from the South Team.'

'Do I know you?' Bobbie asked, brushing flakes of pastry on to the floor.

'You will do soon enough – when I take over your team.'

Aiden stifled a groan.

'We'll see,' Vanda challenged. 'It's not a done deal.'

'What do you mean?' Sheba asked, bristling. 'Quinn has reliably informed me—'

'Quinn Schwinn!' Vanda retorted. 'He hasn't got a clue.'

'But he's the general manager and he told me—'

'Look, we might be merging with your team but that doesn't mean you automatically retain the title of team leader.'

Sheba's cheeks flushed. 'But I have the larger team by far. I'm an *experienced* team leader. I have a very specific set of skills and knowledge.'

Bobbie sat down, passing around a box of croissants. 'Don't mind if I do,' Vanda said, biting the end off one. 'As far as I'm aware, there will be a competitive process for the post.'

'That my coffee?' Bobbie asked, leaning across Sheba to retrieve her mug.

Vanda dunked the pastry into her drink. 'Anyway, it's not always size that counts.'

'Go girl!' Bobbie cried. 'I'll start your campaign right now. Vanda for team leader – woo-hoo!'

'Oh dear, is that really the approach you'll be taking?' Sheba said, pursing her lips. 'Disappointing ... but hardly surprising. It's always the same when you analyse an underdog under pressure.'

'Who are you calling a dog?' Vanda growled.

'Look, I came here out of courtesy – to do the right thing and collaborate on this amalgamation. I thought we could all be adult about the situation but I can see I'll have my work cut out forging you into some kind of order. I might even have to escalate my concerns to Mr Adamson.'

'Ooh, that sounds like a threat,' Bobbie said in mock fear.

'Are you going to get out your whip?' Vanda goaded. 'I hear Aiden likes a dominatrix.'

This time Aiden groaned out loud, his head in his hands.

Sheba stood up, scowling at each individual in turn. 'I'm going now but you haven't heard the last of this!' she cried before slamming the door behind her.

'Are you really going for the post of team leader?' Helga asked.

'Not in a million years,' Vanda laughed. 'She's welcome to it. But I just love winding her up.'

'Job done, I'd say,' Aiden sighed, shaking his head.

A knock at the door silenced their laughter. 'For Christ's sake, don't let her back in!' Aiden shouted. Molly checked the spyhole. 'Don't worry, it's only Chan.' She opened the door as Chan hovered at the entrance. 'Just a wee update about the cordoned-off parking bay.'

'Oh yes?' Molly said, propping the door open with her foot.

'I asked Ray about it and he said he got a call early this morning – about half seven – and was just told to make sure the cones were put out so that no one could park near the centre.'

'Well, who called him?'

'He said he didn't catch the name. It was a man and when Ray started asking questions he just said that they were Mr Adamson's orders. He wasn't about to challenge that so he did as he was told.'

'How strange,' Molly mused.

'I said didn't he even ask what it was for,' Chan recounted. 'But then he got all uppity and said he'd had enough of everyone treating him like an idiot. So, anyway, I've moved them.'

'Right, well, thanks for that.' Molly closed the door and went back to her PC. 'Hey, guys!' she exclaimed. 'Rapid response in! Dr Shah has scanned a referral through for a Mr Dingwall at Baberton Road South.' She handed the referral to Aiden.

'Looks like this might be one for you, Vanda,' Aiden said, reading through the referral. 'Discharged from hospital last week following hip surgery – leaky wound looks like it might be infected. Dr Shah visited this morning and said he was having difficulty mobilising because of the pain but is adamant he's not going back to hospital.'

'You and Bobbie'll need to go,' Vanda said, finishing off her coffee and tossing the mug into the sink. 'I've got to go and check on Miss Sutherland's diabetes – her blood sugars have been all over the place and she keeps getting in a muddle with her meds. If you can go and assess him and I'll try and go this afternoon?'

Aiden nodded. 'Right, Bobster – looks like it's you and I.' Bobbie read over his shoulder. 'Seems like he's not managing with the two sticks. Lucky I brought in a couple of Zimmers. By the way, do you mind if we pop into B&Q? Bob's asked me to bring some slug pellets back.'

'We're not going on a bloody shopping outing!' Aiden protested.

Bobbie ran her hand over his cropped hair. 'Keep your hair on,

Aiden – it's on the way to Baberton.'

'I'm not going on *the way* to a rapid-response call!'

'No, daftie, I meant on the way back!' She winked at Molly, picking up a walking frame.

Chapter 12

'Turn left here,' Bobbie instructed. 'Maoam sweetie?' she offered, chewing with her mouth open.

'I *am* turning left here,' Aiden replied irritably.

'But you haven't got your indicator on.'

'Well, there's no one behind me, smarty-pants. And did you know that it's a minor on the driving test if you indicate unnecessarily?'

'Is it? Anyway, you'll need to go under the bridge – they've closed off the main road for resurfacing.'

'Jesus! You can tell it's near the end of the financial year. Every bloody road in Edinburgh is being resurfaced.'

'Anyway, Sheba looks like she's still got the hots for you,' Bobbie needled.

'Shut up about Sheba!'

'Were you in love?' Bobbie grinned. 'I heard she was pretty head over heels with you.'

'Who told you that?' he growled.

'Laura Ting. Said she knew when you were both working at the Royal that you'd had a fling with the Queen of Sheba.'

'Bloody Laura and her big mouth!'

'Is it true that she used to make you put your uniform on when you were—'

'Bobbie! I mean it!'

'Just asking.'

'And don't utter a word about it to anyone at Harrison.'

'As if,' Bobbie tutted – she and he both knowing it was too late.

Aiden pressed the doorbell twice. 'There should be a Mrs Dingwall about. I doubt she'll have gone out if her husband's unwell.'

'Here's the key safe number,' Bobbie said. 'Six-nine-one-two.' They opened the door and entered the hallway. 'Hello?' Aiden called. 'Anyone home?' They checked the empty living room and kitchen downstairs. 'Hello?' Bobbie boomed.

'Up here.' They heard a gruff voice coming from upstairs.

'Hello?' Bobbie called again as they reached the landing. 'I'm in the bedroom,' a voice answered. Aiden and Bobbie exchanged a look. Aiden tapped on the door as they entered the main bedroom. The plain, sparsely furnished room smelt stale. In one corner stood a carved oak wardrobe, where a woollen overcoat hung from a coat hanger. Little daylight found its way through the small square window that looked on to a grey sky. Centre stage was a wrought-iron bed, where an elderly man with a florid complexion reclined in navy pyjamas. A wisp of cotton wool hair stuck to the top of his head. His knobbly hands looked to be held in prayer. It was then that the team clocked the chrome handcuffs round Mr Dingwall's wrists, fastening him to the bedstead. Bobbie and Aiden took in the scene with mild surprise, Bobbie recovering quickly. 'Mind if I put the light on?'

'Not at all. Please come in. Thank God you're here. I'm Bill Dingwall,' he gasped in relief.

'Good morning, Mr Dingwall,' Aiden said. 'I'm Aiden – an occupational therapist from the Harrison Intervention Team – and this is my colleague Bobbie, who's a physiotherapist.'

'Please call me Bill. Yes, Dr Shah said we might be expecting you.'

'Do you mind if we join you on the bed?' Bobbie asked.

'Absolutely not! I do hope you can help me,' Mr Dingwall said. 'I'd offer you a cup of tea but, as you can see, I'm rather indisposed at the moment.' He rattled the handcuffs.

'Er,' Aiden said, rather at a loss for words. 'Is this, er, normal for you?' he enquired, wondering if the patient was being held captive in his own home. And why hadn't Dr Shah mentioned this in the referral?

The old man chuckled. 'I expect it does look rather queer.'

'We've seen it all before,' Bobbie said. 'Rarely does anything surprise us. Still, if we can help in any way?'

'Well, what it is,' he began to explain. 'Look, would you mind passing me that glass of water? I'm parched and have been longing for a wee sip.'

Bobbie rolled off the bed and fetched the glass from the bedside table. She held it up to his dry lips. 'Ah! Nectar!' he sighed. Bobbie bounced back on to the bed, almost catapulting Aiden off the other side.

'Where was I? Oh yes, well after Dr Shah left I knew she was determined to re-admit me to hospital. I couldn't have that. Poor Agnes, my wife, got taken into a nursing home while I was in the Royal. I fell and broke my hip a couple of weeks ago.'

'Yes, so we see from your notes,' Aiden commented.

'Agnes was a bit muddled before I went in. I normally look after her – do all the shopping and cooking and whatnot. She couldn't be left alone so she got taken off to some God-awful place. They brought her home the same day I got discharged and I barely recognised her – apart from anything, she was wearing someone else's clothes. Now she's gone doolally. I can't risk going back in and her being carted off again. So I asked her to fasten my hands to the bed as a bit of a protest. I wanted to make my point,' he said drily. 'Like a suffragette.'

'Well, I think you've definitely made your point,' Aiden smiled. 'So let's get you out of those, shall we?'

'But that's the problem!' Mr Dingwall wailed. Agnes locked me up ages ago and has gone off with the key. I've no idea where she is. I've been shouting until I'm hoarse.'

'She wasn't downstairs,' Bobbie frowned. 'We checked all the rooms first.'

'She must have gone into the garden. We've got a wee greenhouse round the back. She loves it out there – even in the winter.'

Aiden inspected the restraints. 'These are pretty heavy-duty handcuffs.'

'Like you'd know!' Bobbie sniggered. 'Mind you, I did hear that Sheba was into—'

'Bobbie!' Aiden hissed. 'Not *here!*'

'I used to be a copper,' said Mr Dingwall proudly. 'I still have my badge, whistle and truncheon too. They were the tools of the trade. They won't pull apart without the key.'

'Don't worry,' Bobbie said. 'I'll go and find – did you say Agnes is her name?'

'That's right. Oh, and I hate to be a pest,' said Bill shamefacedly, 'but would you mind passing up my bottle. I've been trying to hold it in for ages.'

Aiden searched under the bed, retrieving a plastic urinal. He was about to pass it to Mr Dingwall, who coughed. 'So sorry, young man. But would you mind doing the honours?'

Aiden sighed as he unbuttoned Mr Dingwall's pyjama bottoms.

'Right, I'll leave you to it.'

Bobbie retreated down the stairs and headed for the back door, which remained slightly ajar. She spotted the greenhouse at the foot of the well-kept garden. Mrs Dingwall seemed to be bent over some plants, although the glass around her had fogged up. Bobbie appeared at the open door. 'Agnes?' she enquired.

'*Wah!*' the woman screamed. A trowel flew out of her hand and cracked a pane.

'Oh! I'm sorry to give you a fright,' Bobbie said, entering the greenhouse. Agnes stepped back in horror, tripped over a ceramic pot and landed on a bag of compost. Bobbie rushed forward to assist. 'I'm not going back!' Agnes screamed. 'Help! *Help!* Police!'

'Shh!' Bobbie said, giving her winning smile. 'Here, let me help you up.'

The frail woman, wearing a thin cotton nightdress with a fleece over the top, cowered in the corner. '*Murder!*' she screeched. Frantically looking around for a weapon, her hand grasped a pair of secateurs. She wielded them at Bobbie. 'Please don't take me away,' she begged.

Then the penny dropped. Bobbie looked down at her uniform. She bent forward and, in a patronising tone, said loudly, 'Hello, Agnes, my name is Bobbie and I'm a physiotherapist. I've come to help your husband, Bill.'

'Bill?' she asked, still brandishing the garden tool. 'Where's Bill? Take me to Bill.'

Bobbie extended her hand. 'Come on, then, let me help you up.' Mrs Dingwall reluctantly allowed Bobbie to assist her to her slippered feet. 'Gosh, you're freezing,' Bobbie said, rubbing the woman's bony hands. 'Let's get you inside and I'll pop the kettle on.' She led Mrs Dingwall back into the warm kitchen and filled the kettle.

'Where's Bill?' Mrs Dingwall asked anxiously.

'He's upstairs in the bedroom,' said Bobbie, wanting to add – *where you left him*!

'Where's the bedroom?'

Bobbie took her hand again and led her upstairs.

'There's Bill!' Mrs Dingwall announced in surprise.

'Hello, love,' Mr Dingwall smiled. 'Now, where did you put the key to these?' He shook the cuffs.

'What's happened to you?' she asked, approaching his side of the bed. She glared at Aiden. 'I don't know who you are but you release my husband this instant!' she cried, swiping at Aiden's head. 'I don't care if you're trying to rob us – I'm giving you nothing. Let – him – go!' She punched Aiden's arm with each word.

'Aya!' Aiden protested.

'Agnes! Calm down,' Mr Dingwall said. 'These young people are here to help us.'

'Don't be ridiculous!' she snapped. 'How long have they kept you prisoner?' And then a thought dawned on her. 'Have you been locked up here the whole time I was in the slammer?'

'Agnes, it was a very nice nursing home. An *expensive* nursing home. The staff were lovely to you.'

'Pah!' she snorted. 'The food was leftover slops and they locked me in a room with a crazy every night. Now you tell me how that's different from jail?'

'Right then, let's all just take a deep breath,' Bobbie said. 'No one is keeping anyone hostage and no one is being forced to leave this house.' *Some people ain't leaving this* room, she thought. 'Why don't I make everyone a nice cup of tea, while you have a wee look for the key?'

'Good idea,' Mr Dingwall said. 'You might want to check the

drawers in the kitchen – that's where we normally keep the keys.'

Four mugs of tea and half a packet of Party Rings later they were no further forward. Bobbie and Aiden had checked every nook and cranny in the house with no sign of the key – although Mrs Dingwall was pleasantly surprised when Bobbie produced a lower denture that had been missing for months from the side of the couch.

'There's nothing for it but to call the fire brigade,' Aiden sighed. 'We've checked everywhere.'

'Oh dear, do you really think so?' Mr Dingwall fretted. 'It would be such a waste of emergency service time. We hated it when we got hoax calls.'

'It's hardly a hoax!' Bobbie said. 'If you don't move soon, you will really start to stiffen up. And then you'll be stuck upstairs even longer.'

'I feel such a fool. What was I thinking?' Tears sprang into his pale eyes.

'It's only because you care about each other so much,' said Bobbie. 'I think it's quite touching.'

'I suppose,' he nodded.

Bobbie turned to Mrs Dingwall. 'I'm saying – you must love Mr Dingwall very much?'

'Who?'

'Mr Dingwall – Bill.'

'Oh, him. Anyway, I'm just going downstairs to watch a bit of television.'

Aiden made the call and within minutes a fire engine rumbled to a halt outside. Bobbie wasn't entirely convinced it required three firefighters to traipse up the stairs into the already crammed bedroom. She overheard one of them chortle, 'I don't think it's quite what that writer meant when she called it *Fifty Shades of*

Grey!' They offered to carry Mr Dingwall down the stairs but Bobbie informed them that wouldn't be necessary, and they left with grateful thanks and the remaining Party Rings.

Helga gazed out at the patchy darkness that surrounded the health centre. She heard the swish of cars as they swept up and down the terrace, and lights prickled on in tenement flats as occupants returned from work.

'Penny for them?' Vanda asked, switching off her PC.

'Oh, just got a lot going on at the moment,' Helga blustered, realising she'd been sitting in front of her spiralling screen saver for too long.

'I bet! The giddy life of an international bestseller!' Vanda checked her reflection in the mirror and swiped scarlet lip gloss across her pouting lips.

'Got a date?' Helga enquired, shoogling her mouse. The screen sprang to life.

'I most certainly have.' She grinned, shoving her arms into a duvet jacket.

'First date?'

'Second, actually. We went out on Saturday night and seemingly he can't wait till next weekend.'

'And who is this young man?'

'He's called Craig and is working at the gym at Edinburgh Uni. He's well fit.'

'Wouldn't it be amusing if you got married and *he* took *your* name – then he'd be Craig Craig!'

'What are you on about?' Vanda frowned. 'Who's talking about marriage? We're just going for a pint. Anyway, I'm seeing Ash on Thursday and he's more my type.'

'Vanda!'

'Well, I'm off. Don't work too late.'

Helga's hand continued to rest on the mouse as one by one the offices emptied. She glanced at her mobile as it vibrated brashly on her desk. It was Kate. *Again*. Looking for the final two blogs for the blog tour. Helga had winced at Kate's impatience, her stomach churning at the thought of having to call her back. She reluctantly switched off her PC and the office lights. By the time she'd fought her way home through the chugging rush hour, it was past six. She drove round the block twice before snatching a parking space along the road. Without a backward glance, she hurried on up the stairs to her tiny flat, turning both locks behind her. There was something odd about that car following her round the block – unless that person was also looking for a space? She dumped her bag and headed for the narrow galley kitchen. Surely she'd be able to concentrate better if she had something to eat? She filled a saucepan with water and reached for the pasta jar but could still hear her phone pinging even from where she'd abandoned it on the settee. Relenting, she retrieved her mobile. Need to keep in touch with her community – mustn't ignore the fans' retweets and direct messages. Not to mention that it had been a week since she'd last posted on her Facebook page. It was almost nine before she typed in *Blog Four – What Makes Candy Tick?*

Chapter 13

The next morning Helga hurtled into the health centre, guiltily checking her watch. She arrived to find a commotion. Chan sat in the centre of their office in tears, cradling a mug of tea. Molly had her arm round her and was offering soothing sounds. Vanda, Bobbie and Aiden had their chairs pulled into a circle. 'What's going on?' Helga asked, reaching for her favourite mug.

'It's Ray. He's been having a right go at Chan,' Molly said, shaking her head. On cue, Chan wailed a decibel higher.

'What for?'

'There's a nutter on the loose,' Vanda said.

'Chan came in early this morning,' Molly recounted. 'And all the lights were on in the offices along our corridor. She, quite rightly, rang Ray to ask him what he's playing at. I mean – his job is to ensure all the lights are turned *off* at night. He went mad, apparently – raged at her for accusing him of not doing his job properly. Says he's going to get the union on to her.'

'Well, I put our lights off when I left,' Helga reported. 'So if they were on this morning, he obviously came in and switched them back on.'

'Why would he do that?' Aiden wondered.

'Maybe he got sidetracked?'

'Anyway, I've reported the incident to Mr Adamson and he's sending Norman over,' said Molly, handing Chan another tissue.

'Who's Norman?' Helga asked.

'You mean you haven't met Norman yet?' Vanda said askance. 'How have you managed to avoid him?'

'He's our building security manager – covers all the health centres in the west,' Molly said.

'Did you not meet him as part of your induction?' Vanda said. 'He gives *everyone* the crime-prevention talk. More like lecture. He goes on for two hours.'

'When I sat through his talk,' Bobbie chipped in. 'He went on so long we had to send out for sandwiches.'

'To be fair – that could have just been down to you,' Vanda said. Bobbie shrugged. 'But have you ever felt the need to check under the pool car for bombs?'

'Eh?' Molly screwed up her face.

'Oh yes, we covered everything from homeland security, to cyber crime to demonstrating the best way to apply a bike lock.' Bobbie rolled her eyes.

'He's on his way,' Molly said. 'And we've all to stay here until he's spoken to us. Aiden, I've cancelled your ten o'clock with Miss Forbes.'

'Cheers.'

'Might as well have a bit of breakfast while I'm waiting,' said Bobbie, popping two slices of bread into the toaster.

'Don't take this the wrong way,' Molly said as Helga stored her lunchbox in the fridge. 'But you're going to have to stop pulling these all-nighters.'

'Is it that obvious?'

'The moon has fewer dark rings than you do.'

'I just need to get through this week.'

'You've got another letter on your desk.'

Molly jumped into the air as the buzzer sounded loudly. 'That'll be Norman.'

She ushered him into the office. Norman was a stout man in his mid-fifties, with a balding head but bristling sideburns over his flushed cheeks. The blue cotton shirt, stretched tautly round his bulging girth, had damp patches under the arms. Bunches of keys jangled from every loophole round his waist. Smoothing down his handful of grey hairs, he commanded the centre of the room.

'Have a seat, Norman. Coffee?' Molly offered.

'Thank you – that would be most appreciated,' he said in a grave voice. The plastic chair creaked under his weight. 'We might be some time.' He withdrew a notepad from his breast pocket, retrieving a biro from behind his ear.

'How long is "some time"?' Aiden asked. 'We've all got patients needing to be seen.'

Norman let out a puff of air. 'Sonny, the patients will just have to wait. There has been a serious breach of protocol here. I am obliged to follow due process. Might as well make yourselves comfortable.'

'I'm very comfy, thank you,' Bobbie said. She put her feet up on her desk and chomped her way through a mound of buttered toast.

'If you don't mind I'd like to take a note of your names and ranks,' Norman said, licking the nib of the biro.

'Aiden's rank.' Bobbie laughed with her mouth full.

'Right, missy, I'll start with you.' Norman glared at Bobbie.

Helga's mobile blared from her bag. 'Sorry, got to take this,' she apologised, ducking back behind her desk.

'Right, well, now that we've got the formalities done, would someone like to explain what's been going on?' Norman's head swivelled like a barn owl. Chan took a gulp of air and repeated the morning's conversation with Ray.

'Now I have spoken to Ray this morning,' Norman said, proud of himself. 'And I *do* know him fairly well. If he says he didn't leave the lights on, then I believe him.'

Aiden snorted. 'You should take up jury duty for a living.'

'So what we have here,' said Norman, ignoring the jibe, 'is the risk of penetration.'

'I'm sorry,' Bobbie giggled, 'but chance'd be a fine thing.'

'A penetration of our *security*,' Norman emphasised. 'We have a serious breach scenario *vis-à-vis* this property. If someone has entered the premises and left all the lights on, what other crimes may have been committed?'

'Such as?' Vanda asked. She jigged her legs impatiently.

'For instance, is anything stolen? Anything disrupted? Apart from which, a person of unknown identity has had the opportunity to browse confidential information.' Norman jabbed his biro towards the whiteboard, where the week's appointments were listed.

'Don't you think we would have reported a break-in?' Vanda tutted. 'As far as we can tell Ray went about his usual business last night and, for whatever reason, forgot to switch the lights off behind him. Maybe he's deliriously in love? Maybe he was fantasising about the saveloy sausage he was having for dinner? It's surely no more a threat to national security than that?'

'But what about the other incidents?' Chan suggested meekly.

Norman pounced. 'What *other* incidents?'

Aiden let out a groan. 'Better cancel all the morning's appointments, Molly.'

Norman flipped over on to a new page. 'Why don't we start at the beginning?'

'I need another coffee,' Vanda sighed.

'Well,' Chan started. 'It all began a couple of weeks ago.' She reeled off the appearance of the pointless flyers, the delivery of the unclaimed Barney and finally the hoax phone call requesting the reservation of the parking spaces.

'Very strange goings-on,' Norman muttered, chewing on his pen. 'So have you been aware of anyone unusual hanging around the health centre these last couple of weeks?'

'No comment!' Bobbie sniggered. 'You don't have enough paper to list all the weirdos we see around here. Molly, remember that time I found one of the patients sitting out on the bench?'

'Oh yes!' she laughed.

'So?' Norman frowned.

'So nothing – except that he was stark naked.'

'Oh, now I know who you mean,' Vanda nodded. 'The bloke who got his testicles stuck between the slats?'

'Don't remind me,' Aiden said. 'You weren't the one who had to remove the splinters!'

Norman winced. 'So could it have been this chappie?'

'No chance,' Vanda replied. 'Mr Findlay can't do stairs.'

'Well, what about anyone new who's started working here?'

'How about that tiler bloke?' Vanda suggested. 'He just popped up recently – and my granny would make a more convincing tradesman. He looks like he's just stepped off a cruise ship.'

'That's true. He calls himself Anver,' Molly stated as Norman wrote furiously. 'And what about that student girl downstairs? She never says good morning.'

'I hardly think a student nurse is going to wage a war of terror whilst on placement!' Vanda shook her head. 'What would be the point?'

'I still think that Ray bloke is the weirdest person here,' Bobbie said.

Norman frowned. 'But why would he make hoax calls to himself?'

'Sorry, what did I miss?' Helga rejoined the group.

'We were just listing potential suspects,' said Norman.

'And I nominated Ray.'

'Yes, he is rather evasive,' Helga nodded. 'And the other evening, when I was leaving late, he was just coming *into* the building.'

'Was he now?' breathed Molly, coming over all *Crimewatch*. 'What time was that?'

'Late-ish.' Helga shrugged. 'Maybe half six?'

'Well, there you go!' Vanda crowed. 'What was he doing here at that time of night? He does all the facilities stuff – why would he be hanging around here in the evening?'

Norman scratched his armpit with the biro. He shook his head. 'I just can't see it.'

'Show him the dinosaur,' Chan urged.

Molly fetched it from her desk and handed it to Norman. He turned the soft toy, with the ribbon round its neck, at arm's length as though it were about to explode. 'Have you got any plastic bags?'

'Of course.' Molly peeled one off a roll.

Norman dropped the toy into the bag and knotted the top.

'Sending it off to forensics?' Bobbie asked, winking at the others.

'I will be examining it under laboratory conditions – yes,' Norman nodded.

'I hope it doesn't belong to anyone,' Chan said anxiously.

'I wouldn't like to tell someone that their thoughtful gift has had its head pulled off,' Aiden remarked. 'And why would it have anything to do with Ray being a lazy bastard?'

Finally, after using his pen to poke and scrutinise every inch of the offices along the corridor, Norman was evicted from the building.

'Jesus, Chan!' Vanda complained. 'Next time you come into work and all the lights are on, just bloody switch them off!'

'I'm sorry,' Chan snivelled, heading back next door.

He took cover from the street, half concealed in a tenement doorway that smelt of piss. It was almost lunchtime and the school kids would be swarming past soon on the way to the chip shop. His blasted mobile began vibrating in his pocket. He tried to ignore the incessant *zzz zzz zzz zzz* as a bus pulled in at the bus stop. A ping indicated a text. He glanced at the screen – Mum. Pulling his cap further down, he watched from the other side of the road as the uniformed guard ambled back to his estate car and drove off. *Finally* – someone had been alerted. And he'd been inside for most of the morning. Good.

Chapter 14

The following week Helga stood at the sink washing out her lunch box. 'Where's Molly?'

'I think she went over to the GPs to hand out the new leaflets. At least, she went out the door with a boxful – could be using them to paper her living room,' said Bobbie. 'Why?'

'She normally helps me set up the room for my Tuesday Chatters group,' Helga replied.

'Sorry, but with me having to get that bloody tooth seen to this morning *and* having to pay a fortune for the pleasure, I'm running late. I'm going to have to squash all my day's visits into the afternoon.'

'Oh well.' Helga found a tray and banged down mugs, opening and shutting the cupboard doors. She continued to ferry trayloads under the watchful eye of Peter, who had arrived early. 'Need a hand, miss?' he offered, raising his hand.

'No, I'm nearly done.'

'Just as well. My mum says I'm a right Clumsy Clarence. What are we doing today, miss? Can I get my photo taken this week?'

'I'll explain when everyone gets here.'

'What are the magazines for, miss?'

Helga gave a thin smile. 'I'll be back in a minute, Peter. Just need to fetch something else.'

'Will I just wait here, then?'

Jimmy shuffled into the room, removing his woollen hat and shaking off a dusting of snow from his winter coat. 'Afternoon,' he smiled, rubbing his hands together. 'That wind's straight from the north.'

'Is it?' Peter asked. 'Are you good with weather?'

'Not particularly. But it's brought the snow with it.'

'My name's Peter.'

'Yes – we met last week. I'm Jimmy.'

'Can you walk now?'

'I beg your pardon?'

'Well, last week you were on one of them scooters.'

'That was Dennis.'

'Oh yes – the one who wishes he was dead.'

'We all wish we were fricking dead,' Lex mumbled, sidling on to a seat.

'Aren't you freezing?' Jimmy asked. 'Look at you with your thin little jacket.'

'I'm not allowed outside – I get picked up by a fricking taxi like some sad day case.'

'Sad day case?' Harry repeated. 'Hello, Peter.'

Helga returned with her MacBook as Kamal slipped in behind her. There was a crash at the door and Dennis could be heard cursing. 'Has someone bloody narrowed the doorframe since last week? Just about took the skin off my knuckles.' He barged into chairs as he headed to the other end of the table.

'Now we're just waiting for—' Helga began.

'So sorry I'm late,' panted Princess, bouncing into the room. She unzipped her red fleece to reveal a full-length Princess Elsa outfit – a long, turquoise shimmering dress complete with silver cloak. She beamed as she sat down. 'I've just been out buying my birthday outfit for next week and I was so pleased with it Mummy let me wear it here. Isn't it gorgeous?'

'But it's so flimsy,' Jimmy commented. 'Aren't you frozen?'

'Exactly!' She grinned. 'Well done, Jimmy. I didn't think old people knew about that sort of stuff.'

'What sort of stuff? Getting cold? It's all I ever think about when I go outside.'

'Who's getting a cold?' Dennis demanded. 'Don't bloody sit next to me. The last thing I need is someone coughing and spluttering in my face.'

'Anyway!' Helga said, rapping the table. 'Welcome to our Tuesday Chatters. I hope you've all had a good week?'

'What are the magazines for, miss?' Peter repeated.

'I'll get to that shortly,' Helga answered. 'Shall we all get a hot drink first?'

'I can't reach from here,' Dennis grumbled. 'Will someone give me a coffee?'

'Ah!' Peter cried. 'But you told us not to give you any coughing!'

'*Coffee!* You dimwit!' Dennis retorted.

'Now, now,' said Helga. 'I'll get you your drink. How do you like it?'

'With whisky.'

'Hear, hear,' Harry agreed. 'I keep asking for something more substantial but alas nothing has appeared.'

'Kamal, would you like a drink?' Helga offered. He shook his head, looking down at the floor.

'What's the point in asking a mute to join a social group?' Dennis asked.

'He's not a fricking mute!' Lex leapt to Kamal's defence. She looked at him from behind her green fringe. '*Are* you?'

He shook his head again.

'Maybe the lad's shy?' Jimmy added. 'He'll come round in his own time.'

'My mummy says *I'm* shy,' Princess said. She fiddled with her plaited hair. 'She says that's why I haven't met a prince yet.'

'Really?' asked Harry. '*That's* the reason?'

'Okay, so as Peter has mentioned – you'll see I've brought down a whole pile of magazines,' Helga said. 'What we're going to do this afternoon is take a blank piece of paper each.' She handed them out. 'I want you to go through the magazines and cut out any picture or word or photo that you think says something about you. Then, we'll go round the group and each say a bit more about ourselves. Is that clear?'

'Fricking hell!' Lex complained. 'I've bloody died and gone to therapy.'

'*What* do you want us to do?' Dennis asked. 'Cut out pictures and stick them on paper like bloody nursery children?'

'Do you need help?' Princess asked. 'Here, I'll help you.'

'No, I don't need bloody help,' Dennis said. 'I need a bloody shotgun to put us all out of our misery. Jesus wept!'

'Now, Dennis,' Helga said patiently. 'Just think about what you normally do of an afternoon. You sit in your bedroom looking at the four walls. Now, we're all having a jolly time here. I think, once you get started, you'll find it very absorbing.'

Lex snorted. 'I wish I'd fricking been charged with shoplifting.'

As the group reached for magazines, glue and scissors, Helga opened up her MacBook. She clicked on her documents. *Blog Five: How I Meet My Deadlines.* She frowned in concentration as her fingers hovered above the keyboard. *I love it when my agent presents me with a deadline*, she wrote. *It provides me with the focus I require. Some writers find this creates unnecessary pressure but I welcome it with—*

'Cut it out!' Peter cried. 'Helga, Dennis keeps taking the glue when I need it.'

'I am cutting it out,' Dennis responded smugly. 'Isn't that what we've been asked to do? Cut it out?'

'There's plenty of glue to go round,' Helga called across. 'Please just share it.'

She reread her blog. *The best thing to do is set aside some time and absolutely stick to—*

'It keeps sticking to my fingers!' Peter exclaimed.

Helga blocked out the commotion as Peter thrashed his hands. *… absolutely stick to your plan. Another way to ensure I manage my workload is by having a Blog Day. One day a week that I allocate to this task. Blogs are a key way to communicate with my readers—*

'I wish I'd brought my readers,' Jimmy grumbled. 'No one mentioned I'd be reading anything.' He turned to Harry. 'Does that say *IMPORTANT* or *IMPORTED*?'

'It says *impotent*,' Harry replied. 'But feel free to glue it on. We're all friends here.'

'No, I …' Jimmy discarded the cutting.

'Hey, Princess!' Peter called. 'Here's a photo of a pretty lady. Do you want it for your collage?'

'Oh, yes, please!'

'That's fricking Theresa May!' Lex guffawed.

'Who?'

'The fricking prime minister!'

Peter frowned. 'I thought that was Nicola Splurger?'

'Sturgeon,' Jimmy corrected.

'Oh, that's not a very nice picture.' Princess frowned. 'I like something with more glitter.'

'Gary Glitter?' Dennis laughed.

'Oh, I remember him,' Jimmy nodded. 'Wasn't he in the charts?'

'In the charts, in the prisons. He got around,' Dennis replied. 'Here's a picture of Celtic – does anyone want it? No? Oh well.'

'I'm more of a Jambo,' Jimmy confessed.

'What's a Jam-bow?' Peter asked. 'Is that like a jamboree? My mum goes to them sometimes at the church. Says she always gets robbed at them.'

'Yeah, that's about right,' Jimmy agreed. 'Jambo. Jam Tarts – Hearts,' said Jimmy. 'I support Hearts.'

'So sorry,' Dennis smirked.

I try to cover a range of topics, Helga typed, *but everyone always wants to know more about Candy*. Ping! An email alert popped up. She clicked it open.

Just a wee email to say that I've been checking the ticket sales for the upcoming Writers' Block event next week. The other authors have sold all their ticket allocation but yours are rather paltry ☹ – any chance you can shift these by the end of the week?
Cheers, love. Kate XX.

Helga groaned. She'd punted as many as she could around her small circle of friends. She supposed she could have extended the invitation to her mother's entire creative writing class but she didn't want to encourage their attention. Helga sipped her coffee and ignored the plea. *Fans often ask me whether Candy Martini is based on a real person. I like to think she's a better version of myself – for example, people are always telling me what excellent lifestyle advice I offer and how I can listen to them for hours—*

'Miss! Miss! Dennis has stuck a photo of ladies' bosoms on his paper!' Peter declared.

Helga jammed her fingers in her ears. *Having empathy for those trying to negotiate life's difficulties is a gift that I cherish—*

'Don't get glue on my pretty dress!' Princess shrieked, bursting into tears. 'You've got it all over my sparkly dress. Helga, he's ruined my outfit – what will I do?'

'It's only glue!' Helga barked. 'Can you just give me five minutes?'

'It'll wash off,' Harry said. 'Come over to the sink and I'll give you a hand.'

'Are you taking it off?' Dennis asked hopefully.

'Finished!' Peter shouted. 'Miss Helga – I'm finished.'

'Give the man a fricking coconut,' Lex said. 'I was finished after the first five minutes but I'm not looking for a fricking medal.'

'Ooh! Is there a medal?' Peter asked, clapping his hands. 'I've never won a medal for anything before.'

'Not even for Prize Twat?' Lex asked. She flicked a blob of glue at Peter's chest.

Helga sighed, snapping her MacBook shut. 'Alrighty! Well done. Let's have a look at what you've produced. Who wants to go first?'

Peter's hand shot in the air. 'Pick me, miss!'

'Fine. Hold up your paper for us all to see.'

Peter proudly displayed the collage of half-cut, half-torn images.

'So do you want to tell us why you've picked these particular images?'

Peter jabbed a stumpy finger. 'This is a house as I live in a house with my mum. That's a picture of a pie cos I like pies.' He grinned.

'I didn't know what to put for a telly so I just stuck this square of windows. And my favourite drink is cola so I put this advert here.'

'Very good. Thank you, Peter. Has anyone got any questions for Peter?' Helga asked, looking round the group.

'What's with the photo of Katie Price?' Harry asked.

'Oh,' Peter said, blushing. 'That's my dream girlfriend.'

'Keep fricking dreaming,' Lex commented.

'Right, who's next?'

Peter tried to put his paper down but the edges were stuck to his fingers. He flapped the sheet around until the paper ripped, leaving torn remnants attached to his fingertips.

'I don't mind,' Princess offered. She pointed to a castle that she had glued in the centre of the page. 'One day I think I'll meet a handsome prince and we'll live in this amazing castle.'

'Will you tell her or will I?' Lex remarked.

Princess carried on. 'I've put this pot of pink paint as that's my favourite colour. *Obvs!* This lady sitting on the phone is because I'd like to get a job again and I think I'd be really good at talking to people. This here,' she pointed to a photo of a heart, 'is because inside, my heart is breaking since I'm all alone and I don't know why. My daddy says it's because no one is special enough for me. But I just feel if I had a chance I'd—'

Helga's mobile trilled. 'Sorry! Must get this.' She moved to the other side of the room and spoke quietly into the handset.

'Do continue,' said Jimmy.

'Doesn't matter,' Princess mumbled, folding her sheet in half.

Helga hung up. 'Okay, where were we? Lex, what have you got there?'

'This is so fricking lame,' Lex protested.

'But all you've done is cover the sheet in black pictures,' Helga said, frowning. 'A black wall, black box, black floor, black door. What's that all about?'

Lex shrugged. 'What's the fricking point?'

'Right, well, what about you, Kamal?' Helga asked. 'What have you found to tell us about?'

Kamal silently held up his paper. There was only one image glued on: a picture of a green velvet curtain. He lifted up the curtain and underneath was a photo of a boy lying in bed. He let the curtain drop.

'Would you like to say a few words about why you've picked those two images?' Helga asked, leaning forward. He shook his head.

'Lazy bugger would rather stay in bed all day!' Dennis commented.

'Well, mine's easy,' Harry drawled. 'A picture of a packet of fags and a bottle of Famous Grouse.' She coughed into a handkerchief.

'And what about the photo of the young man?' Helga enquired. 'Does that represent your late husband or a love lost, perhaps?'

'What? I've no idea who it is – just some random bloke with a nice arse.'

'Jimmy – you're next,' Helga smiled stiffly. 'How did you get on?'

'Oh well, I don't really go in for all this arty-farty stuff. I just cut out this picture of a Ford Focus because I used to drive one. Oh, and a photo of a ship, as the best holiday Elsie and I ever took was a cruise around the Mediterranean.'

'So,' Helga clasped her hands together. 'Hopefully that gave you a bit more insight into who we are?'

'But what about you, miss?' Peter asked. 'Where's your sheet?'

'Or have you been otherwise occupied?' Harry muttered, raising an eyebrow.

'What? I … Oh well. Actually, since you ask, I have a bit of a proposition for you.'

'Oh aye?' said Dennis.

'Next week – next Wednesday evening, actually, I wondered whether you were all up for a bit of an evening activity for a change?'

'You mean a pub?' Dennis asked, grinning.

'I don't normally go out after tea,' Peter fretted. 'Do we have to?'

'Of course you don't *have* to,' Helga smiled. 'It's just that I'm participating in an event next week at Musselburgh town hall and I thought you might all like to come along? As a bit of a *social*.'

'What kind of social?' Jimmy asked. 'I can't abide bingo.'

'Will there be alcohol?' asked Harry, brightening.

'Definitely no alcohol. It's just me and a few other authors talking about our work.'

'Sounds shite,' Dennis muttered. 'Why don't we just go to the pub?'

'How will we get to Musselburgh?' Harry asked.

'Ah, well, I've thought about that,' Helga said. 'I can ask the centre's driver to pick you all up in the minibus. He isn't booked for the evening and can drop you off after the event.'

'Will there be dancing?' Princess chirped.

Helga took a deep breath. 'I think it will be good for all of us. If we think about why we're here – it's to make friends and chat. So, this just gives you another chance to get out of the house – for *free*. You'll be collected and dropped off. So, what do you say?'

'I'm only here under fricking duress,' Lex complained. 'Sounds like torture.'

'Will there be pies, miss?' Peter asked. 'There's a Greggs in Musselburgh.'

'Anyway,' said Helga, collecting up the mugs. 'That's the end of our group for today. Now I thought for next week it might be a good idea if we all brought an item from home that means something special.'

'Like my mum?' Peter asked.

'*You're* the one that's special,' Lex muttered.

'I meant an object – something you own. It will give us another opportunity to share what makes us tick.'

'Like a clock?'

Helga tutted. 'I didn't mean it in a literal sense.'

'How big should it be?' Princess asked.

'The size isn't important,' Helga answered, already regretting her suggestion.

'That's what all you ladies say,' Dennis sniggered.

'I'll ignore that comment. And when you come to next week's Tuesday Chatters I'll confirm all the details for our wee social. Now take care how you get home – looks like the weather's taken a turn for the worse.'

'Will you give me a note for my mum?' Peter asked.

'I need to start upping my offences,' said Lex, shaking her head.

Helga placed the laden tray on the ground so she could punch in the code before pushing the door open with her back. She banged the tray down on the draining board, emptying the mugs into the overflowing sink.

'Right, darling, calm down!' Molly spoke into the telephone.

'What do you mean you think you've blown up the microwave? Sorry, Caz, you're going to have to stop being hysterical long enough to tell me what happened. So the fire's out? And what were your shoes doing in there in the first place? Honestly, Caz, I'll kill you if you've broken the microwave – you know it's how I like to do all my cooking! I'll be home soon and you better stay *well* out of my way!'

She slammed down the receiver. 'Bloody kids! How was your group, Helga?'

'Oh well, they're a bit of a handful too. Look, I've got some catching-up to do – would you mind doing the mugs?'

'Sure. I'll just save what I was doing …'

Chapter 15

Vanda brushed the snow from her spiky hair. 'I can't believe we've got as far as March and *now* it decides to snow.'

'You should see it up by us,' Molly moaned. I had to high-step all the way from my house to the bus stop – no way was I bringing the car in this weather.'

'Get an email from Sheba?' Vanda asked as she joined the morning run-through.

'Yes,' came a collective response.

'I didn't,' said Molly, offended.

'She wants to see us each individually,' Vanda said. 'God knows what she needs to say to us one by one.'

'She wants to get Aiden on his own,' Bobbie grinned.

'That's what I'm worried about,' he muttered. 'By the way, you've got orange stuff all over your face.'

'Oh, that'll be the Wotsits,' Bobbie replied, wiping her mouth on her sleeve. 'What slot did you get?'

'Four o'clock today.'

'Ooh! She's keen!' Vanda said. 'She doesn't have time to see me until next week.'

'Me neither,' said Bobbie.

'Or me,' Helga added.

'By the way.' Molly clicked on her Outlook. 'I've had an email from Mr Adamson asking what approach we're taking to boosting our numbers. He seems to think that the launch at Westside was a complete disaster.'

'Well, it was for his suit!' Bobbie giggled.

'I've printed off the referral data so you can see who has the lowest numbers.' She handed round a sheet.

'Just as I thought,' Aiden nodded. 'Baberton has two new GPs and they probably don't know anything about us.'

'And Hailes Practice is pretty low too.'

'That's because they send referrals for all their patients to about ten different services, hoping that one of them will respond. By the time we do get them passed to us everyone has had their sticky fingers on them,' Vanda said in exasperation.

'Shall I make an appointment for you to go along to those two practices, then?'

'Please,' said Vanda.

'Also, just a heads-up,' said Molly. 'Norman is coming back today – says he wants to go through the building's security strategy with us.'

'Good God!' Vanda exclaimed. 'What time is he coming?'

'Just said some time this morning.'

'Right, let's whizz through the patients so we can get on the road.'

'Thanks, guys!' Molly frowned. 'And leave me with Numbskull Norman?'

'Actually, I could do with catching up with some admin this morning. Does anyone mind if I work from the office next door? Chan says the desk next to her is free all week.' Helga gathered up her files and made an exit.

'What's up with her?' Vanda whispered. 'She's been a tad tetchy this week.'

'Think she's under a bit of stress,' Molly replied. 'Got a lot on.'

'We've *all* got a lot on,' Aiden complained. 'Talking of which, I better shoot. Got that new man to see – Mr McGibbon?'

'Go on, then – skedaddle!' Vanda said.

'S'pose I ought to go and see some patients as well. Hmm, who can I face this morning?' Bobbie rifled through the pile. 'Maybe I'll just have another coffee to set me up.'

The buzzer sounded and Molly jerked her tea in shock.

'Christ, that'll be Norman!' Vanda hissed. 'I'm *off*.' She snatched up her bag and ran out of the office, careering straight into Anver. 'Help ma boab!' he cried as Vanda spilt her notes all over the floor. He massaged his stomach. 'Hey, lassie, you just about mashed me breakfast! What's the emergency?'

'Sorry.' She knelt down, scooping up the scattered papers. 'Are you really sliding around Gorgie in a pair of boat shoes with no socks?'

Anver bent to help her. 'You know, all this rushing isn't good for you. Why don't you take it easy?'

'Like you, you mean? Start a job and come back a week later?'

'Exactly!' He grinned, tipping his pork-pie hat to her.

'The world would grind to a halt if everyone moved at your speed. Anyway, now that you're here, when will the ladies be open again? I've had enough of running up and down those stairs.'

Anver shrugged, his hands in his chino pockets. 'I plan to start the tiling today but I can't say for sure when I'll be finished. Tell you what, why don't we have lunch together and I'll let you know my progress?'

'What? Are you mad?'

'Mad – or *bad*?' He winked.

Molly opened the office door. 'I thought I heard your voice, Anver. Like a coffee?'

'Yes, please, that would be rare.' He entered the ladies' toilets, whistling to himself.

Later that afternoon Aiden yanked open the grimy glass door to the utilitarian single-storey neighbourhood office. He fidgeted at the reception desk behind a dishevelled man who reeked of cheap whisky and stale cigarette smoke. 'Just tell your boss that I'm no' leaving here until I get my welfare. I've been up here every day this week and every day get sent away but I'm no having it!' He kicked the wooden counter for good measure.

'I've already explained to you, Mr Wallace,' the tight-lipped woman informed him, 'Your key worker is not available today and no one else can deal with your appeal.'

'How no?' he demanded, spitting on the floor.

'Excuse me,' Aiden interrupted, leaning past the enraged client. 'I'm here to see Sheba Mount. It's Aiden James.'

'Whoa, whoa, whoa! Hold your horses, son. There's a queue here.' He grimaced a few inches from Aiden's face, his breath able to fuel a large Christmas pudding. Aiden recoiled in disgust.

'Just take a seat,' the receptionist instructed. 'I'll let her know you're here. Mr Wallace, please leave before I alert security.' Her hand hovered over the phone.

'Well, I hope that *he's* not your man,' Mr Wallace slurred in Aiden's direction. 'That streak of piss couldn't fight sleep!'

A couple of minutes later Sheba appeared at a side door. 'Aiden,' she called. 'Glad you could make this appointment at short notice.'

Aiden mumbled something indecipherable, following her through the faceless corridors like a well-disciplined puppy. She stopped abruptly and opened a door to a windowless room – empty except for a chipped table and three aluminium chairs.

'Thought we'd get more peace in here,' she said crisply. 'Coffee?'

'Er, no, thanks.' He held up his sports bottle.

'Quite right – hydration is so important for one's complexion.' She sat at the head of the table and kicked out the chair to her side.

Aiden perched on a corner of the chair and pulled out a notebook and pen from his rucksack. Sheba leant forward, resting her hand on his forearm. 'Please, Aiden, this is really just an informal catch-up. No need to take notes. I just wanted a chance to speak to you on your own – without the *others*.'

'Oh, er …' He returned the notebook and sat staring straight ahead.

'So, Aiden, how would you describe our relationship?' She reclined in the chair, crossing her legs with a swish. He blushed crimson to his ears.

'Well, y-you're …' he stammered.

'I'm what?'

'You're, er, a team leader?'

'Is that all I am to you? After what we've been through? Are you seriously telling me that there isn't a tiny knob of Aiden that doesn't still hanker for some Sheba?'

'I just don't think. I mean …' He coughed nervously. A line of sweat appeared on his upper lip.

'I hope I'm not making you feel uncomfortable? It's just that I'm certain we can have the kind of relaxed relationship that means we get the work done – but can have a laugh too?'

'Oh, I'm all about the laughing,' Aiden said, giving a strangled chuckle.

'I'm not a great believer in harking back to the past … but I do recognise it would empower me to share my feelings on our brief liaison. I want you to know that I was actually pretty devastated by the way you broke things off. I know I come across with supreme confidence, but I'm really rather fragile. And you trampled over me without a backward glance.'

'Oh, I don't think—'

Sheba held up her hand. 'As I say, it's all in the past.' She suddenly sat upright and looked him in the eye. 'Let bygones be bygones, I say. So – moving on to the present! I'm going to disclose something that I'd rather you kept absolutely confidential for the moment.'

'Uh-huh?'

'As you know, our teams will be merging.'

'Yes.'

'I've scrutinised your referral numbers and I don't think I can justify bringing an extra four members of staff into the South Team. Helga I can use as we don't have a link worker and I think she will be an asset. As for Vanda, Bobbie and yourself – well, I could probably take one of you at a push.'

Aiden stared at her in disbelief. 'What are you saying, Sheba?'

'I'm saying I could probably take one of you at a push.'

'Yes, I heard that, but what do you mean? We all have different roles – you can't just need one of us.'

Sheba screwed up her face. 'Thing is, Aiden – *our* team is fully staffed. On the other hand, the acute hospital service always has vacancies. It would make sense for two of you to shift over there – to go back into hospital work.'

Aiden sat in furious silence.

'Aiden? Your thoughts?'

'I don't know what you want me to say,' he answered, certain that his thoughts would be to knock her lights out. 'Are you asking me to suggest who should stay and who should go? I mean, we all work in the intervention team because that's where we've chosen to work and been *employed* to work. None of us wants to go back into acute.'

'I'm merely letting you into my confidence. As I said, I'm requesting radio silence on the matter but I *will* be asked to make a decision. I can swing it either way – maybe we need another OT, maybe another physio. Maybe I don't need you *or* Bobbie. I certainly have no requirement for any admin staff.'

'This isn't right!' he exclaimed. 'It's not fair!'

'Not fair?' Sheba mocked. 'Of course it's not fair. It's organisational change. Suck it up.'

Aiden reached for his rucksack, ready to bolt.

'Let me leave you with this thought, Aiden. I'm giving you a chance to prove yourself. If you can get your referrals up I'll be more than happy to hang on to you. Otherwise I'll be recommending you get punted back on to the wards, where you'll be covering whatever service has a vacancy. I hear orthopaedics is always short?'

He grabbed his rucksack and stormed out of the room, slamming the door behind him. Striding across the reception area he sidestepped the security guard, who was grappling with Mr Wallace on the floor as a mother and her toddler watched on with interest. 'You need to sign out!' the receptionist shouted.

Chapter 16

'How'd'ya get on with the Queen of Sheba yesterday?' Vanda asked, checking her reflection in the mirror. She prodded at a spot on her chin.

'Fine,' Aiden replied moodily.

'Do I detect trouble in the James' household?'

'Piss off, Vanda!'

'Oh, Aiden, that's not like you!' Molly scolded.

'It's exactly like him,' Vanda laughed. 'Grumpy bastard! So do I get any pre-warning about what she wants to see us about?'

Aiden sighed. 'She just wants to know how we feel about joining her team.'

'Pfft! I'll soon tell her my thoughts on that. Morning, Bobbie.'

'Hiya,' Bobbie puffed. She waddled into the office in her wellies, carrying a stuffed bin bag.

'Council not collecting your rubbish this week?' Vanda asked. Bobbie dropped the bag with a thud. 'Linda is collecting bras for Africa.'

'Bloody hell, Bobbie! I knew you were a D-cup but have you really enough spare to pack a bin bag?'

'Well, I started off with bras but then I found some old knickers and socks. I piled them up and before I knew it I had a massive heap.'

'Not being funny, but does the developing world really want your old knickers?'

'Oh yes!' Bobbie exclaimed. 'Apparently so. My used underwear will be like proper designer lingerie to the disadvantaged.'

'Don't you think the continent is in enough trouble without a deluge of Bobbie's bloomers?'

'I'm merely responding to a crisis,' Bobbie shrugged. 'Now … who wants a Pop-Tart?'

'Go on, then,' Molly said. 'It feels a long time since I had my porridge. Now I know Helga's not in yet but I've had a response from Baberton. They're able to accommodate your visit tomorrow lunchtime?'

'That's fine for me,' Aiden jumped in.

'Oh – first off the starting blocks,' Vanda remarked. 'I think that's OK for me too. Unless you want to go, Bobbie?'

'Carry on,' Bobbie said, fishing the Pop-Tarts out with her biro.

'Something smells good,' Helga said, dropping her bag at her desk.

'Morning, Helga.' Molly smiled. 'How are you?'

'Much better today. Managed to deliver the next five thousand words to the publisher, so feel rather relieved.'

'We're so happy for you,' said Vanda. 'Right, let's do the run-through.'

'Be with you in a tick. Just putting on the next batch of Pop-Tarts.'

'Quinn's sent round an email this morning,' Molly announced. 'Says "Due to the inclement weather I would strongly recommend that staff engage in ESSENTIAL – capital letters – travel only and ensure that vehicles are properly equipped with the Cold Pack as recommended in our Inclement Weather Guidance, appendix III".'

'Jesus!' Vanda objected. 'Surely *all* our travel is essential. Does he really think we like schlepping around Edinburgh, visiting patients for fun?'

'What's in a cold pack?' Bobbie asked. 'Ow! *Hot!*' She dropped the Pop-Tart on to the floor. '*Damn!*'

'"Shovel, blanket, water, torch" etc.,' Molly read from the screen.

'It does make you wonder how we possibly function at home without bloody guidance!' Aiden griped.

'I know!' Bobbie laughed. 'I mean, it's amazing how I ever manage a camping trip without a health and safety assessment.'

'Or bringing the Christmas decorations down from the attic,' Molly agreed.

'Or, God forbid, we should attempt to negotiate a weekly shop without four appendices,' Vanda said. 'Anyway—'

She was interrupted by a loud and persistent alarm blaring out in the corridor. 'Fire alarm!' Molly exclaimed.

'Probably just a test?' Helga asked hopefully.

'Nope,' Molly confirmed, grabbing her jacket. 'And it's constant, which means it's in this building. Come on, everyone out.'

'But I've just put in some more tarts!' Bobbie protested.

'Get a move on,' Vanda scolded. Bobbie hoicked them out of the toaster and grabbed her coffee. They bundled along *en masse* with the alarm reverberating around the stairwell. A crowd huddled in the car park as snowflakes tumbled from the grey sky.

'Great bloody timing,' Aiden grumbled, zipping up his fleece.

A tank of a woman in high-vis tabard came storming up to their group. 'What on earth do you think you're doing?' she shouted at Bobbie.

'Thought there was a fire?'

'Yes! And? You're standing out here with your entire breakfast it seems. Coffee and hot snacks?'

'Oh, sorry,' Bobbie said, 'where are my manners? Pop-Tart?'

'You are contravening the building's evacuation procedure!' she snapped, referring to her clipboard.

'What's going on?' Vanda asked, muscling her way between the two.

'Is she yours?' the woman demanded.

'Who – Bobbie?'

'This member of staff has ignored the fundamental rule of evacuation, which is to immediately leave one's workspace to exit the building. Now, she,' she jabbed a finger at Bobbie's chest, 'has dawdled in a potentially life-threatening environment to prepare herself a hot drink and snacks.'

'I did offer to share it,' Bobbie said with her mouth full.

'Members of staff are advised that they must not detour, even to retrieve their coats.' She sniffed as her nose dripped on to the snowy path.

'Are you suggesting that my team should leave the office and stand out here in the brass-monkey chill just to comply with your sodding rules?' Vanda retorted.

'They're not *my* rules.'

'Well, they're certainly not ours. And I think my staff are more at risk of frigging pneumonia than of getting trapped in a towering inferno.'

'Well, I shall be alerting Mr Adamson in my fire report.'

'Oooh – fire engine!' Bobbie cried.

'There's smoke coming out of one of the windows!' Helga said, pointing to the ground floor. The crowd stood back to let the two fire appliances – lights blazing and sirens clamouring – manoeuvre into the tight turning space.

'This would be quite exciting if it wasn't so flipping perishing,' Molly commented. 'What if the whole building goes up in flames?'

'Good riddance, I say,' Vanda muttered.

'I bet it was someone smoking in the gents' toilets,' said Aiden.

'Normally the community project knuckleheads smoke outside but I bet the cold has driven them indoors.'

'Oi! I heard that. We're not *all* knuckleheads.'

'Whatever.'

'Shit – talking of knuckleheads – here comes Norman,' Vanda cursed. 'We'll be here all bloody day now. *God,* it's cold.'

Norman waved regally to the crowd as he conferred with the lead fire officer. There was much head shaking and pointing of fingers.

'What's *he* doing?' Aiden asked, screwing up his eyes.

They followed his stare as Ray hovered on the edge of the rabble, before slinking back into his locked shed.

'Anyone want a hot drink?' Helga offered. 'I'm going to nip over the road.'

'Oh, cheers, Helga. Get me a cappuccino,' Vanda replied.

'Shh!' Helga said. 'Keep your voice down. I'm only getting some for us lot – not the whole corridor.'

'Can I have a hot chocolate?' Bobbie asked. 'With extra chocolate and marshmallows if they have them.'

'I don't think you're meant to leave,' Molly chided. 'What if what's-her-face is counting numbers?'

Helga shrugged. 'Not likely.'

The fire warden was giggling at something one of the fire fighters was saying as he wielded an axe. Helga slipped away from the frustrated huddle. She had an uneasy sensation that a pair of eyes was focused on her as she crossed the road to the Turkish café.

Teeth could be heard chattering by the time Norman reappeared at the building's entrance.

'May I have everybody's attention?' he bellowed, hitching up his trousers. A hush fell upon the crowd – either that or they were frozen in time.

'Now, in the instance of a genuine, actual fire, I will be producing a fire report, including lessons learnt, for Mr Adamson.'

A murmur of interest rippled through the audience.

'But what I will divulge, at this point, is that we do believe a fire was started *intentionally*.' He let the word hang in the air like an icicle. 'I will therefore be interviewing each team to try to identify any possible perpetrators.'

'Jings – I'd burn the building down if it got us out of this cold!' Vanda exclaimed.

'So, you may now re-enter the building but please be cognisant of potential on-going danger.'

'What does that mean?' Molly wondered.

'It means the whole frigging building is falling apart,' Aiden said, shaking his head. 'Could that man really waste any more time if he tried?'

The team returned to their office, keeping their coats on until they acclimatised. Helga returned with a cardboard holder of steaming drinks.

'Here you go,' said Helga, passing round the cups.

'Well done!' said Molly. 'My hands are like ice!'

Chapter 17

That afternoon the snow swirled around the building and, when the skies darkened not long after three p.m., the team was sent home. 'It's meant to turn to slush by tomorrow,' Molly announced, closing the door.

'Fingers crossed!' Bobbie smiled. 'See you tomorrow.'

Helga regretted bringing her ancient Hyundai to work as the back wheels skidded on the snow. It took her forever to reach her street, although the snow wasn't even lying. The traffic was in a go-slow paralysis. She had been aware of her phone vibrating in her bag and couldn't wait to see who had been trying to get hold of her. Four missed calls from Kate! As she climbed the stairs she could hear Dolly's yapping growing nearer. *Shit!*

'Oh, Helga, thank goodness you're here,' said Donald, her lanky neighbour who had ears like satellite dishes and eyes that pointed east and west. 'I was getting worried about you. I've been looking out the window all afternoon for your wee car.'

'That's very kind of you,' Helga replied, making to climb the next flight.

'Now, I'm just taking Dolly out – we've been cooped up indoors all day. Would you like me to get you anything from the corner shop?'

'No, thanks, Donald – I really must get into my flat.'

'What about a Pot Noodle? They're selling two for a pound?'

'I'm not really a fan of—'

'I just thought with you being on your own and all. They're quite handy. Oh, I know! They've also got two Scotch pies for a pound? They're kind of just out of the sell-by date but I had one yesterday and I'm alright.'

Helga kept climbing. 'Bye, Donald.'

'Sticky ribs?' he shouted.

Her flat felt chilly, so Helga closed the curtains and switched on the small flame-effect fire for some cheer. Her mobile was still cold in her hand. Twenty notifications! Her eye caught an email from Kate – subject line:

OMG!!

She clicked it open.

Helga, you will never guess! Scot Today is doing a feature on the ten most promising writers in Scotland and they want to do a feature on you! Can you believe it? This is MASSIVE! They're offering a makeover and everything. This will do wonders for Candy Martini. Call me!

The next morning, as Molly had predicted, the snow was melting rapidly and the roads were back to normal, the buses sending fountains of grey slush up on to the pavements.

'You've got a spring in your step!' Molly noted.

'Got a new man, have you?' Vanda asked from behind her PC.

'I told you, I'm not looking for a man,' Helga replied. 'But I *am* rather chuffed with myself.'

'Oh aye?'

'I'll wait until everyone else is here, if you don't mind, Vanda. It'll save me repeating myself.'

'If you insist,' Vanda shrugged.

'I'm just asking,' said Bobbie as she entered the office at the same time as Aiden, 'which would you rather do? The jungle one or the Big Brother thingy.'

'And I'm telling you neither,' Aiden insisted, picking up his uniform.

'I don't believe you! If someone offered you the chance for your mug to be on TV I bet you'd jump at the chance.'

'Nope!' Aiden shook his head. 'Face it, Bobbie – you've got me all wrong. I wouldn't want that type of fame, whatever they were offering.'

'Well, funny you should mention that ...' Helga started.

'That's bollocks, Aiden, and you know it. You've got a price just like all of us—'

'As I was saying ...' Helga interrupted.

'Never!' Aiden retorted. 'Why would I want my face blown up on the big screen for everyone to comment on every little aspect of my—'

'Shhh, you two!' Molly scolded. 'Helga has an announcement to make.'

'Du-du-du-du-dah!' Vanda trumpeted with her hands.

Suddenly Helga looked embarrassed. 'Perhaps not so much an announcement as more of a sharing of—'

'Just get on with it!' Vanda exclaimed. 'Bloody hell – for a writer you don't half prattle a load of nonsense.'

'Sorry,' Helga said from behind her desk. 'Just thought you'd be pleased for me – I'm going to be in *Scot Today*! They're doing a bit of a feature on the most promising writers in Scotland. It'll be great exposure for me.'

Vanda whistled. 'Good on you, Helga! A star is born!'

'That's great,' Aiden nodded.

Bobbie ambled across and gave Helga a big hug. 'I can finally say I know someone famous!'

'Well,' Helga blushed.

'That's fabby!' Molly grinned. 'Wait until I tell my kids – they'll be so excited. Maybe you should be signing copies of the HIT leaflets?'

'I suppose I could do a few,' agreed Helga. 'Might be worth something one day?'

'Ah! Now about the leaflets,' Vanda said. 'I've just had a call from Miss Sutherland's GP – he's worried she's got all her meds in a muddle again. The best time for me to go is over lunchtime so I can't make the meeting with Baberton. Aiden, are you still okay for it?'

'Yep, no problem. What about you, Helga – are you free to come with me?'

'What about *me*?' Bobbie asked indignantly. 'Usually it's me that pairs up with one of you. No offence, Helga, but you're kind of second-line staff.'

'No offence, Bobbie,' Aiden echoed, 'but last time we did a joint promotion you tried to kill at least three people.'

'What? A slight exaggeration. The tai chi man merely lost his balance on Mr Happy and that Gail woman should never have been charging around the centre like a demented bull.'

'And Mr Adamson? You're telling me that chucking hot wax all over our general manager has helped our team's cause?'

'Och, no one cares about Quinn! What's another ruined suit to him?'

'So do you need me or not?' Helga asked. 'Only I really have to prep for this interview.'

'Yes, your presence will be required – *Hello* magazine will just have to wait.'

'Please yourself,' Bobbie shrugged. 'Anyway, the café does two baked potato fillings for the price of one on a Friday.'

'Right, Helga, will I meet you there?'

'Actually, I think I'm just going to base myself in the office this morning – can you come back to pick me up?'

'Fine,' Aiden snapped. 'See you lot later.'

'What's up with him?' Vanda asked.

'If I didn't know better,' Bobbie replied, 'I'd say he's suffering from PMT.'

Chapter 18

'Knock, knock!' Norman declared as he rapped on the door of Ray's shed. A key turned and the door opened an inch. 'Oh, it's you,' said Ray sourly. 'What do you want?'

'I need to speak to you. It's freezing out here – let me in.' He pulled the zip higher on his anorak as though to emphasise the point. Ray scowled, nudging the door ajar. The gloomy shed was crammed with discarded equipment from the health centre: old hoists, stacks of broken chairs, lopsided tables and battered filing cabinets. The shack had a lingering odour of mould combined with industrial disinfectant. A plate with a half-eaten bacon roll sat on the dilapidated wooden desk; a cracked mug of coffee going cold. Ray returned to his threadbare swivel chair. Norman took in the scene with incredulity. 'What are you doing with all this crap in here?'

Ray shrugged. 'Staff give me a ring and ask me to uplift their old stuff and I bring it in here to get it out of their way.'

'But what's it doing in here, man? You're supposed to arrange removal to the council dump.'

Ray propped his feet on the desk as Norman searched for somewhere to perch. He settled on a rusty wheelchair, the seat of which sagged under his weight. A paint-splattered radio was blaring out 'Dignity' until Ray reluctantly flipped it off. Norman opened up a shiny black folder. He clicked his pen, writing the

136

date and *Witness Number One* at the top of the page.

'Is this going to take long? Only I'm supposed to be emptying all the bins and they get very upset when I don't turn up.' As if on cue the phone trilled.

'Ignore it,' Norman commanded. 'Perhaps you don't realise the gravity of the situation here.'

'Perhaps I don't. Please – enlighten me.' Ray leant back in his chair, cracking the joints in his hands.

'We are having to consider the possibility of a serial offender, whose main objective or target is unclear. The series of events appears to be escalating in criminality and we cannot afford to be complacent in disregarding this individual's efforts.'

'So,' Ray sighed. 'We've got a nutter on the loose.'

'Apparently. So, if you'd be so kind as to provide me with the exact details of your movements yesterday?'

'What are you implying?'

'Just answer the question.'

'I came to work as I do every morning at seven thirty. I did my rounds checking everything was all A-okay. I had my breakfast.' He indicated the half-eaten meal. 'Then I started on my duties.'

'Which include?'

'Look, would it be easier if I forwarded my job description?'

'Just a rough idea.'

'Emptying the bins, doing the mail, carrying out minor repairs, responding to urgent requests for stuff.'

'Such as?'

'Uplifts, parking issues, equipment not working.'

Ray's eyes darted across to where a mobile phone vibrated on the desk. Norman shook his head. 'So did you see anyone or anything suspicious yesterday?'

'Not unless you include that moron administrator in the community health project?'

'Who, Lance?'

'He goes mental if they run out of paper towels.'

'I think he's what's known as "on the spectrum".'

Ray snorted. 'Is that what they call it nowadays – please excuse my ignorance.'

'And what about the rest of the day?'

'Look, mate, if I saw something I'd say so. Why would I want the building burned down any more than you? No building – no job!'

'Ah, but it wasn't actually a fire,' Norman confided.

'I see – that's why there was smoke billowing out the gents' toilets and we called the fire brigade? Did we think they just fancied a wee jaunt to get them away from the snooker table?'

'According to the incident report, a plastic bin was filled with a mix of ammonia and hydrochloric acid, which set off a chemical reaction – hence the smoke. The perpetrator then – we think – set off the alarm to give the illusion of a fire.'

'Then you really do have a bampot on the loose. A loon who doesn't set fire to a building but pretends to? A half-arson, effort eh?' He grinned.

'This is most certainly *not* a laughing matter! But it brings me to my next question – do you store or are you aware of anyone on the premises storing these particular chemicals?'

'I'm not bloody sitting here mixing up crystal meth like *Breaking Bad*! Anyway, if it's chemicals you're after, speak to the feet folk. They have all sorts of stuff. *And* – they're the ones who are agitating to get moved. It would suit them no end if this place got torched.'

'But it wasn't—'

'Whatever! Look, I need to go before I get the sack. Come on –
out!' Ray jostled Norman out of the shed, locking it behind them.
'I'm *coming*!' he barked into his phone.

Chapter 19

Aiden sent Helga a text:

`I'm waiting downstairs - remember to bring the leaflets.`

Almost ten minutes later she appeared, flopping on to the passenger seat, her bag bulging over her lap. He glared in her direction as he belted out of the car park. 'Sorry, Aiden – got a call just as I was heading out.'

Aiden shrugged, turning up the hill. 'Busy morning?' he enquired sarcastically.

'Oh yes – lots to do. I needed to amend my biography and Kate asked for a wee blog – just to help with the build-up.'

'I meant *work*?'

'Och, I'll catch up with that soon enough. These chances rarely come along – I must seize every opportunity. It'll be such good exposure for my profile. Kate's set me a target of ten thousand Twitter followers, which is pretty ambitious.'

'Move – it's *green*!' Aiden tooted his horn at the car in front as it stalled and the traffic lights turned back to red. 'Bloody learners.' Aiden thumped the steering wheel.

'Are we late?' Helga asked, checking out a comment on her Facebook page.

'We will be if this twit doesn't get into gear. If the new GPs are anything like the old ones in this practice, they won't hang around for us. We'll get a five-minute slot the same as the patients.'

'Oh – sorry.' Helga looked out of the window at the dirty piles of slush along the gutters. 'At least the snow's almost gone.'

Helga and Aiden were shown into a cramped staff room, where a low coffee table was laden with mugs, empty food cartons and half-eaten packets of biscuits. The three GPs – two men and one woman – sat in sagging chairs, their knees almost touching. The woman, bundled up in a woollen suit, was eating pasta from a Tupperware box. The two men had progressed to coffee. As Helga and Aiden squeezed past to take the remaining seats, the older man announced. 'Hi, I'm Dr Donaldson – I'm the senior partner here.'

'Grant McKinley.'

'Beth Thomson – no *P*,' said the woman, sloshing from a litre bottle of water.

'Well, thank you for having us,' Aiden began. 'I'm Aiden James, occupational therapist, and this is Helga Trumpet our link worker. We're from the Harrison Intervention Team.'

'Are you?' Dr Donaldson frowned. 'I thought we were getting someone from the community psychology service?'

'Sorry,' Helga replied.

'Damn! I had a referral ready to hand over.'

'What do *you* do?' Dr Thomson asked. 'What kind of intervention – that's a bit vague, isn't it?'

Helga swiftly passed round handfuls of leaflets that all three immediately pored over.

'We offer assessment, rehabilitation and community integration for any of your patients at this practice – anyone over sixteen,' Aiden recited to the tops of their heads.

'It says here you do falls assessments,' Dr McKinley read. 'I've got loads of patients who've had a fall. Shall I just pass them all on to you?'

'Hmm,' Aiden faltered. 'It depends if they've already been seen by another service – there would be little benefit to the patient if they've recently had an assessment or are already being seen by another team.'

'Well, how am I supposed to know that?' he snapped. 'If someone comes out of hospital, I've got no idea what they've been referred for.'

'What about bathing?' Dr Donaldson asked.

'Yes – we have been known to maintain personal hygiene.' Aiden's joke was met by a stony silence. 'Of course I would carry out a bathing assessment as part of my overall functional assessment,' he rushed on.

'But you wouldn't actually *give* someone a bath?' Dr Donaldson peered over the top of his glasses.

'No,' Aiden replied, fidgeting in his seat.

Dr Thomson smiled smugly at her colleague. 'I'd have thought that putting someone *in* the bath would be the best way to see how they manage, wouldn't you, Colin?'

'Quite.' He nodded.

Helga's mobile bleated loudly. 'Oh! Sorry, must get this,' she said, stepping over their legs to exit the room.

'But what about the social services folk?' Dr McKinley asked. 'Surely if I want an occupational therapy assessment I'd just refer to them?'

'Ah, well – you see, the thing about our team is that we're multidisciplinary. If you refer one of your many frail, older patients it's very likely they'll have a range of complex needs and co-morbidity. Since we have a district nurse and physiotherapist in our team, we can address multiple problems at the same time. And of course we have Helga – whose key role is to ensure the patients feel part of the community.'

The three nodded their heads. 'And,' said Aiden, checking the door, 'you know how long you have to wait for the local authority to respond. If you want an occupational therapy assessment quickly – just send in the referral and mark *for OT*.'

'Isn't that jumping the queue?'

'We're just trying to support you as GPs.'

'About time *someone* did,' Dr Donaldson grumbled.

'Yep. If you want us to go out and visit a patient all you have to do is call or scan a referral and we'll assess immediately. We offer a rapid-response service too – so if you visit a patient and are really concerned about them or you want to avoid a hospital admission, just give us a call on that mobile number.' He pointed to the foot of the leaflet. 'We can be there within the hour.'

'Amazing!' Dr Thomson said.

'Have you got any referral forms with you?' Dr McKinley asked.

Aiden retrieved a bundle from his rucksack.

'Hang on a tick.' Dr McKinley grabbed a stack and disappeared out of the room.

'My apologies,' Helga said, taking her seat. 'That was my agent and I've got a big feature coming up next week in *Scot Today*.'

'As a link worker?' Dr Donaldson queried. 'What angle are they taking?'

'Oh no!' Helga beamed. 'I'm a writer too, you see. My debut novel is one hundred and fourteen on the bestseller list.' She observed their bemused faces. 'Helga Trumpet?'

'Helga, I'm sure they don't want to hear about all that,' Aiden said through gritted teeth.

'Are you the one who writes about bodies in the canal?' Dr Thomson asked. 'Aren't you from Dundee?'

'My book's called *Candy Martini Reaches Out*,' Helga continued. 'It's been met with literary acclaim.'

'So do you work in the team as well?' Dr Donaldson asked.

'Barely,' Aiden muttered.

'Here, take one of my promotional cards – I've just had these printed up *professionally*,' Helga said, scattering brightly coloured glossy postcards over the coffee table. 'And if any of you are interested in hearing more about my writing, I'm presenting at a Writers' Block next week in Musselburgh. Would either of you like a ticket?'

'I … er,' Dr Thomson frowned, gathering up her lunch box, 'think I have a patient waiting.'

'Yes – must dash,' Dr Donaldson echoed, shooting out of the staff room.

'Helga! What are you playing at?' Aiden fumed. 'Come on – let's go.'

Dr McKinley returned holding the wad of referral forms. 'There you go – I've marked them all *for OT* like you asked.'

'That's not for us,' Helga replied. 'They're for—'

'Great! Cheers, Dr McKinley.' Aiden smiled, gripping the sheets.

'But I thought …'

Aiden booted up his PC and entered all the referral information. Ten new patients! That would give him a bit of a cushion. *And what was that Helga like? Selling book festival tickets to GPs?* He shook his head.

Chapter 20

The wind whistled through the stairwell as Helga poked her head out of the front door. She closed it as quietly as she could, locking it behind her.

'Morning!' Donald chirped from nowhere.

'Oh, Donald, you gave me such a fright!'

'Sorry, Helga. How are you today? I didn't see you at all over the weekend.'

'I'm fine, but I'm in a bit of a hurry – Monday morning rush and all that.'

'Of course. You're a very busy lady. How is your latest novel coming along? I can't wait to read it!' He focused on Helga's left shoulder.

'Oh well, you know …' And then a thought struck her. 'Donald, what are you doing on Wednesday evening?'

He blushed and stared down at his feet. 'I … er …'

'It's just that I'm participating in a writers' event in Musselburgh, where local authors will be talking about their work.'

'So kind of like a date?'

'*Nothing* like a date,' Helga replied sternly. 'But if you'd like a ticket just let me know – they cost—'

'Yes, please! I don't usually go out during the week – or at weekends either for that matter – but that would be lovely. Wait till I tell Mum I'm going out with a famous author!'

'Must fly!' Helga cried as she dashed down the stairs.

'How was you weekend, Helga?' Vanda asked from behind her PC.

'Oh well, I was mostly busy writing,' Helga lied, knowing that composing tweets and posting on Facebook wouldn't be the kind of words the publisher was expecting.

'I don't know how you do it,' Molly added. 'By the time it gets to the weekend I just want to flop on the settee and vegetate. It's as much as I can do to keep the kids fed and watered. See on Saturday? One of Mandy's wee pals was having a birthday party at the leisure centre. *Ten minutes* before I was due to take her I remembered I hadn't bought a present. I was all for sticking a fiver in the birthday card but Mandy was in tears – said she'd "never live it down". She's seven, by the way. I had no choice but to gift-wrap a box of Frosties and a tin of fruit cocktail. Mandy never spoke to me for the entire weekend! Honestly, the stress of having kids.'

'Aye, well I'm with you there, sister,' Vanda nodded.

'Oh, and here's another letter for you, Helga,' Molly said, passing it over. 'You've been getting an awful lot of post recently.'

'You know, if they're referrals you should really be encouraging referrers to go online,' Vanda said, frowning. 'We're trying to discourage all that letter-writing carry-on.'

'Shall I take them and put them on the system?' Molly asked.

'Oh, they're not referrals.'

'Fan mail?' Molly teased.

'Something like that.'

The door opened and Bobbie and Aiden tumbled in at the same time. 'What a farce!' Aiden protested.

'Aiden's got to go into an identity parade!' Bobbie giggled.

'Been holding up Aldi's again?' Vanda asked.

'It's that bloody Norman – he's mad!' Aiden snatched up his uniform and went to get changed.

'What's going on?' Molly asked, filling the kettle.

'We were just coming in when Norman stopped us downstairs. Apparently one of the podiatrists saw someone dodgy hanging around the centre last week on the morning of the fire. Thanks,' said Bobbie, adding milk to her coffee. 'And now he wants ten men to line up in an identity parade to see if this bloke can be picked out.'

Aiden returned. 'It's crazy – most of the podiatrists would know who I am and how are they going to get any potential perpetrator to come forward?'

'Does seem a bit daft,' Molly agreed.

Bobbie lathered hummus on to two oatcakes. 'Says he wants to rule out any staff who work here. That tiler chap …'

'Anver?'

'Yeah – Norman's trying to track him down for this morning.'

'I think I already saw him going into the ladies,' Vanda said. 'Who else is being nobbled?'

Bobbie licked her fingers. 'Lance from community health – although he couldn't start a fire with a flamethrower and a can of petrol.'

'What about Ray?' Helga asked. 'He gives me the heebie-jeebies.'

'Me too.'

'Oh, this day just gets better and better,' Aiden complained.

'S'up?' Vanda asked.

'I've got an email from Quinn – sent on Sunday evening, for God's sake! – *demanding* that I explain why I've "blocked" the work for Mrs McGowan. He wants to see me immediately.'

'Want me to come with you?' Bobbie asked. 'Hold your hand?'

'No, thanks, Bobbie – I'd rather come out of this meeting with my balls intact.'

'Aiden!' Molly blushed.

Vanda pushed open the door to the ladies, where Anver was kneeling under the row of basins. Tiles were strewn across the floor. He looked up in surprise. 'Hey, it's my comic-pal who likes to charge about.' He stood up, reaching towards the ceiling and flexing his back. His Hawaiian shirt rode up, revealing a brown belly. Vanda covered her eyes. 'Oi, calm down – I don't get paid enough for this.'

'Thought you'd be used to seeing naked bodies?' He grinned, a gold tooth gleaming from a top molar. 'Anyway, can't you do something about my back? It isn't half giving me grief – mind you it could be coming from my wonky hip.' He rubbed his knees where his chinos were dusty from the floor. 'To tell the truth, my knees aren't much better.'

Vanda shook her head. 'Ever thought you're in the wrong job?'

'*All* the time, lady.' He winked. 'So you can't help me?'

'Not unless you'd like me to take you out the back and shoot you?'

'I'd do it myself only I can't stand the sight of blood.'

'Anyway, I'm just here to tell you that Norman, our security manager, wants to see you downstairs.'

'And *I* told him I only picked up those tiles cos I thought they were being chucked. How was I supposed to know Mr Adamson had them delivered to his workplace?'

'It's about the fire last Thursday morning. Someone spotted a dodgy-looking character hanging around and – can't think why – but your name came up.'

'Lady, I wasn't even here last Thursday!' Anver protested. 'That was the day I had to work from home as I was getting my drains unblocked.'

'How can you possibly do what you do from *home*?'

Anver tapped the side of his nose. 'I'm not just a pretty face, eh?'

'Well, take your good looks downstairs before Norman really gets on the warpath.'

'So no rub-down, then?'

Anver reattached the hazard-warning tape over the entrance to the toilets and headed downstairs. 'You been called up too, sonny?' he asked Aiden as they entered the community room. Aiden recognised Ray slouched in the corner, but there was a stocky man wearing a boiler suit he didn't know and two lads he presumed had been kidnapped from the local high school. Norman stood in the centre, writing down names on his clipboard.

'This is a piece of bloody nonsense!' Aiden declared, standing with his arms folded. 'Why would I want to set fire to my workplace while I'm still in it?'

'And I wasn't even here,' Anver added. 'I was ankle-high in unflushed effluent.'

'All in good time,' said Norman with a swagger. 'Remind me of your names?'

'Aiden James.'

'And you? Are you from the ethnic minority team?' Norman enquired.

'Flipping cheek! I'm the tiler – Anver.'

'So what's the occasion? Montego Monday, is it? And where's your ID badge?'

Anver raked around in his back pocket before producing a bent plastic card.

'Hell, it's not doing much good in there,' Norman barked. 'Get it out, man, where people can see it. Anyway,' he peered at the image, 'that's not even a photo of you!'

'No flies on you, eh?'

'So?'

'The day I went for my photo the lad had been throwing up all night after a pint and paella session. I never quite got round to going back. I found this one in the toolbox.'

'Saints preserve us! Let's hope this building isn't blown to pieces and we end up knocking on some random person's door to tell them her beloved husband is scattered over Gorgie.'

Lance stuck his head round the door. 'Are you ready for me yet, Norman? I won't come in until you're absolutely ready. I can't afford to be breathing in all your airborne pathogens.'

'Yeah, get a move on,' Ray complained. 'I'm due a fag break.'

'And we need to get back to school,' one of the lads in uniform grumbled.

'Fine – in you come, Lance. I'll fetch Simon from the clinic. Now all stand in a line, facing that wall. Don't turn round until I've fetched the witness.'

'What a joke,' Aiden muttered. 'Does he not realise Simon has a visual impairment? He wouldn't know me from Elvis.'

A few minutes later Norman led Simon into the room. 'Okay, chaps I want you all to turn round and face me – look straight ahead and do not attempt to speak to the witness. Now, Simon, in your own time, I want you to study each man and tell me if you recognise the person you saw loitering at the patients' entrance early last Thursday morning.'

'Right, got that,' Simon answered in a serious tone. 'Have they turned round yet?'

One of the teenagers giggled.

'Yes, Simon, they've all turned round. Take your time.'

Simon shuffled forward, his hands held out in front.

'I can't have him touching my face!' Lance cried anxiously, stepping backwards.

'I said no talking!' Norman shouted. 'Stand your ground!'

Simon peered into Aiden's face, close enough to give a blast of stale coffee. He moved along the line until he reached Ray. He sniffed the air and nodded.

'This isn't a bloody smelling contest!' Ray protested.

'I knew that was you, Ray,' Simon said smugly.

'Cheers.'

Simon reached out and ruffled the hair on one of the lads. 'Oi! Paedo! No touching he said.'

'I said no *talking* but that doesn't seem to have made a jot of difference.'

Simon inched along the line, reaching Anver. 'It wasn't a black man.'

'Hallelujah!' Anver squawked. 'Can I get that in writing? For once it's not the black one getting fitted up for a crime he didn't commit.'

'Enough of this ranting,' Norman declared. 'It was only proper that I included a mix of backgrounds.'

'Sorry, mate,' Anver replied. 'But surely you got even a vague description first?'

'This is turning into a travesty!' Norman growled.

'Will I keep going?' Simon asked, halting in front of the boiler-suited stranger. He scrutinised the height and build, shaking his head sadly. 'It definitely wasn't this one. He wasn't as big and bulky.'

'No offence taken.'

'Right, I'm off,' Aiden announced. 'What a farce!'

Lance scooted gel on to his hands, rubbing them fiercely as he bolted from the room.

Aiden took a deep breath and tapped on the door.

'Come!' Quinn boomed.

'Good morning, Mr Adamson,' Aiden gushed, holding out his hand to Quinn, who remained seated behind his desk.

'Sit down.'

Aiden was halfway seated when he caught a flash of movement to his right.

'What's *she* doing here?' Aiden growled.

'Who, Miss Mount? Well, she's going to be managing your team shortly so I've begun the handover process already. Thought I'd get her up to speed.'

'Morning, Aiden,' Sheba smiled sweetly. 'Always a pleasure to see you.'

Aiden snorted.

'So it's about this letter of complaint we've had from Mr John McGowan – Mrs McGowan's son,' Quinn began, holding the letter between finger and thumb as though it were infected with TB.

'Yes, and as I've explained already to Mr McGowan—'

'Don't interrupt, Aiden, I wasn't finished speaking. His son says you've been deliberately obstructive and incredibly unhelpful – although clearly he doesn't have access to a dictionary.' He smirked at Sheba, who returned his smile.

'Mr McGowan says that you've refused to listen to common sense and that you're contravening her human rights by withdrawing her opportunity for self-care.'

There was silence in the office, broken only by Quinn's digital watch peeping the top of the hour.

'Well?' Quinn demanded. 'What have you got to say for yourself?'

'Sorry, I was just waiting for you to finish.'

Quinn scowled. 'And?'

'Look, these aren't my rules. The council decides the criteria for removing a bath and installing a shower. There's obviously a cost involved in this work and they have to prioritise cases where they feel the work is absolutely necessary.'

Quinn was reading something on his iPad and glanced up.

'I've assessed Mrs McGowan on two occasions and she can manage to transfer into and out of her bath safely – therefore she doesn't meet the council's criteria. All I've done is explain this to him. If he has a complaint, he must surely take it up with the council?'

Quinn puffed. 'He is already disputing his case with the council – and they've come back to me, urging me to resolve the issue.'

'How?'

'I think what Mr Adamson is asking you to do is to review Mrs McGowan's ability to manage the bath,' Sheba proposed.

Aiden glared in her direction.

'So is that the matter settled?' Quinn asked, swiping at his iPad.

'What do you mean?' Aiden said. 'I don't follow.'

'Just rewrite your blasted assessment so that she meets the criteria and let's be done with it. I don't have time to get dragged into this type of service-client argument.'

'But that's not right!' Aiden protested. 'You're asking me to make up the outcome of my assessment? I might as well not bother providing my professional opinion at all. Perhaps we ought to just ask the plumber to assess her ability while he's ripping out the bath?'

'There's no place for flippancy in my office,' Quinn concluded. 'I've asked Miss Mount to monitor your competencies and I'm happy for her to review your performance on an ongoing basis. Satisfied?'

'Fine by me,' Sheba twittered.

Without another word Aiden left the office, stormed across the car park and it wasn't until he reached the canal did he remember he'd brought the car.

Chapter 21

The rain splattered against his bedroom window in waves as he raked through the photos. He lay on his stomach on his sagging bed, the albums spread across the candlewick cover. Most people he knew stored their images on a phone or tablet, but he was one of the few who still printed off photos and slipped them methodically between plastic pages. Bad-tempered noises from the kitchen downstairs indicated dinner was on its way. He reached for an older album, flicking through the pages. Now where was it? Squint and blurry photos of Applecross and Kirkcudbright flashed by. That camera he'd been given as a present was rubbish! One of him licking a cone outside Woolworths – how old was *that* picture? He picked up a newer album – yes, there it was. It was one of his favourite images of Helga – she didn't even know he'd taken it. It must have been during May when the pink candyfloss blossom in the Meadows drew photographers from all over. It looked like early morning with a weak sun filtering through the avenue of trees. She was watching something or admiring the view and had an expression of contentment. He wondered if he'd been responsible for any of that.

The oven door opened and slammed shut. A pot banged down on the hob. He kept browsing, lifting out photos and carefully cutting round the shapes before gluing them on to a montage. It was coming along nicely. He wondered if he ought to add captions

– witty little comments to personalise the gift? His head poking out from an orange tent as the wind whipped the flap in his face and water streamed over the canvas – *Another day in paradise*? Or one of Helga at her very first book-signing event – *Next stop Hollywood!*?

'*Dinner time!*' came a roar from the foot of the stairs. He tucked the montage under his bed and blew his nose.

Chapter 22

'How's our marketing strategy working?' Vanda asked, joining the morning run-through.

Molly tapped her keyboard, her back to the team. 'Referrals are definitely up this month – although most of them seem to be for Aiden.'

Helga shot Aiden a look. Vanda pursed her lips. 'Really? They're not usually that specific.'

'Yes, we've had quite a run on requests for OT,' Molly continued.

'So what other ideas can we come up with?' Aiden said swiftly.

'I still like the idea of gathering some patient stories, especially if we can find some patients who've had involvement from us all.'

'But what would we do with them? Quinn's not interested.' Aiden sipped from his water bottle.

'Well, there's all this current focus on "What matters to me",' said Helga. 'In fact there's been something on Twitter – I'm sure there's a whole day dedicated to it. Maybe it'll get some attention from the senior management team?'

'You could be on to something there,' Vanda nodded. 'Bobbie, what *are* you doing?'

'*Paaah!*' Bobbie exhaled loudly. She regained her composure. 'I was at the hairdresser's last night and I read that if you hold your breath for extended periods of time it boosts your respiratory rate. Which impacts on your energy consumption.'

'What a load of—' Aiden started.

'S'true!' Bobbie protested. 'I've been doing it off and on since yesterday and I've already lost a pound.'

'I can lend you a pound,' Molly called over her shoulder.

'Sixth of June,' Helga said, checking her phone. 'We could set up a wee stall at Westside and you can request a "WMTY" pack.'

'I think Bobbie's banned from Westside.'

'*Paaah!*' sighed Bobbie, slumping.

'What about the Dingwalls?' Vanda proposed. 'We've all been visiting them – and we've definitely kept him out of hospital. Helga, you haven't seen them yet but if you could do something with Mr Dingwall then we'll all have seen him.'

'What sort of thing?'

'S and M,' Bobbie giggled.

'Sorry?'

'Ignore her,' Aiden said. 'She's deprived of oxygen. And, as you can see, she's fading away before our very eyes.'

'You know, I think I *am*. Maybe I'll have a coffee. Ooh – are these doughnuts fresh?'

'Yes – actually Anver brought them in as he's finished tiling the toilets.'

'Woo hoo!' Vanda cried. 'Normal service resumed.'

'I mean it!' Molly shouted into her mobile. 'Caz, you get out of your bed right now and get to school! I've had the office on the phone saying you missed registration again. I don't care if it's only RME first thing – shift it. And don't be dobbing in your brother again – I'll see to him when I get home!'

'You tell 'em,' Vanda smiled.

'Sorry, guys – sometimes shouting is the only thing that gets through to them.'

'I find the silent treatment works best for me,' Bobbie added. 'Drives Bob mad.'

'That's not much use on the phone, though, is it?' Aiden frowned. 'Calling someone up then saying nothing?'

'Oh, I don't know. I think that would be a bit creepy,' said Vanda.

'Funny you should mention that.' Molly swivelled round. 'Have you been getting those calls too?'

'*What* calls?' Vanda asked.

'Well, the phone rings and when I answer it the person doesn't say a word.'

'How do you know there's someone there?' Bobbie asked.

'I can sort of hear breathing.'

'Are you sure it's not old Mr Walker?' Helga said. 'Apparently he keeps doing that to his daughter. I think he forgets what he called for.'

'Nah!' said Aiden. 'He wouldn't know our number. How often has it happened?'

Molly shrugged. 'Maybe six or seven times.'

'What?' Vanda cried. 'And have you tried—'

'Yes, the number is withheld.'

'Well, don't be reporting it to Norman or he'll be having our bloody phones tapped.'

They heard a timid knock at the door. 'Talking of tapping,' said Molly, opening the door to Chan. She handed over a piece of paper.

'What's that?' Molly asked.

'It's the new door code. Norman says it's a security measure. Oh, and this present was left at the top of the stairs. It's for Helga.'

'What present?' Helga said.

Chan passed her a rectangular gift-wrapped box, red ribbon

tied in a bow on the front.

'Ay-up!' Bobbie grinned. 'Methinks someone has bought you some fancy-schmancy chocolates by the look of it.'

'I shouldn't think so,' Helga mumbled, throwing the box on to her desk.

'What? Aren't you going to open it?' Bobbie said.

'Here, you take it. It probably is chocolates,' said Helga. She removed the gift label and held out the box.

'Och, no!' Bobbie shook her head firmly. 'I'm on a diet.'

'Please, they're not a kind I like.'

'Really? I thought all chocolate was chocolate.' Bobbie ripped off the paper. 'Wow! Harvey Nics! We don't have any patients who shop at Harvey Nics, do we?'

'*Spar*-vy Nics maybe!' Vanda said. 'Ooh! Lush!'

'*Who* did you say gave them to you?' Bobbie asked.

Helga shrugged. 'Think it was from a fan.'

'The same one who bought you roses?' Molly wondered. 'Looks like he's got a bit of a thing for you.'

'Or *her*,' Bobbie chucked in. 'You shouldn't speculate.'

'Wish I had a wealthy admirer,' Vanda complained. 'But until such time … let's run through the patients.'

'I can't believe it's Tuesday already,' Molly said, laying the mugs out on the table. 'Your wee group comes round so quickly.'

'Hiya!' Peter beamed, crashing on to a chair. 'I'm Peter – are you new?'

'Me?' Molly laughed. 'No, I work with Helga.'

'Aw – shame. You smell nice.'

'Do I?' Molly blushed, dashing out of the community room.

'And I'm telling you that if the council spent the same amount of money filling in potholes as they do on making bloody parks that no kids want to play in cos they're all too busy on their phones – I'd be gliding here on air,' Dennis grumbled to Jimmy as they arrived. 'My teeth have just about been shaken oot my heid!'

'You don't notice it so much on the bus,' Jimmy commented. 'But the drivers do like to slam on the brakes. I thought the one we had today was practising his tap dancing!'

Harry followed, cigarette holder in hand. 'You pair are like those Muppets.'

'What muppets?' Jimmy asked.

'Statler and Waldorf,' Lex answered. She threw her jacket over the back of her chair.

Dennis shook his head. 'I've no idea what you're saying, lassie.'

Princess bounded into the room, this week wearing a white fur dress and long white gloves.

'Heavens!' Harry exclaimed. 'What have you come as this week? A polar bear?'

'No!' Princess sulked. 'I got this outfit from my Auntie Jean for my birthday. I'm a snow queen. It's actually very cosy.'

'All very well and good for Narnia,' Harry drawled, 'but there's not much call for a permanent state of winter in Gorgie.'

'It's all slush now, anyway,' Dennis added.

'Well, I think you look fabulous,' Helga said encouragingly. 'How did you enjoy your birthday?'

'Oh, it was wonderful!' Princess gushed. 'Mummy, Daddy and I went out for supper.'

'Nice.' Helga smiled. 'Where did you go?'

'Just to our local pub – the Jolly Swagger. It's two meals for eight pounds during the week and Daddy was in the darts match. We stayed out until pretty late – well, at least until Daddy had to punch someone in the face.'

'Oh dear – what happened?'

'A rude man said I looked like Humpty Dumpty. I think he was a *little* bit tipsy as I was meant to be Rapunzel!'

'Anyway, where's the dark lad?' Dennis chuckled. 'Run out of things to say?'

Kamal hovered at the doorway before taking a seat next to Lex. Dennis coughed. 'Alright, son?'

'So! Welcome to this week's Tuesday Chatters!' Helga said. 'I hope you've all had a good week?'

'If you call being fricking imprisoned by ageing tossers, then yeah – it was spot on,' Lex growled.

'I had a good week!' Peter said with excitement.

'Oh – perhaps you'd like to share with the group?' Helga suggested.

'My mum got extra benefit for looking after me.'

'What?' Dennis cried. 'You're a grown man, for goodness' sake. Why would she get paid to look after you?'

'Can't say.' Peter suddenly looked embarrassed.

'You can't leave us in suspense,' Harry complained.

'It's just that I sometimes need help at night,' said Peter, focusing on his hands.

'Well, we all need help at some point,' Helga smiled. 'Do you have nightmares?'

Peter nodded. 'And then I get *very* scared.'

'He's a bloody bed-wetter!' Dennis snapped. 'And it's our flipping council tax that's paying for his ma's extra laundry.'

'I don't mean to!' Peter protested. 'But sometimes it's just sooo dark. And there's a bogeyman under my bed.'

'There's a bogey living in your fricking nose!' Lex tutted.

'Right!' Helga clapped her hands. 'Why don't we all help ourselves to a lovely hot drink.'

'Shall I just have my cola, miss?'

'Yes, Peter. Kamal – would you like a tea or coffee?'

He shook his head.

'Do you prefer, like, proper coffee?' Lex asked.

Kamal looked at her with dark eyes and shook his head again.

'What about a beer?' she persisted.

'They don't drink alcohol!' Dennis exclaimed from the other side of the table.

'Dennis!' Helga scolded. 'You can't go making assumptions about people.'

'Ask him, then.'

'*Do* you drink alcohol?' Lex asked quietly.

Kamal stared at the floor, giving an almost imperceptible shake of his head.

'Ha!' Dennis crowed.

'Well, we can't all be fricking alcoholics like you!'

'Let's just calm things down.' Helga flapped her hands. 'Now that you've got your coffee …'

'And cola!'

'… and cola, perhaps we could move on to our discussion for this week? At the end of last week's session I asked you to bring a personal item that had special meaning or said something particular about you.'

'Oh, shit!' Dennis muttered. 'Forgot.'

'Can I go first, miss?' Peter's hand waved frantically as Lex rolled her eyes.

'Of course – what have you brought with you?' Helga's attention was caught by the twenty-one Twitter notifications on her mobile;

she wondered what that was all about?

Peter reached down with a plump hand into his coat pocket. He held up a cheap frame that mounted a photo of a suited man, so the group could see.

'Who's that, then?' Dennis demanded. 'That your dad?'

'It's Suggs,' Peter replied proudly. '*And* it's signed.'

'Who the hell is Suggs?'

'He's from Madness.'

'Aren't we all?' Dennis muttered.

'What's madness?' asked Jimmy.

'Don't!' Helga held up her hand as Lex opened her mouth.

Peter beamed. 'That's my favourite band *ever* – they're brilliant. They're a ska band?'

'Nope, you've lost me, son.'

'They dance like this.' Peter jumped up from his seat and proceeded to run on the spot, his arms pumping. 'You must know Madness?' he puffed, collapsing back into his seat. 'I got this when they came up to Edinburgh.'

'Gosh,' Helga said. 'Did you get to see them?'

'Nah.'

'What about meeting Suggs?'

Peter shook his sweaty head.

'So how did you get a signed photo?'

'Oh, my mum bought that at Ingliston market.'

'Nice,' Helga smiled. 'What about you, Jimmy?'

Jimmy ran a gnarled hand over the maroon and white football scarf tied round his neck. 'I'm wearing mine but it's not just to keep me warm. This scarf is ancient. I've supported Hearts for as long as I can remember. My dad always took me to the game every Saturday without fail.'

'That's child cruelty, that is,' Dennis remarked.

'And then I took David, my lad. Took him for years until he discovered rugby.'

'You like football, then?' Helga prompted.

Jimmy shrugged. 'I've never really thought about it – it's just what we did back then. Football has been a constant throughout my life: when I was a kid, when I was married, after I retired. People come and go, but there's always football. I stopped going when I got moved into the high-rise – it's too far away now.' He patted his scarf. 'But I've got plenty memories of wearing this – happy *and* despairing.'

'I hear you, brother!' Dennis agreed.

'Thank you for sharing,' Helga nodded. 'What have you got there, Harry?'

Harry was fingering a black velvet collar. 'Oh well, I couldn't really think of what you meant so I brought my Bibi's collar.'

'Is it a flea collar?' Peter asked. 'My mum says all cats have fleas.'

'It is not,' Harry snapped.

'Do you love your cat?' Princess asked. 'Is it sweet?'

'Bibi and I happen to share the same flat. She's no more sweet than I am.'

'I'm guessing you're very like your cat?' Helga suggested.

'Have *you* got fleas?' Peter persisted.

'I meant that cats are such independent souls – they like their own company?' said Helga.

'I suppose.' Harry sniffed. 'I'm a bit of a loner and Bibi certainly doesn't need me.'

'Have you ever been married?' Princess asked. 'I can't imagine *never* being married!'

'Oh, it's surprisingly easy.'

'But did you *want* to get married?'

'Maybe once, when I was young. I nearly got married. Turns out he was a right bastard so I was well shot of him.'

'My dad says he won't just let *any* man marry me.'

'I'm not sure any man *will* marry you,' Harry commented.

Helga finished her coffee. 'So, Kamal, have you brought anything?'

Kamal studied the floor for several minutes as rain rattled against the windows. Dennis coughed impatiently. Eventually Kamal lifted a worn paperback from his lap and laid it on the table. Helga read the upside-down title. '*The Outsider* by Albert Camus.'

'Is it a book about the country?' Peter asked. 'I hate being outside, it's always freezing.'

Helga put a hand on Kamal's arm. 'Is that how you feel? Like an outsider?'

She felt Kamal's arm stiffen under his jumper. He let his hands fall back into his lap and stared at the floor.

'You'll always be an outsider unless you get forced to join in like the rest of us,' Dennis moaned. 'Why don't you speak up for yourself?'

'And why don't you fricking well leave him alone?' said Lex, glaring.

'Would you like to tell us a bit about how you feel?' Helga asked in a kind voice.

Kamal shook his head, his lips tightly closed. 'All in good time,' said Helga. 'So Lex, are we on to you?'

'If we must be,' she growled, continuing to sit in silence.

'Not you as well!' Dennis complained. 'You youngsters aren't really getting the hang of this social group at all!'

'Give her a minute,' Helga tutted.

Lex's right arm lay on the table, a plastic object gripped tightly in her hand.

'Lex?'

Gradually, she unfurled her slim fingers to reveal a purple plastic Hot Wheels car. It sat on the table as she stared at its painted silver wheels and black tinted windows. With her index finger she propelled the car back and forth.

'You're going to have to explain this one,' Harry said.

Lex sighed, her eyes fixed on the toy car. 'My brother Chris bought me a Happy Meal. I was twelve and thought, *How old does he think I am? I'm practically a fricking teenager!*'

'*I* still like Happy Meals,' Princess offered.

'Me too,' Peter agreed.

'So your brother bought you a McDonald's?' Harry asked. 'Is that a big deal?'

Lex continued to focus on the car as it rolled along under her finger. 'It was a Saturday evening and I was in my room watching TV. He threw me a Happy Meal and said not to tell Mum. Then he went off with his best mate, on the back of Allan's motorbike, and never came home again.'

'Oooh! Did he run away somewhere?' Princess asked.

'No, he didn't. A Mercedes pulled out from a junction without looking and they were both wiped off the planet.'

'What, dead?' Peter asked.

'Yes, fucking dead, you retard!'

'Now, Lex,' Helga warned.

'Sorry!' she barked. 'Yes, fricking dead. And now I have to go on living with my parents who walk around the house like stuck-up zombies. They don't even know I exist. In fact, it's worse than that. They *do* know I exist but wish it had been me not him that was killed.'

'Lex! You don't mean that,' said Helga. 'What makes you have such thoughts?'

'Because they say, "Why can't you be more like Chris?" So like, what, *dead*?'

'They're still grieving, though. You all are. When did this happen?'

'Seven years ago … and it's never got any fricking better.'

'But it's easy to put someone up on a pedestal who can't ever be seen in another light.'

Lex snorted. 'He was a head boy at high school – captain of the rugby team. This was his last summer before he went off to Aberdeen Uni to do medicine. He was every parent's wet fricking dream.'

'I'm sure you did well at school too?'

'How *could* I?' Lex protested. 'That was me just going into high school. I didn't sleep for a year. I … well, what does it matter? Now I'm sitting here with a bunch of fricking saddos and I can't say anything because I'm not much better.'

'Would you like a hug?' Peter asked.

'What do *you* think?'

'That's just the saddest thing I've ever heard,' Princess wept. 'But maybe, if I never meet a prince, perhaps we could share a flat together?'

'Jesus!' Dennis exclaimed. 'If she wasn't suicidal before …'

'She's not suicidal – *are* you?' Helga checked.

Lex shrugged, tucking the car back in her pocket. She pulled the hood up over her head and yanked the toggles.

'Am I the only one who needs a drink?' Harry asked.

'Good idea!' Helga said. 'More coffee, anyone? Now before you go, remember we've got our wee trip tomorrow evening.'

'Will we need to bring anything?' Jimmy asked.

'Just wrap up warm,' said Helga. 'It can get pretty cold on the minibus. Now Jimmy, you're furthest away so the driver will pick you up first. If you can all be ready for six o'clock, we should have everyone picked up and taken to Musselburgh for seven.'

'We normally have our tea then,' Peter said anxiously. 'I hope I have time for pudding.'

'I'll be lucky if I get anything chucked my way,' Dennis grumbled. 'Last night I got served faggots! I tell you, the bloody dog gets better quality meat than I do.'

Helga's fingers were numb with cold as she put the key in the front door.

'Hiya, Helga!' Donald leapt out from his flat. 'How has your day been so far?'

'Busy,' she replied, keeping her head down.

'Me too. I had to take Dolly to the vet this morning. Mum must have given her chocolate again and she shat all over the kitchen.'

'Well, I must be getting on.'

'Absolutely! By the way, I've got my seven pounds – thought I could get my ticket just now so I'm all prepared for tomorrow?'

'Tomorrow?'

'Your special book talk – *duh*!' His head almost spun 360 degrees with excitement.

'Of course – I'm just a bit tired. Wait here and I'll get it for you.' Helga pushed her door open and went in search of the envelope Kate had posted. She found it on the hall table and fished out one ticket.

'Super!' Donald said, standing right behind her. 'Gosh, you've got lots left over – do you want my mum to see if anyone down the club wants one? Mind you, they're probably all concessions so you won't make a penny out of them. They're all either pensioners or on disability.'

Helga gave a tight smile. 'Thank you, Donald, but I'm sure we've got enough people coming. I'll just see you out.' She ushered him back along the hall.

'How are you getting there? Shall I chum you on the bus?'

'Actually, I'm accompanying a group from the health centre and we're getting picked up by minibus.'

'Perfect! What time shall I be ready for?'

'He should swing by here about six thirty,' sighed Helga, closing the door firmly.

'I'll bring my camera!' Donald shouted from beyond the door.

Chapter 23

'Isn't it today that you're doing your big feature thingy?' Molly asked, handing over another two letters.

'It is,' Helga nodded.

'You don't look like you had much sleep. Still – you did say you were getting a makeover, didn't you? They can do wonders with foundation these days. And – worst-case scenario – all the celebrities get airbrushed.'

'Thanks, Molly!'

'I just meant … oh, here's Bobbie.'

'What have I done now?'

'I'm just saying – Helga has the magazine feature today.'

'Oh yes!' Bobbie peered at Helga. 'Were you up all night worrying?'

'I've got one hell of a day today,' Helga snapped. 'The *Scot Today* interview is at lunchtime, then this evening it's my Writers' Block. I'm a bag of nerves.'

'Lunchtime?' Bobbie echoed. 'Where do you have to go? It'll have to be a pretty quick interview!'

'Don't worry – I'll make up the time.'

Bobbie shrugged. 'Hot cross bun?'

'Got any spare?' Molly asked. 'I didn't have time for breakfast this morning. Connor threw up all over his bed and I wanted to get the sheets in the washing before I left. Then I had to drop him at my mum's and she wasn't too happy as today she's getting her kitchen laminated.'

'Have you tried lighting a lavender candle?' Bobbie suggested, stirring her coffee.

'Does that help with vomiting bugs?'

'I meant for Helga. It makes the bedroom nice and calm.'

'Who wants a calm bedroom?' Vanda asked, hanging up her coat. 'Surely one's *chambre* should be all juju and fireworks!'

'Maybe in *your* room,' Bobbie muttered. 'I'm more likely to be sending up a flare!'

'I think we'll all be sending up flares soon. Did you see how many slates came off the roof last night in the storm? They're smashed right over the car park. Ray's cordoned off a complete corner while he sweeps them up,' Molly reported.

'I saw that,' said Vanda. 'What's he like with that hard hat? He looks like one of the Village People!'

'If *only,*' Molly giggled.

The door opened as Aiden and Sheba entered the office at the same time.

'Oh aye?' Bobbie grinned. 'Been car sharing again?'

'I came by bike!' Aiden said moodily, snatching up his uniform.

'And to what do we owe this honour?' asked Vanda from her corner.

Sheba sauntered into the office, dumping her bag on an empty desk. 'Mind if I sit here today? Thought I'd do a bit of shadowing – see what you lot get up to in the west.' She leant back in the swivel chair, rotating slowly as she absorbed the morning's routine.

'Helga's doing a big feature at lunchtime for *Scot Today!*' Bobbie blabbed. Helga glared over her MacBook.

'Is she now?' Sheba smirked. 'Rubbing shoulders with the rich and famous no doubt?'

'It's a marvellous opportunity for me – great exposure.'

'Whatever.'

Chan's timid knock at the door was answered by Vanda. 'Hi Chan, how are you?'

'Fine,' she said, not looking fine at all. 'I've just come to tell you that one of your pool cars is out of action.'

'Is it? What's happened?'

'Ray just rang to say that a slate has cracked the windscreen on the Corsa.'

'They're all Corsas, Chan. Did he say which one?'

'I don't even know why he calls me!' she cried. 'I think he just likes shouting. It's not my fault half the roof has blown off!'

'Don't worry about him,' Vanda tutted. 'He's just a knob.'

'Who's a knob?' Aiden asked, still adjusting his tunic.

'I've got to go now,' Chan mumbled, closing the door.

'That Ray is such a bully,' said Vanda, flicking on the kettle switch. 'I have to say your morning ritual could do with a bit of resuscitation. It's –' Sheba checked her watch – 'nearly eight forty and I haven't even heard so much as a peep about a patient.'

'You should have been here half an hour ago,' said Bobbie, popping a hot cross bun into the toaster. 'By eight o'clock I had Dr Brand on the blower referring a rapid-response patient. She was in a right tizzy about one of my ladies who had a fall last night.'

'Really?'

'Yep,' Bobbie winked at Molly. 'So this is nearly elevenses for me.'

'Perhaps I could come out with you to observe your holistic assessment?'

'If you like. Watch the master at work, eh?'

The phone rang and Molly snatched it up. 'Harrison

Intervention Team – Molly speaking. How may I help you?' she recited.

Sheba cocked up one ear.

'Of course.' Molly took notes on a pad. 'Yes, right. Uh-huh. I see ... well. Of course I'll pass that on to our physiotherapist. *Fire!*' she screamed. A spiral of blue smoke snaked up from the toaster. '*Fire!*' Molly repeated, flapping her free hand at the appliance. 'Bobbie – your bun's on fire!'

'Oh, crap!' Bobbie exclaimed.

'Get the window open!' Vanda shouted from across the office. 'The bloody fire alarm will go off again.'

Molly hung up and began tugging at the sash window. The smoke billowed up towards the ceiling. 'It's no good! It's painted shut!'

'Move over,' Aiden commanded. He gave the window a mighty heave and it shot up with a creak. A blast of cold air blew in.

'Thank God!' Vanda muttered.' I couldn't bear another episode of Storming Norman.'

Bobbie poked at the toaster with a knife.

'Are you seriously trying to kill yourself?' Aiden demanded. He tipped the toaster upside down until a charcoal bap fell to the floor followed by a mound of crumbs.

'Aiden!' Molly protested.

Sheba reclined in her chair with her arms folded. 'It's like a bloody Carry On film here! The sooner we get you integrated the better.'

'Oh, it's not always like this,' said Bobbie. 'Normally it's quite disorganised in the morning.'

Chapter 24

Helga admired the majestic George Street Hotel with its series of international flags whipping against their flagpoles. She posted a selfie on Instagram – *My date with* Scot Today*!* The heavy entrance door led into a plush foyer with its gilt and oak polished reception desk. A suited man with slicked-back hair was seated at a PC. He glanced up over the top of his glasses. 'May I help you?' he asked in an Eastern European accent.

'I'm here for the *Scot Today* interview,' Helga announced. 'I've to ask for Lianne?'

'And your name?'

'Helga Trumpet.'

He lifted a clipboard, running a silver pen down the list.

'Helen, did you say?'

'*Helga*. Trumpet.'

'Hmm, we have a Helen McBryde.'

'That's probably not me. Perhaps if you call Lianne?'

He glared at her as he put aside the clipboard and lifted the receiver. 'Good morning, Lianne – we have a Miss …' he covered the receiver. 'Sorry, what did you say your name was?'

'Helga Trumpet.'

He nodded. 'A Miss Trampet here. I see. Very good.'

'Please have a seat and Lianne will be with you shortly.'

Helga sank into one of the low leather armchairs that were

arranged round a glass coffee table. She noted several copies of last month's *Scot Today* fanned in one corner, a toothy model grinning on the front cover. Her watch showed it was already twelve thirty. *They better get a move on! And where were the others?* She observed the smartly dressed guests as they crisscrossed the reception area – some dragging pull-along cases, others grasping briefcases. Stiletto heels tip-tapped over the marble flooring. Finally, a young girl wearing a scarlet suit and patent black heels headed in her direction. A froth of blonde hair framed the girl's made-up face. She held out her hand. 'Hi, I'm Lianne – sorry to keep you waiting.' Her other hand also gripped a clipboard.

As Helga struggled to rise from the low chair, the girl almost pulled her up with her handshake. 'Please follow me – we're going to the Calton suite. Is that what you're wearing?'

'Yes – why?'

'Oh, didn't you receive the email asking everyone to wear either black or white? A mix of colours looks rather cheap.' She frowned at Helga's checked shirt and woollen skirt. They arrived in a large room, set up cabaret-style – empty except for a photographer who was changing a long lens for an even longer one. A range of silver and black backdrops had been pinned against one wall.

'Where's everyone else?' Helga asked, setting down her shoulder bag.

'What do you mean? Right, Archie, ready to go when you are.'

'I mean the other writers?'

Lianne scowled. 'Oh, we don't bring in everyone at the same time – we bring in the novices first. Couldn't have the pros hanging around all day.'

'But I thought we were having a group photo.'

'Did you?'

'So I won't get to meet any of the other writers?'

'No, they're mostly still having lunch in the dining room. Archie's going to take your photo.'

'Don't I get a makeover?'

'Sorry?'

'Kate – my agent – said we'd be offered a makeover.'

'Oh … yeah. Well you had to be in this morning for that. The girls have all gone now. Okay, Archie?'

Archie stood up, camera at the ready. 'Over here, please.' He switched on a bright light.

Helga snatched up her bag, rummaging in the bottom for a lipstick. She ran a brush through her hair and blew her nose.

'Mind taking your glasses off?' Archie asked from behind his camera.

'Oh, well, I – I'm so used to seeing my face with glasses.' She folded them in one hand.

'Now look straight into the camera,' Archie coaxed. Helga squinted into the light. 'If you could just look *at* me,' he said, irritated.

'But you keep moving.'

'Don't worry about that. Chin up. And look to the right. No – *your* right. Lianne, can you sort her collar, it's sticking up.'

Lianne gave a tug at Helga's collar. She frowned. 'I'm just not sure about that shirt. Have you got a suit jacket you could wear over the top?'

Helga shook her head. 'I just wore my raincoat – it's chucking it down out there.'

Archie sighed. 'Perhaps if she stands side-on?'

'Really?' Lianne asked. 'I'm not sure that would be any better. Never mind – just take a few and we'll sort it out later.'

'I think that's the best I'm going to get.'

'Fine. Now, if you go back to reception and take a left you'll find the Tay room – Dawn wants to ask a few questions.'

'And the lunch?' Helga asked hopefully.

Lianne swiped at her phone. 'That'll be finished by now. Just head round to the Tay.'

It was mid-afternoon by the time Helga made her way back to the office. Sheba looked up sharply from her desk. 'There you are, Helga! You've been away for more than *three hours*. You've been completely out of contact and *I* have had to deal with your – quite rightly – furious patients.'

'Furious? Who would that be?' Helga slumped behind her desk. 'I'm really sorry – it took longer than I expected. I'll make up the time.'

'Of course you will – you'll have to stay on late this afternoon.'

'This afternoon? But I can't, not this evening.'

'How so?'

'I have another engagement, that's all.'

'Well, Molly and I have had to pick up the pieces while you've been out gallivanting. We've had a Mr Cormack on the phone—'

'Mr Cormack!' Helga said. 'I completely forgot!'

'He was devastated that you weren't there to take him down to the bowling club. He'd been looking forward to it all week. Now, Helga, Molly is here to support the team with admin – she is not here to manage your caseload.'

Helga glanced at Molly, who mouthed, 'Sorry.'

'I'll give him a call but I must have some lunch first.'

'*Lunch?*' Sheba exclaimed. 'You can't stop for lunch now! You'll be heading off soon.'

'Right,' Helga nodded. 'Can I at least grab a coffee?'

'I'll get you a coffee,' Molly offered, jumping up.

'You may be a budding author and think you have everyone wrapped round your little finger,' Sheba seethed, 'but I *will not* be tolerating this intractable behaviour when we merge.'

'Ooh – big words!' Bobbie smiled, returning to the office. 'Who's done what now? Molly, don't tell me you've been online gambling again while we've been out visiting patients?'

Molly handed Helga her coffee. 'You know me too well!'

'Thanks,' Helga said with an appreciative smile.

'Right, well, I think I've seen enough nonsense for one day,' Sheba announced, gathering up her belongings.

'That you off?' Bobbie asked. 'Hope your write-up about me this morning gets me extra Brownie points. I can't let Aiden beat me. Mind you, he *does* have an advantage over me.'

Sheba blushed, letting the door slam behind her.

Chapter 25

Donald gave his woolly scarf an extra wind round his neck as he and Helga stamped their feet on the frosty pavement. The odd car swept past, slowing as it approached the end of the road. 'We could have watched from my window,' Donald offered. 'I hate to think of you catching a cold or flu.'

Helga blew into her mittened hands. 'I wouldn't trust the driver to wait. One toot of his horn and if we hadn't appeared in thirty seconds he'd be off.'

'Oh! Is this him coming now?'

A dented white minibus drew in at the kerb, a rusty scrape running its length. Helga opened the door on the passenger side, Donald close behind. 'You'll need to sit in the back,' she said.

'What? Aren't they dangerous?'

'Don't be ridiculous, Donald! Get in the back.'

Donald reluctantly slid open the side door as seven faces glared back at him. 'Hiya!' He waved. 'I'm Donald.'

'Shut the bloody door, man!' Dennis barked from the corner, where he was strapped into his mobility scooter.

'I'm here to accompany Helga,' said Donald, jerking to release the seat belt.

'Are you her boyfriend?' Princess gasped.

'I'm her—'

'Neighbour!' Helga shouted from the front. 'Right, that's

everyone, driver – let's get to Musselburgh town hall.'

The driver parked next to the old civic building, its spire hidden in the gloomy darkness. He used the hydraulic lift to assist Dennis to the pavement. 'I can take it from here,' Dennis grumbled. 'I'm not a bloody sofa delivery.'

After everyone had alighted the driver sat back in his seat and unfurled a newspaper.

'Aren't you going to come in?' Helga asked. 'I'm going to be sharing my thoughts about my writing.'

'If it's all the same to you, I'm just as happy here.'

'Suit yourself. But it's freezing.'

The driver unscrewed the lid of a Thermos flask. 'Don't you worry about me, hen.'

A uniformed clerk manned the entrance to the building, his breath rolling in clouds. 'Tickets, please.'

Helga handed each of the Tuesday Chatters their ticket. 'Got mine!' Donald flapped it in the face of the guard, who released the glass door.

'This is so exciting!' Princess shrieked, clapping her hands. 'I wonder if we'll see anyone famous?'

'Do you think Ewan McGregor will be here?' Peter asked, scanning the faces of the guests.

'Why would Ewan McGregor possibly be in Musselburgh on a Wednesday winter's night?' Harry said, exasperation in her voice.

'But Helga might have written the next Star Wars film!'

'Peter, that trilogy is well gone. His lightsabre days are over. It's the young team now.'

'But maybe he would like Helga's book?'

'Are we bucking going in or not?' Lex demanded. 'It's Baltic out here.'

'You need to learn to layer up – that's the secret,' said Jimmy, patting his woollen overcoat.

'There is no bucking *secret*,' Lex retorted. 'Just stay indoors. It's not exactly breaking news.'

Helga herded them into the expansive hall, where plastic chairs had been arranged in rows facing a low stage, where four seats faced the audience.

'It's not much warmer in here!' Dennis complained.

'Apparently the boiler's on the blink,' Helga replied. A number of electric heaters had been positioned along the sides, cables trailing from extension cords.

'Watch you don't trip,' Helga warned as she guided her group to the seats. 'Perhaps if you all sit in the back row, then your scooter won't block the aisle, Dennis?'

'God forbid I should stop anyone leaving the building.'

'Shall I come up with you?' Donald asked. 'I *am* supposed to be accompanying you.'

'I think I'll be fine from here. *Blast it!*'

'*Yoo hoo!* Helga, darling!' her mother yelled from the entrance. 'We're here!' She and her friend Mags joined the group. 'Are these all your little friends, Helga?'

'Less of the little,' Harry objected.

'Less of the "friends",' said Lex.

'Hi, Mum.' Helga squirmed as her mother gave her a brief hug.

'Hello, folks! My name's Eileen and this is Mags.'

'Irene?' Jimmy asked. 'My aunt was an Irene.'

'*Eileen.*'

'These are some of the people I work with.' Helga gave a vague sweep of her hand.

'Really?' Her mother frowned at Lex's green hair, piercings

and tattoos. 'They must have a pretty relaxed dress code at the health centre. And what's *your* job?' She bent her knees to speak to Dennis.

'My job is to top myself before my bloody family does it for me!'

'Come along, Mum, let's find you and Mags a seat.' Helga propelled her mother towards the front. '*Donald!*' she hissed. 'You're in charge.'

'Absolutely!' Donald saluted.

'Is she your boss?' Princess asked.

'No.'

'Then why is she bossing you around?' Peter asked. 'Anyway, is there a shop here because my mum's given me money for sweets?'

'A shop?' Harry echoed. 'It's a town hall, not a blooming mall. Why can this generation not last five minutes without spend, spend, spend!'

'Look, I've got plenty of sweets here.' Donald unzipped his rucksack to reveal bags of boiled sweets and toffees. I got them three for a pound!'

'Can I have some?' Princess asked. 'Pink ones are my favourite.'

Donald enticed them into their seats as if he were *Chitty Chitty Bang Bang's* Child Catcher. He gave each person a handful. 'That's to last you till the break.'

'Thanks, Dad,' said Lex.

'What about you, pal?' Donald asked Kamal. 'Want a sweet?'

Kamal shook his head and stuck his hands in his jacket pocket.

'Look!' Helga's mother waved her manuscript.

'What's that?'

'It's the first fifty pages of *Rose-Marie Gala Touches Love.*'

'But why have you brought it here?'

'Well, there are bound to be lots of editor-type people and literary agents. Maybe even publishers!'

'Mum, there won't be. It's just us three writers and the audience.'

'You don't know who might be here.' She gave a furtive glance at the rows behind. 'Just take it.'

'And what am I supposed to do with it, Mum?'

'Pass it around the writers – see what they think. It would be super to get some early feedback.'

'It's very good,' Mags nodded. 'Better than what I've wrote.'

'Oh, yours is good too,' said Eileen, patting her friend's knee.

'But we're meant to be talking about *our* writing this evening,' Helga insisted. 'There won't be time for much else.'

'Ah! I've thought of that,' said Eileen smugly. She reached into her briefcase and removed a handful of manuscripts. 'Just take these and make sure each writer gets one to take home with her. I've put my email address on the front. I know it's only the first fifty pages but I know how it ends so I can tell them if they need more info.' She piled the sheets on to Helga's lap.

'Mum!'

Mags leant across. 'Is there an interval, Helga?' she asked. 'Or should I go to the toilet now?'

'Look, I have to go and find the organiser. Yes, there's an interval – I'll see you later.'

'Good luck!' Eileen winked.

Helga found the organiser, a heavyset woman in her forties with dyed black hair and Doc Martin boots who looked like she'd just finished a shift at Saughton Prison. Helga was greeted with, 'Where have *you* been? You should have reported in at seven.'

'Sorry, I had people to organise.'

'*I've* got people to organise!' She stabbed her pen at her oversized clipboard. 'This lot has paid good money for tonight – they want a bit of bang for their buck. Thought I was going to have to tell them there are only three speakers,' she grumped. 'I don't want a riot on my hands.' *You'd know*, thought Helga. 'I'm sorry, I should have let you know I was here.' Suddenly she felt exhausted.

'Anyway, I've had to swap you round. I told the other lassie she could go on before the break. I've put you last.' She made a point of writing HELGA TRUMPET – LAST SPEAKER on her sheet. 'You need to sit at the front. I'll call you up one by one. At the end we'll be having a panel discussion.'

'Right – who's leading that?' Helga said.

'Some bint called Judy. She was here first thing – now *she's* gone missing. Honestly, you lot are worse than kids. If you see an interrogator in an orange trouser suit that looks like she's got piles, give me a shout.'

By seven thirty the lights dimmed and a spotlight shone on the trouser-suited chairperson who gave the first speaker a glowing introduction. She handed the microphone to the lone writer who sat quivering centre stage. After the two women had relived their tortuous writing careers, the lights came up and the chair announced, with a pinched mouth, a fifteen-minute interval. She gestured towards a tea station set up outside the gents' toilets as the audience dispersed.

'That was sooo boring!' Peter declared. 'And I've finished all my sweeties. I wish I'd brought some cola. Excuse me, mister?'

'Me?' Donald asked, edging towards the aisle.

'Does that shop sell cola?'

'Hmm, I think it's just tea and coffee.'

'My hands are actually numb,' Dennis said, rubbing them together.

'I've been in warmer graveyards,' Harry agreed.

Princess pulled a beanie over her ears and stuffed her hands in her fur muff. 'My daddy wouldn't like me being cold. He'd give me a big hug.'

'It's not Helga's fault it's freezing in this hall,' Donald said through his scarf. 'Here – help yourselves to my cache. I'm going to see if she's okay. She must be really nervous.' He elbowed his way through the audience to the front.

Helga and Eileen were hovering by the stage, cradling plastic cups of instant coffee. 'I oughtn't to,' said Mags. 'I'll be desperate the whole second half.'

'It is fabulous, though, isn't it?' Eileen effused. 'I feel so energised by all this creativity! I wish I'd brought my typewriter.'

'Hardly practical, Mum.'

'I swear I'll be up until midnight dashing off the next chapter.'

The organiser stomped past, ramming the last of a chocolate bar into her mouth. She nodded at Helga.

'Who's that?' Eileen shrilled. 'Is she someone important? Is she from one of the big London publishing houses?'

'Calm down! I've no idea what her job is – she seems to be organising this event.'

'But do you think she's something to do with the literary world?'

'I've no idea, Mum! I've never met her before in my life. For all I know she's a clerk at the town hall! Maybe she's in charge of the bin lorries!'

'Alright, keep your hair on! I know you're nervous,' said Eileen. 'Oh, I've just had a thought – if she's the organiser, do you think they'll let me go on at the end? I could be the voice of the grassroots writer. *Excuse me!*' She chased after the prison warder.

Donald popped up in front of the stage, giving Mags a fright. 'How are you bearing up?'

'I'm fine, Donald,' said Helga, checking her watch. 'Be glad when it's over, mind you. It's been a *long* day!'

'It's a brilliant show! Thank you for inviting me. Maybe we can do more things like this together?'

'Oh, er, I ... look, you better get back to your seat. The second half is about to start.'

'So are you in or are you out?' Dennis asked the group.

'Which pub do you mean?' Jimmy asked. 'Is it near?'

'It's right next door – the Auld Tavern. It'll be as cosy as you like – if I remember rightly it even has a real fire. And we can all have a wee nip to warm us up.'

'I'm paying – my treat,' Harry grinned, shaking her purse.

'There you go! Even better,' Dennis said. 'It would be rude to turn down a lady's kind offer.'

'I *could do* with being warmed up,' Jimmy agreed. 'My circulation is a plumber's nightmare.'

'What about you youngsters?'

'Freaking-A!' Lex said, giving the thumbs up. Kamal shrugged his slight shoulders.

'I've never been in a pub before,' said Peter with a worried expression. 'Does it sell cola?'

'Lots of cola!' Princess laughed. She took Peter's chubby hand. 'Come on, Peter. Oh! Your hand's icy cold, you should put it in my muff.'

As the lights dimmed, the group tiptoed towards the exit, Dennis leading on his mobility scooter.

A blanket of warm air engulfed the Chatters as they trooped into the Auld Tavern. Four locals perched on barstools, four pints of beer lined the counter. Four heads were turned to a screen behind the bar where a wintry game of football was being played out. A wood-burning stove gave off a smoky autumnal aroma. 'Honey, I'm home!' Dennis gloated as he manoeuvred himself into a corner.

'Smells like a bonfire,' said Peter, holding his nose.

'Take a seat – Harry and I'll go to the bar,' Jimmy said, hooking his Hearts scarf over the back of a chair. 'What will you be having?'

'Malt for me,' Dennis said. 'Any chance of a double?'

'Sounds like a marvellous idea. I'll be having a double cognac,' Harry agreed. 'What kind of malt?'

Dennis shouted to the barman, 'Got a Macallan, son?'

'Sure.'

'Princess, what would you like?' Jimmy asked.

'My daddy usually buys me a snowball drink – at the Jolly Swagger it always comes in a wee bottle.'

'Can you do a snowball?' Jimmy asked the barman, who scratched his head. 'I think I've once before in my life been asked for a snowball ... and that was my granny at our millennium party.'

'Lex, what are you having?'

'Vodka coke – no ice.'

'She got ID?' the barman asked. Lex flicked her card out of a black billfold and handed it to Jimmy.

'Oh no! I haven't got any ID,' said Peter, panic in his voice.

'You don't need it for coke, you bucking loon,' Lex replied.

'You want a cola?' Jimmy asked.

'Yes, please.'

The barman reached for a glass. 'Ice and lemon?'

'What do you mean? Issanlemon? Is that cola?'

'Do-you-want-ice-and-lemon?' the barman asked slowly.

'I don't know – do I?'

'Yes!' Dennis cried. 'Son, if I don't get my whisky because of your bloody stupid questions, I'll run you over in a heartbeat.'

'Kamal, what are you having?'

Kamal looked at the ground. Lex put her hand on his arm. 'Do you want a drink?' Kamal shook his head. Jimmy shrugged. 'Okay. Well I'll have a half of your local – what've you got?'

'Belhaven?'

'Sounds good to me. Look, Harry, let's split the bill – you shouldn't be buying the whole round.'

'Nonsense, you can get the next round.' She held out a fifty-pound note.

'*Sláinte!*' Dennis toasted, raising his glass. 'Ah, 'tis the nectar indeed.'

'Bottoms up!' Jimmy smiled. 'Well, this is mighty cheerier than listening to those downtrodden women moaning on.'

'I think it's known as being a tortured soul,' Harry commented.

'*We* were the ones being tortured,' Dennis complained. 'Who cares about every person who'd ever inspired them? I'd never heard of any of those writers they were going on about. Not a single mention of Alistair MacLean or Wilbur Smith.'

'My favourite story is Cinderella,' said Princess, nibbling on a maraschino cherry.

'Away!' Harry muttered.

'I'm just waiting for my Prince Charming to arrive.'

'I doubt he's in Musselburgh.'

'Sometimes when I'm out,' she confided, 'I kick off one of my shoes. I keep praying that, one day, a real gentleman will kneel before me and ask, "Does this belong to you, fair maiden?" and it'll glide on like a glass slipper.'

'That's a bit of a long shot,' Jimmy mused.

'I know,' Princess sighed. 'And one time, when we were at the Jolly Swagger, someone went off with my shoe and I had to hop all the way home!'

Their chat was interrupted when the door swung open with a bang and two straggly youths in sports hoodies and skinny jeans staggered in. They gave a cursory scan of the pub and weaved their way to the bar. 'The usual, Derek.' One of the pair turned his back and leant against the bar as his pal tried to mount a barstool. 'What are you lot of morons staring at?' he demanded. 'Escape from the asylum, did you?'

The Tuesday Chatters put their heads down and concentrated on their drinks.

'Permission to take them out?' Lex seethed. She curled her fists.

'Denied,' Jimmy replied.

'They're *scary*,' Princess whispered.

'Just ignore them – don't be put off by their bravado,' said Jimmy reassuringly. 'They're probably meek on the inside.'

'You mean like Shrek?' Princess asked, doubt in her voice.

'Oi! Did you just call me Shrek? Do I *look* like an ogre?'

'Actually—' Princess began.

'Ignore them – I mean it,' Jimmy repeated. 'Hey! How about we have a wee game of darts?' He lifted the set of darts from the board hanging next to their table and wiped the scoreboard blank with a grubby cloth. 'Come on, Peter, how about we have a quick game?'

'Oh, I don't know,' Peter faltered.

'Have you played before?' Jimmy asked.

'I've never seen this board in my life,' Peter answered.

'Go on, son,' Dennis said. 'Give it a shot.'

Jimmy threw the first three darts, the final one bouncing off the wire and landing on the floor. He passed them to Peter.

'Now, stand behind this line,' Jimmy said, 'and just aim for anywhere in the circle. We'll do a few practice throws.' He wrote *360* in chalk under *Jimmy* and *Peter*.

The thugs picked up their pints and took charge of a nearby table. 'Right, you bunch of twats, *we* came here to play darts so shove off.'

'Come on now,' Dennis said angrily from his scooter. 'We were here first. Let the lad have his game.'

'And I said, *hand them over*,' the youth growled, his acne flaring.

'Settle down over there!' came a shout from the bar.

The ogre stood up unsteadily. 'Look, I don't know which nuthouse you've broken out of but we come here every Wednesday. You'll be at it for hours. We'll have our game first then you can play after.'

'Yeah, hand over the darts, doughnut,' Acne-Boy sniggered.

Peter clenched the darts. 'But I want a go.'

'Derek!' Ogre yelled. 'Tell him we should play first and they can go after us.'

Derek shrugged. 'Not up to me, mate.'

Now both lads were on their feet, towering either side of Peter, who was staring at his trainers.

'Maybe you better sit down,' Harry suggested. 'Let the boys have their toys.'

'You're big bullies!' Princess declared.

'And you're bloody ugly!' Acne-Boy retorted with a sneer.

'Now, there's no need for rudeness,' Jimmy asserted, as Ogre rounded on him. 'And what are you going to do about it, old man?' He held out a skinny hand. 'Pass them here.'

Peter shook his head, lining up his trainers behind the white line. Ogre shoved him from behind so that Peter stumbled forward, dropping the darts. Acne-Boy scooped up the darts triumphantly. 'Ha!' he cried. 'That's what you get for being a spastic!'

'Are you alright?' Jimmy asked Peter, who nodded mutely. His forehead creased into a frown.

'Aw! Are you going to cry?' Ogre jeered as tears sprang into Peter's eyes.

'Look, tell you what,' Acne-Boy said, slinging his arm round Peter's pudgy shoulders. 'Why don't I let you have one throw? We each get one dart and the nearest to the bullseye can get a game. How aboot that?'

'What do you think, Peter?' Jimmy asked. 'Do you want a shot?' Peter shrugged his shoulders sullenly.

'Okay, then, here we go! Watch and learn!' Acne-Boy slurped half his pint and handed one dart each to Jimmy and Peter. 'Right, I'll go first – move out my way.' He faced the board, his toe-capped boots over the line. Peter glared at the floor. He tugged at Jimmy's jumper, but Jimmy shook his head. Acne-Boy pitched the dart with force and it hit the green ring of the bullseye with a *thud*! 'Way-hey!' he declared, his fists pumping the air. 'Champion-ey!' His pal gave him a high five.

'Over to you, old man – try to hit the board!'

Jimmy shuffled into position, making a point of squaring his foot behind the line. He leant forward and, with a quiet swish, landed the dart on segment four.

'You need to clean your glasses, Grandad.' The lads shook hands. 'Come on, fat boy – you're up.'

Peter rolled the dart uncertainly between his finger and thumb.

'Get a move on, you're throwing it not smoking it!' They fell about laughing.

Peter lingered at the line; he adjusted his sweatshirt and rocked his head from side to side.

'Get *him*!' Acne-Boy guffawed. 'A right bloody Phil Taylor!'

'Go, Peter!' Princess squealed.

'Concentrate!'

'Take you time,' Jimmy offered.

Peter squinted at the dartboard, holding the dart in front of his nose. With a grunt he flicked his wrist. The dart pierced the centre of the bullseye with a satisfying *clunk*. A roar went up from Dennis and Jimmy. Princess leapt up from her chair and hugged Peter tightly. 'My hero!'

'No *way*!' Acne-Boy fumed.

'What the fuck?' his friend scowled, lashing out at a chair.

'Now clear off,' said Jimmy. 'You were beaten fair and square.'

'Let's get out of here,' Ogre barked. 'This pub is full of fucking losers. You should piss off to your loony bin!' They downed their pints and stormed out the door.

'Well done, Peter!' Harry patted Peter's back.

'Where did you learn to throw like that?' Jimmy asked. 'You play like a pro.'

'I thought you said you'd never seen a dartboard before?' accused Dennis.

Peter grinned. 'I said I'd never seen *this* board before. The one in my bedroom is much nicer.'

'Well, I think this calls for another drink! What do you say?' Dennis suggested.

'You bet!' Harry nodded. 'Another round!'

Chapter 26

As soon as Donald returned to his seat he spotted the seven unoccupied chairs in the back row. His stomach clenched. *Shit! Where were they?* Maybe they were all in the toilet? Hardly likely given there were only two cubicles. Maybe they were waiting at the entrance? Again, why would a bunch of complainers be standing in the even chillier reception area? He couldn't go chasing about after them now. The lights dimmed and the Trouser Suit began to introduce Writer Number Three, reading from her notes. He tried to pick out the back of Helga's head in the front row but it was too dark to see anything. *What to do?*

Finally it was Helga's turn and she took the hot seat with chin held high. Her hands felt sweaty and her heart thumped in protest. She tried to ignore her mother in the front row, who was waving a copy of her own manuscript. The bulk of the audience was a blur of faces. She had to admit they didn't have the expectant look of diehard fans that might be hanging on to her every word. In fact, she spotted three people dozing, one woman scrolling through her mobile phone and a man in the second row who was reading a magazine! And there, at the back of the hall, she glimpsed Donald standing in the aisle, flapping his hands and hopping from foot to foot. What the hell? Unless a black mamba had bitten him on his arse, she found his distracting behaviour entirely unacceptable. No wonder he was never allowed out of the house in the evening.

Her concentration slipped and she was aware of an uncomfortable silence as she groped hopelessly for her line of thought. Someone coughed and one of the dozers jumped awake with a start.

The chair prompted in a tetchy voice, 'You were telling us about how you formed the idea for Candy Martini?' *Christ, who booked this one? No wonder they left her until last.*

'Oh yes – Candy Martini. I, well …' And now Donald was pointing frantically at the back row with both hands as though he were guiding an easyJet aircraft into the town hall.

'Come on, love!' Her mother gave an encouraging smile. 'Don't be nervous!'

The chair trotted on to the stage with a glass of water. 'Here, drink this,' she instructed, meaning *Get a bloody move on!*

Donald launched into a one-man game of charades, tapping his forearm and cupping his ear. He mimed what appeared to be *all* or *everything* – everyone in the audience? Then he held up seven fingers – ah! Seven people? *Seven Brides for Seven Brothers? The Magnificent Seven?* Despite hating charades, Helga was actually quite good at it. So, seven people? Next word: *shoo? Off? Away? Gone?*

'Yes, so the idea for Candy really came when I visited Findhorn as a teenager. I found it such an inspiring and uplifting place to be – almost ethereal. I felt that anyone born in such a magical locale could so easily possess an out-of-this-world psyche.'

And then her thoughts collided. Fuck! *Seven people gone!* She garbled a lot of rubbish about coping with success, cantered through her writing paradigm and summarised the follow-up to her debut novel as 'It does what it says on the tin – *Candy Martini Goes Viral'*. The chair stared open-mouthed, unable to comprehend that such a gifted writer, acknowledged for her contribution to Scotland's emerging talent, had just likened her body of work to an advert for outdoor varnish. She stumbled up on to the stage, mic at the ready. 'Can we please thank Helga Trumpet for a most, er, insightful presentation.' The audience gave a bemused spattering of applause. Helga's mother held her head in her hands. 'Now, if the other three writers (*read = professionals*) could please come up on to the stage, we will welcome questions for our panel discussion.'

'Do I have to stay?' Helga appealed.

'Yes, of course!' the chair snapped. *Let's see how you deal with some serious heckling, which I hope gets hurled your way.*

The questions from the audience triggered heated and lengthy discussions regarding the nurturing of primary school literacy and the underpinning of Scotland's arts budget to shore up creative writing as a career. And then there was the inevitable book signing. Helga stared with dismay as the entire town hall formed a queue up on to the stage, as though this was *their* opportunity to participate in the world of publishing.

After the third round of drinks, it had been Harry's idea to play *Never Have I Ever*. She tried to explain the rules to a sea of blank faces. 'Okay, look. I'll go first. I have to think of something that *I've* never done but I think some of *you* might have done. If you have, then you need to take a drink.'

'Oooh! Sounds like fun!' Princess bounced in her seat.

'I don't understand, it's too complicated,' Peter complained.

'Right,' said Harry. 'Never have I ever been abroad.'

Princess's hand shot up. 'I have! I've been to France.'

'Then you take a drink,' said Harry. 'Now who else has been abroad?'

'Does Wales count?' Peter asked.

'No!'

Dennis, Jimmy and Lex all took a gulp. 'So someone else goes now.'

'Shall I go next?' Peter grinned. 'Never have I ever been abroad.'

'We've just bucking had that!' said Lex. 'You're supposed to think of something different.'

'Oh.' He frowned in concentration. 'Mmm. Never have I ever had cola.'

'You drink it all the bloody time, man!' Dennis said, exasperated.

'But *you* don't,' Peter retorted.

'Oh, for God's sake. Right,' said Dennis, shaking his head. 'Never have I ever eaten fish.'

'Now I do like a fish supper,' said Jimmy, taking a swig.

'Do you count prawns?' Lex asked.

Dennis shuddered. 'Anything that lives in the sea. When I was in the Merchant Navy I saw what went into the sea and, if you had too, you'd be the same.'

'What about fish fingers?' Peter asked.

'Of course!'

'So what do I do now?'

'Take a drink, man!'

'This *is* fun,' Peter agreed.

'Me next?' Jimmy asked. He pondered a moment. 'Never have I ever been arrested.'

'What are you trying to bucking say about us lot?' Lex demanded.

Jimmy blushed. 'Oh, I didn't mean to cause offence. Of course I wasn't implying anything. I was just trying to think—'

'Ha!' Lex quaffed her vodka. 'Got you!'

Dennis and Harry also took a swill. 'Long story,' said Harry.

Kamal watched with wide eyes.

Princess smiled coyly. 'Me next! Never have I ever been married.'

'That's me again,' said Dennis.

'And me,' Jimmy nodded. 'Right, Lex, over to you.'

She thought hard for a minute, then shrugged. 'Never have I ever had a job.'

'That *is* a good one,' Princess smiled. She sipped her Snowball. 'My most favourite job ever was when I got to unpack all the pretty dresses when I worked at the Disney Store.'

'I hated working,' Peter said. 'I tried it once when I left school but my mum let me quit because I was crying all the time. My boss – Mr Clarke – was a really mean man. He kept shouting at me for getting things wrong and always making a mess.'

'What was your job?' Jimmy asked.

'Filling doughnuts. It was really hard! But I got my own back,' Peter smiled. 'Laura was my friend and when she heard I was leaving she took this powder from her granny that makes you go to the toilet. We filled a doughnut with it and I topped it up with jam.'

'That's terrible!' Princess cried.

'He was really cruel to me,' Peter protested. 'Anyway, on my last day Laura and I laughed all afternoon when *he* made a mess of his trousers!'

Dennis shook with laughter. 'Oh hell, talking of the toilet – I better visit the gents.'

'Do you need a hand?' Jimmy offered.

'Actually, I might. This bloody thing won't fit anywhere near the toilet.' He eased himself off the scooter, making a grab for a nearby chair.

'Give's a hand, then.'

Jimmy stood to help but before he could reach, Dennis's knees buckled and he dropped to the floor. His head cracked off the corner of the table. Princess screamed as dark blood gushed from the open wound. In seconds the barman leapt over the bar and crouched by Dennis's crumpled body. He whipped out his mobile, barking, 'Ambulance, please.'

'Is he dead?' Princess gasped, her hand held over her mouth.

'Everyone move away – give him some room,' the barman ordered. The Chatters leapt back, knocking over chairs in their haste. Dennis's eyes were closed as drool seeped from the corner of his mouth. The barman pressed a tea towel against Dennis's forehead. Within minutes the towel was soaked red. 'Is he on any medications?'

'We've no idea,' Jimmy mumbled. 'We hardly know each other.'

'Who's in charge?'

The Tuesday Chatters looked from one to the other. 'Shall I go and get Helga?' Princess asked fearfully.

Chapter 27

Helga sprang off the stage in a state of panic as Donald – who had tried to swim upstream – grabbed her by the shoulders as though a lifebuoy. 'They're gone!' he gasped. 'Your patients have disappeared.'

Helga's mother popped up at her side. 'What's he on about? What patients?'

'Not now, Mum! Gotta go.'

'But what about my manuscript?' she wailed. 'Did everyone get a copy?'

Helga charged after Donald as he pushed through the dawdlers. 'What happened?' Helga demanded as they reached the foyer.

'I've no idea!' Donald stammered. 'I left them at break time with all my sweets and by the time I got back they'd disappeared.'

Helga jogged around the small lobby, checking each crevice and behind pillars as though looking for a misplaced handbag. Spotting a security guard, who was sweeping the crowd towards the exit, she clutched his arm. 'Excuse me, have you seen a small group of people who might have left the building?'

'Funnily enough, I have,' he grumbled. 'There's a small group. Oh, and there's *another* small group.'

'I mean,' said Helga through gritted teeth, 'a group of mixed abilities.'

'What the hell's that when it's at home?'

Donald stepped up. 'Did you see seven people – four men and

three women – who might have left during the break?'

'To be honest I was trying to finish my sudoku during the break.'

'They ranged from aged nineteen to eighty-four?' Helga prompted.

'Hmm, well I'm not a great judge of people's ages. My wife says I'm always offending folk by thinking they're older or younger than they should be. I mean take you, for example—'

'One was on a mobility scooter!' Helga interrupted.

'Ah, now why didn't you say so?' He looked very pleased with himself. 'Yes, now that I can tell you. They left after the first half seeing as how it was such a load of rubbish. What did *you* make of it? All those women blabbing on about their "inspiration". It wasn't much of a show, was it? I left after about ten minutes. Wasn't even as interesting as the AGM – and that's a shocker.'

Helga resisted grabbing him by the throat. 'Did you see which way they went?'

'Again, yes, I did. I do believe they were heading for the Auld Tavern.'

'Please tell me that's not a pub?' She thought she might faint.

'It does sound a bit like a pub,' Donald said helpfully.

'Serves great ale,' the guard nodded.

'Oh my God! What will I do?' Helga cried. 'Two of them are alcoholics.'

'Think there'll be more than a couple of alcoholics in the Auld Tavern.' The guard winked. Helga snatched her coat off the rack and bolted out of the building, Donald in pursuit. The street was ablaze with blue flashing lights as an ambulance stood with its doors open outside the pub. Two paramedics were manoeuvring a stretcher into the lit ambulance as Helga stopped in her tracks. 'Oh, Donald, what's happened?'

They rushed towards the ambulance as the gurney was being locked into place. The six remaining Tuesday Chatters shivered mournfully on the pavement.

'Where's Dennis?' Helga cried, knowing the answer.

Peter pointed to the ambulance. 'He fell and banged his head, miss.' Helga seized the handle on the door as the paramedic pulled it closed. 'Sorry, I'm Helga Trumpet. This is my group of patients,' she blurted.

'Patients? Where are you from?' one asked.

The other member of the crew jumped into the driving seat. 'Sorry, love, we've got to get him to hospital. Are you his escort?'

'I suppose I'd better. Can you hang on a minute?'

'Not really, he's losing blood here.'

Helga shouted out of the door as it was being closed. 'Donald! Can you see that everyone gets to the minibus and gets home safely? I'll let you know what's happening.'

'Message received and understood. Come on, folks, let's get back to the bus.'

'Oh, what a sad way to end such a super evening,' Princess said.

'Do you think Dennis is going to die?' Peter asked.

'I'm sure he'll be fine,' said Jimmy. 'He's in good hands now.'

'But such a lot of blood!' Princess exclaimed.

'What were you lot up to?' Donald demanded. 'I hope Helga doesn't get into trouble over this.'

'Helga is in such big trouble!' Sheba declared, pacing up and down the office.

'Hey, give the girl a chance – you haven't heard her side of the story yet,' said Vanda. She stuck her tongue out at Sheba's back.

'Why don't you sit down and have a coffee?' Molly suggested.

'Helga's not usually in this early.'

'She better be in soon, after last night's fiasco.'

'Oooh, what did I miss?' Bobbie asked, dropping a bulging bag-for-life at her desk. 'What fiasco?'

Sheba took a breath but Vanda interrupted. 'We don't know the facts yet. All we know is that there was an incident yesterday evening with Helga's social group.'

'Evening?' Bobbie queried. 'I thought it was an afternoon group? What were they doing? Bingo or something?'

'I think it was "or something",' Sheba said darkly.

'Morning,' Aiden chirped, entering the office. His face fell as he clocked Sheba behaving like a caged tiger. 'Is this about Mrs McGowan?' he growled. 'Because I haven't started on her bloody appeal yet.'

'Helga's had a fiasco!' Bobbie revealed.

'Oh aye? What happened?'

'We don't know yet,' Vanda said irritably. 'Let's all just carry on as usual and Helga can join us after Sheba's had a wee word.'

Sheba snorted. 'It'll be a mighty big word! And today of all days! I don't have time for this unnecessary diversion. I'm supposed to be on my Essential Leadership course today – this is so inconvenient!'

'I'm happy to pass on a message to Helga if you want to get on?' Vanda offered.

'You're really not grasping the gravity of the situation.'

'Of course we're not!' Bobbie puffed. 'You've haven't told us a bloody thing! You keep going on about a *fiasco*. Well, in my book, that can mean anything from knocking a glass of red wine over your pal's cream settee to getting to Manchester airport to find you've left your passport on the microwave.'

'A glass?' Vanda said. 'It was a whole flipping bottle and I'd already warned you about playing Twister in the lounge.'

'I can assure you that this will take more than a spot of dry-cleaning to resolve.'

'It looked like a scene from *Taggart*,' Vanda muttered.

'Anyone else want a coffee?' Molly said to lighten the mood. 'Kettle's just boiled.'

'Good idea. And if anyone wants a crumpet I can pop one in the toaster?' said Bobbie. 'Sheba? Aiden? Anyone interested in crumpet?' She winked at Molly.

They heard the door code being entered and Helga slunk in. She wore the same clothes as the day before; her eye make-up was smudged like a vampire and one side of her hair was flattened where she'd tried to sleep in the hospital waiting room. She dropped her bag on her desk and slumped into her chair.

'Helga, there you are at last!' Sheba pronounced. 'I've booked the quiet room along the corridor. I need to take a statement.'

'A statement?' Helga whispered. 'I suppose so.'

'Here, have this cup of coffee,' said Molly. 'I've just made it.'

'Let's get this over with.' Sheba held the door open as Helga trailed behind.

'What do you think she's done?' Bobbie whispered. 'What's the fiasco?'

'All I know is that she was out with her social group and they ended up in a pub …' Vanda began.

'A *pub*?'

Vanda nodded. 'And Sheba says all the patients were pissed and one fell over and now he's in the Royal with a head injury.'

'Bloody hell!' Bobbie exclaimed.

'Why would she take the patients to a pub?' Aiden tutted. 'That's suicide! Imagine carrying on like that when we've got Sheba watching our every move.'

'She might be watching *your* every move,' Vanda said, 'but she hasn't paid a jot of attention to Helga.'

'She's certainly making up for it now,' said Molly. 'Maybe I will have a crumpet after all.'

'I'm going nowhere till I find out what's happening,' Bobbie said. 'Do you want banana or marmalade on yours? Or both?'

Chapter 28

He couldn't believe how awful Helga looked. What was going on? She should have been bursting with pride. First a photo-shoot and interview with *Scot Today* – that would have made her high as a kite. And then the Writers' Block – what a coup! She'd have been in her element with all that fawning from the literary world and the chance to show off about her writing. Helga should have been on cloud nine. And instead she looked bedraggled, as though she hadn't slept for a week. And he was sure she was still wearing the same clothes as yesterday. This wasn't good. She didn't look like she'd be in any kind of mood to delight in the collage he'd spent days constructing. And all those witty little annotations he'd come up with. Helga Trumpet is a blast! and Edinburgh author gets it write! His legs numb with cold, he crouched behind a Volvo estate in the car park biting his nails anxiously at the thought of his gift completely missing the mark.

Chapter 29

Sheba balanced on the edge of her seat, leaning on an occasional table, a writing pad flipped open and biro poised. 'Let's begin with the current status of Mr Beattie – what's the latest?'

'He's been admitted to ward 101,' Helga reported in a small voice. 'Apparently he's stable. He was somewhat confused on admission but the doctor wasn't sure how much was related to … er … to alcohol. The laceration to his scalp has been steri-stripped and he suffered some facial bruising to his temple and cheek.'

'And his family? Have they been informed?'

'We called his daughter from the hospital last night and she arrived early this morning – she apparently can't function without a night's sleep. I know *that* feeling.'

'And how was she when she arrived?' Sheba quizzed. Helga knew what she was implying. 'Dennis's daughter was, quite rightly, furious that he had been given the opportunity to seek out alcohol. And that he hadn't been supervised at all times and they plan to—'

'Don't tell me …'

'I'm afraid so. They were shouting about legal action and suing the health centre.'

'Heavens above, Helga! What were you *thinking*?' Sheba roared.

'I was thinking it would be a nice wee treat for the group – a social evening to get them out of the house. They were picked up by minibus and taken home again. I was in the same hall the whole time. Anyway, I hate to be derogatory but Dennis's family has probably waited their entire lives to pounce on this type of situation.'

'That is an outrageous accusation and I will not tolerate such discrimination!'

'But if you knew how they treated him at home ... All this sudden affection and concern for his welfare – it's all fake.'

'That is irrelevant. We need to stick to facts and the fact is, you allowed their precious father to escape.'

'He didn't exactly *escape*,' Helga protested. 'They're not prisoners and I wasn't in the role of custodian!'

'Yes, but they were *your* responsibility – they're all vulnerable adults and, as such, their safety and well-being should be assured.'

'I left Donald in charge while I was presenting.'

'Who's Donald?'

'My neighbour.'

'Your what? Honestly, Helga, I seriously doubt your professional judgement here. And talking of which, had you carried out a risk assessment of the area prior to the event? I mean, to take two alcoholics to a venue with a pub right across the road! You were practically goading them! This is a right bloody predicament you've got us into.' Sheba thrust her pen at the pad while she processed the information.

'So can I go home and get a shower – then I promise I'll come straight back to work?' Helga asked.

'What? No! Out of the question!' Sheba snapped.

'But I can't carry on looking such a mess.'

'Helga, you're not "carrying on". Surely you appreciate that we have no option but to suspend you immediately, pending a formal enquiry?'

'Oh *no*!' Helga burst into tears, covering her face with her hands. 'Suspended?' she sobbed. 'But what does that even mean?'

'It means Mr Adamson has already advised me of the course of action we require to take. While the Beattie family is involved in any type of dispute regarding your behaviour or competency, we can't have you working with other patients.'

'So should I be speaking to my union rep?'

'I'd say so. Not to mention your solicitor!'

'Why?'

Sheba shrugged. 'There may be some judicial case to be answered – we'll need to consult our legal department. Negligence? Misadventure? Who knows? I've never had to manage a case like this before.'

'But surely this could go on for months? Years?'

'Very likely.'

'But what will I do? I can't just sit at home waiting – I'll go mad. How long will it take to arrange the formal enquiry?'

'I've no idea, Helga. You should have thought about that when you exploited a vulnerable group of patients to boost your ego. Anyway, look on the bright side,' Sheba said grimly, 'maybe you'll get a good story out of this!'

Helga opened the office door, quietly retrieved her bag and coat and made to leave the office.

'Hey!' Bobbie protested, spraying crumpet over her desk. 'Where are you going? What's this all about?'

'Sorry, guys,' Helga mumbled through her tears. 'I'm not allowed to say a word to you.' She closed the door and stumbled out into the car park.

Helga had come straight from the hospital so didn't have her car with her. By the time he'd spotted her exiting the building, she had already crossed the road and boarded a number four. *Now where was she going?*

Hours passed as Helga travelled mindlessly on buses from one end of Edinburgh to the other. When she reached a terminus, she shivered numbly in the sleet for the next bus to anywhere. As she ran out of change, she found a nearby shop and bought a Mars bar to break a twenty. It didn't register that she'd ridden the number twenty-two for three full circuits until the driver threw her off. Standing on the dockside at Ocean Terminal she stared blankly at the dingy brown water as it slapped against the harbour wall. An approaching drunk slurred, 'Dinnae do it, hen!' as he staggered towards her. 'Got any spare change?' *No* – she thought. Reaching into her bag she found the chocolate bar, which he accepted with an aggrieved grunt.

The vibration in her pocket was like toothache as she ignored Kate's mounting emails and messages:

How did it go yesterday with *Scot Today?*

Who did you get to meet – anyone famous?

What kind of questions did the journalist ask?

Call me! I want to know ALL about the Writers' Block!

How many people were there? Anyone I should know about?

How many books did you sell?

Where are you?

Helga, I'm getting worried – are you okay?

Seriously – CALL ME!!!

Helga?

And then from her mother:

where did U get 2 last night?

Why did U rush off?
Why aren't U ansring my calls?

Streetlights blinked on as she unlocked the door to her building. She could hear Dolly's yapping as she wound her way up the stone steps.

'*Oh, Helga!* I'm so relieved to see you!' Donald cried as he wiped his nose on his sleeve. He stretched his scrawny arms wide for a hug but she brushed him off.

'What happened at the hospital? Is the old boy okay?'

Helga inserted the key in her front door. 'Not now, Donald. I have to get home.' She closed the door behind her and leant against the wall. Her knees bent and she collapsed on to the floor. The letterbox sprang open. 'Helga, are you all right? You must let me in. Please … talk to me!'

She closed her eyes and, a few minutes later, she was crossing between two skyscrapers on a tightrope as the wind buffeted her from side to side.

Chapter 30

'Right, well I don't mind doing that if it keeps him happy.

Fine, I'll give him a call,' Bobbie tutted, hanging up. 'That Sheba hasn't half got her knickers in a twist. Mind you, some people might find that quite a turn-on, eh, Aiden?'

'Shut it, Bobbie!'

'What's she on about now?' Vanda asked.

'She says that we need to go through the diary and make sure we cancel all Helga's appointments.'

'For how long?'

'She was a bit vague – at least for this week and next. But she said Mr Cormack was so disappointed at missing the bowling yesterday that one of us had to take him. I said I didn't mind – I need to see how he's getting on with his mobility anyway. She said she's hoping they'll get the initial panel thing sorted out maybe the week after.'

'What panel thing?'

'You know – for Helga. She has to face up to Quinn and Sheba.'

'Oh, crap.'

Molly returned to the office carrying a large rectangular parcel that she laid on Helga's desk. 'Anyone know what this is?'

'No idea.' Vanda shook her head. 'Did she make a poster or something? Maybe she ordered a picture for the community room? Something for her social group?'

'Talking of which,' Bobbie said. 'What's the latest?'

Vanda sipped her coffee. 'According to Sheba she's been suspended.'

'What!' Bobbie exclaimed.

'Yeah – she invited her group—'

'The Tuesday Chatters?'

'Yes. Apparently she arranged for them to go along to that Writers' thing she was trying to get us lot to go to. Seemingly, the group left during the interval and ended up in a pub. They all got a bit hammered and one of the old men fell and knocked himself out.'

'How terrible!' Molly gasped.

'He's in the Royal.'

'Actually, I meant for Helga.'

'It wouldn't be so bad but his daughter is kicking up a right stooshie – says she's going to sue the health centre.'

'Good luck with that,' Aiden muttered. 'She's welcome to it.'

'I feel awful now,' Molly said. 'I wish I'd gone with her and then none of this might have happened.'

'But it's not like they were patients from a locked ward or anything,' Aiden protested. 'I mean, they all live at home. They can go to the pub whenever they like. It's not Helga's responsibility to keep them sober.'

'But she did look dreadful when she left,' Molly said. 'Do you think we ought to send her some flowers or something?'

'Or a cake?' Bobbie suggested. 'Everyone loves a cupcake. Or even better, what about a trifle?'

A tap at the door interrupted them. 'That'll be Chan.'

Vanda opened the door. 'Come in.'

'Sorry to disturb your meeting,' Chan said, hardly daring to step into the room.

'Have a seat,' Bobbie offered.

'No, I won't stay. Just two things today.'

'Uh-huh?'

'Firstly, the medical centre next door is having a Fun Day Friday next week and wondered whether you wanted—'

'What's a Fun Day Friday?' Bobbie interrupted. 'In a doctors' surgery? I can't imagine it's the sort of fun I'd want to have!'

'Well, it's the Friday before Mother's Day. They thought they could have a bit of fun and raise awareness of women's health issues at the same time.'

'Sure,' Vanda said. 'Nothing says ovarian cancer like a bouncy castle.'

'Ooh, do you think they'll put a bouncy castle in the car park?' Bobbie asked. 'I *love* them – especially when I get to show off my backflips.'

'I didn't know you were that gymnastically-inclined?' said Vanda. 'Can you properly do somersaults and stuff?'

'How do you mean?'

'You said "backflips".'

'Did I? I meant belly flops.'

'What are they asking from us?' Aiden queried. 'It's a great chance for us to raise the profile of the team but there's no way I'm getting dressed up in a ridiculous costume or having my face turned into a Ninja Turtle. The very words *fun* and *day* fill me with dread.'

'Cheer up, Scrooge,' Bobbie laughed. 'Wait until you have kids. You'll be begging to climb into a Mr Blobby outfit if it keeps them amused for five minutes.'

Chan frowned, checking her notebook. 'I don't think there is any guidance on fancy dress. I've just been told to let you know about it and if you want to do something you can.'

'Like what?' Vanda demanded. 'I'm with Aiden on this one. I don't mind handing out some leaflets on the HIT team, but I can't be bothered getting roped into a tug-of-war or mini-disco.'

''Scuse the pun.'

'I don't know,' Chan fretted. 'Someone said they're looking for people to bring their dogs to work or—'

'There you go, Aiden – you could bring Sheba,' Vanda quipped.

'Or if you wanted to bring in some home baking?' Chan suggested.

'Oh!' Bobbie cried. 'I could bring in my chocolate fountain! Kids love that – they get in a right mess.'

'And I could bring some chopped fruit to dip in?' offered Molly. 'I've got plenty of skewers too.'

'Okay, I'll leave it with you,' said Chan, turning to go.

'What was the second thing?' Vanda asked.

'Sorry?'

'You said two things?'

'Oh yes. Well, just to let you know Norman has convened a security meeting for the building first thing on Monday morning.'

'Shit! That's ruined my weekend,' Aiden grumbled.

'It's in the community room. Nine o'clock. He says everyone must be there.'

'*Everyone?*' Bobbie repeated. 'Everyone in Edinburgh, or Scotland or the whole world?'

Chan checked her notebook again. 'He just says everyone.'

Helga woke up to find her flat in darkness. What was she doing on the floor? *Ow!* She put her hand on the crick in her neck. Her whole body felt cold and stiff, as though she had died already.

She checked her watch – nine p.m. With caution she unfolded her limbs and fumbled towards the kitchen. Perhaps a cup of hot coffee would help? She filled the kettle and removed a carton of milk from the fridge, gave it a sniff. As she poured the lumpy milk down the sink, she switched off the kettle. Her stomach complained bitterly but she knew she couldn't face food.

The dream of sinking into a hot bath full of creamy bubbles seemed like heaven. Shame she only had a shower cubicle with a wonky door and unreliable thermostat to warm her bones. By nine thirty, she crept under the duvet, knowing that she faced a sleepless night of hell.

Chapter 31

'What are you doing back here?' Vanda accused Anver as he shuffled into the community room, a Starbucks coffee in hand.

'Oh, that's charming – I've missed you too.'

'But you don't work here.'

'Excuse *me*, lady, but who do you think does all the tiling this side of Edinburgh?'

'I mean, you don't *have* to be here – not like us muggins that have no choice.'

He winked. 'I had no choice, either. I've got a job in the foot clinic and I was going about my business this morning when Ivan the Terrible chased us all in here.'

'What job?'

'What do you care?'

'I'm just making conversation.'

'Is that what you call it? Why don't you ask me how I enjoyed my luxury weekend on my yacht or how I keep so buffed?'

'Seriously? I'm being given a lesson in the art of etiquette from a tiler?'

'Hark at Miss Snootypants! You're not exactly hobnobbing down at Holyrood Palace this morning, are you?'

'True.'

Bobbie gave Vanda a shove. 'Move along, it's standing room only at the back.' All the seats were taken, the health centre personnel crammed against the walls. At least four staff began a coughing match, sneezes were quashed and noses blown at scale.

'See if I get a cold from attending this bloody meeting,' Aiden fumed.

'Guaranteed,' Vanda said. 'Think of all the germs whizzing around this room. We don't stand a chance.'

'Can someone let in some fresh air?' Aiden shouted. A hand reached up and the window was popped open an inch.

'Shut the window! It's bloody freezing.'

Norman pushed his way through the rabble, clapping his hands to silence the crowd.

'Good morning, all,' he began, surveying the scene.

'Good morning, Headmaster!' someone called from the front, sending a titter around the room.

'Thank you for attending this unscheduled meeting – I know you're all extremely busy. However, it is really rather imperative that I get you up to speed on this building's security breaches.' He hooked his stout thumbs through his trouser belt loops and rocked on his heels. 'Let me start by saying how shocked I am at your lackadaisical approach to security.' A rumble of irritation could be heard. 'I'm standing here and I can count two, no three – in fact, *four* members of staff who are not wearing their ID badges.' Heads swivelled in search of the culprits. 'How do I know that we're not being infiltrated by individuals who *do not* work at this health centre?'

Vanda jabbed Anver in the ribs.

'I'm sorry,' Aiden interrupted, 'but surely there is no one in this room except those of us enforced to be here?'

'No one made me come, mate,' Cameron replied. 'I so look forward to these wee get-togethers. My weekend dragged, so it did.'

'And,' Norman continued, unflappable, 'I see an unattended bag in the corner. What are you people thinking? I watched you from outside and not *one single person* challenged where the bag came from or what it might contain.'

Bobbie's hand shot in the air. 'Please, sir! Those are my bras for Africa. I brought them in for Linda.'

'Cheers!' Linda replied, giving a wave.

'Point three,' Norman declared, holding up three fingers for all to see. 'You'll note, we're on the ground floor and yet –' he paused for dramatic effect – 'your window is clearly left unlocked.'

'Unless a passing jellied eel wants to break in I shouldn't be too worried,' Anver offered.

'Good point,' someone agreed.

Chan raised a timid hand. 'Yes?' Norman said tetchily.

'Are we expected to deliver airport-standard security in this building?' she asked. 'Only, I'm the building's representative but I can't be checking everyone's ID.'

'And that man's brought in a drink that's more than a hundred mils,' a voice piped up. 'Aren't you going to make him chuck it away?'

'Look, people,' Norman grunted, 'I'm simply trying to ensure we maintain security vigilance at a time when we have a heightened risk of a breach. The building is currently operating at an amber alert.'

'Shouldn't it be a ginger alert, sir?'

Norman grimaced. 'It's not a case of *if* we have an incident but *when* we have an incident. It's only a matter of time.' He took in the murmurs of concern with self-satisfaction. That got their attention!

'Do you know when this incident is taking place?' Bobbie asked. 'Only there's a Family Fun Day next Friday – that's not easy to say with these teeth – but we wouldn't want to go to a lot of trouble to have it ruined by some incident.'

'*I* don't know!' Norman exclaimed. 'I'm asking you to keep your eyes and ears open.'

'Sorry, I didn't hear that,' Aiden said.

'Did you catch the fella who started the fire?' Cameron asked.

'Well, it wasn't strictly a fire,' Norman responded. 'It was more of a chemical reaction to generate smoke and the appearance of a fire.'

'So did you catch the fella who didn't start the fire?' Cameron goaded.

'No, not yet. The investigation is still underway.'

'We heard it was Lance,' joked Cameron. 'He was washing his hands so fast he started a fire.'

'That's a lie!' Lance cried, folding his arms.

'Is that it?' Vanda asked. 'Only we've got patients to visit.'

'I'm coming to my final point,' Norman pronounced. 'Now I need your full attention. Some of you may have heard about the incident last Thursday in the car park?'

Vanda and Bobbie exchanged a look – both shrugging. 'This can't be about me dropping my eggs on Dr Mitchell's new BMW, can it?' Bobbie whispered.

'Was that *you*?' Vanda hissed.

'No,' said Bobbie.

'*Full attention!*' Norman shouted.

'Imagine you're on an aeroplane!' Cameron added.

'Thank you, son, but there'll be no emergency exits here. So … last week an unknown man was behaving suspiciously in the car park but, when approached, he ran off.'

'Aiden?' Vanda smiled.

Norman indicated for a petite woman wearing a pale blue uniform and panda eyeliner to come forward. 'For those of you who don't know her, this is Ruth from the breast-screening clinic. She's here to tell us what happened.'

Ruth went to open her mouth but Norman continued. 'Last Thursday a man was seen hiding behind cars in the car park off and on during the morning. He was spotted by at least three members of the team but they thought nothing of it until they discussed it at their break. It was at this point that they jointly observed him concealing himself behind a visitor's car. Two of the staff decided to challenge him but, as they approached, he ran off up Ardmillan Terrace. Now Ruth got a good look at this man, didn't you?'

Again Ruth began to speak but was interrupted. 'So Ruth, can you describe this man and let's see if anyone else recognises this description.'

'Now?'

'Yes, now,' he barked.

'Well, I'd say he was aged about thirty. Maybe this tall.' She held her hand about a foot above her head. 'He was wearing a dark jacket with the hood pulled up and black trousers.'

'How on earth can we recognise him from that description?' Cameron complained. 'That could be every man in this room.'

'What colour was he?' Anver lobbed in from the back.

'Colour?' Ruth faltered. 'Well, he looked a normal colour.'

'White?' asked Norman.

'Yes … Scottish, I expect.'

'So,' Norman announced, 'we have a Caucasian male, aged approximately thirty, wearing a dark jacket and black trousers. Now does that ring any bells with anyone? Has anyone else seen a man of this description hanging around the health centre?'

'Phew! That's me off the hook,' said Anver, finishing his latte.

'Can I sit down now?' Ruth asked.

'Thanks,' said Norman.

'What about CCTV?' Aiden asked.

'Ooh, hark at Inspector Morse!' Bobbie said.

'That's an excellent observation,' Norman nodded, 'but unfortunately we only have one actual camera at Breast Screening and it's focused on the entrance.'

'And talking of CCTV,' Bobbie whispered to Vanda, 'where's Ray? He's supposed to be our on-site security.'

'Sorry, Norman, we really have to go,' Cameron pleaded. 'Our patients have been waiting since nine.'

'Right – well, before you go I'll leave you with one pledge,' said Norman in a serious tone. 'If you see someone you don't know – whether it be doctor, or patient or tradesman or whatever – please, *please* ask them their name and the purpose of their visit. People, you must be on your guard and may God be with you.'

'... *and may God be with you,*' Bobbie repeated in an American accent. 'Bloody hell – you'd think he was auditioning for *Homeland*.'

'It is a bit worrying, though,' said Molly. 'I don't like the idea of weirdos hanging around the health centre.'

'Then you're in the wrong job,' said Vanda. 'Our work provides a service to the weirdos of this world: the eccentrics, the disadvantaged, the lost, the misanthropes. Oh, here's Aiden!'

'What's he like?' Aiden moaned. 'I wouldn't mind but last year, when my bike got nicked, he couldn't have cared less. Now we've got some pervert who likes to hang around nurses and suddenly we're on high alert!'

Chapter 32

This wasn't good at all. Helga definitely didn't turn up for work today. He had shivered in the tenement doorway, before daylight had even cracked over the health centre, without a sign of her arrival. He checked his watch again – it was almost nine thirty. She was clearly a no-show. And after rushing out of work looking so dishevelled last week? Something was going on but he had no idea what. And not a peep since he'd sent his masterpiece to her office. His feet were numb as he stamped his boots on the stone path. He'd better get to work himself or they'd start to ask questions.

Chapter 33

Sipping her second cup of black coffee, Helga lay low on her settee with her bedding wrapped round her. With the heating off during the day, it was warmer under the duvet. She had made the mistake of checking her Twitter account – the feedback from the Writers' Block had been mixed. Of course her fans had responded with endless praise but there, lurking in the background, were the doubters.

> **Did anyone else pay to see @HelgaTrumpet sprint through her presentation as though on speed?**

> **So disappointed at the #WritersBlock appearance by @HelgaTrumpet – asked for a refund!**

> **Does @Helga Trumpet think she's above signing her fans' books?**

> **@HelgaTrumpet gets mum to sign her books!**

And her excited tweet:

> ***About to go on stage at the #WritersBlock – so nervous!***

had been quoted along with:

> ***@HelgaTrumpet – stage fright or just frightful?***

And:

> ***Never mind #WritersBlock, what about verbal block?!***

Helga dropped her mobile, feeling sick to her stomach. What a disaster! In the early hours she had given up the pretence of sleep and slumped in front of the TV as images jumped around the screen. She absently scratched at her scalp, sending a cloud of dry skin on to the floor. And who had poured sand into her eyes during the night?

Dolly's whining became more insistent as the door to Donald's flat opened. Helga heard a yelp outside as her letterbox clanged open and something fell on to her carpet. The sound of Donald's high-handed voice faded as he wound down the stairs. With a sigh Helga reached for her MacBook and eased it open. 'Go to … Page 150'. Where was she? She read back over the last couple of paragraphs. Ah yes, Candy Martini had been invited to attend a European conference on crystals and their healing uses. She'd been invited as a keynote speaker and, as such, had been offered a penthouse suite at the Mandarin Oriental Hotel in Geneva. A limousine whisked her from her hotel to the conference centre, where a small group of her fanatical followers were waiting with bouquets of flowers. She had already received, with delight, a bottle of Taittinger that had been gifted by the celebrity presenter of *Playing at Life*. Helga's stomach rumbled. She tightened the duvet round her shoulders and shuffled into the kitchen. Two crusts wrapped in a plastic bag loitered at the back of the bread bin. She shoved them in the toaster, wishing she had Bobbie nearby to ply her with warm croissants or chocolate-chip muffins.

How could she have messed things up so monumentally? Had her invitation to the Tuesday Chatters been so misjudged? Sheba's comments about exploiting the vulnerable struck a painful nerve. The toast popped up but, by the time she'd registered, it was cold and chewy.

Helga lumbered back through to the living room and picked up her mobile as though it were infectious. The messages were piling up. Her Twitter followers had sent direct messages asking why the radio silence? They couldn't understand the frenzy of tweets prior to the *Scot Today* interview and the Writers' Block – and then not a single self-congratulatory tweet to celebrate the literary jamboree. Where was Helga Trumpet? Indeed, *who* was Helga Trumpet? Helga gripped her phone at arm's length and squinted at the messages from Kate, barely able to face a potential diatribe. Her gut clenched with anxiety. How should she respond? A mammoth effort at PR damage limitation was required. It would be like convincing the public the *Titanic* had experienced teething problems.

In the end she did what any daughter in distress does – she called her mother.

'Oh, Helga, I've been so worried about you! Where did you rush off to on Wednesday? There were still people asking for you to sign your book! But don't worry, I signed them on your behalf. After all, I'm surely the next best thing?'

'Sorry, Mum. There was a bit of an incident with the group of people I brought along. During the interval they left the hall and went to a local pub. They all got a bit tipsy and one of them had a fall and banged his head.'

'But surely you can't be held responsible for your colleagues' behaviour? They shouldn't be carrying on like that on a works' night out!'

'They were actually a group of my patients. We have a social group in the afternoon and I thought they might like a wee change.'

'Of course you did, darling! It was a wonderful evening! There's no helping some people. I mean, you try to do the right thing and they go and take advantage ...'

'Well, one of them ended up in hospital.'

'Oh dear! I hope they're not blaming you?'

'It *is* my fault, Mum. I've gone and messed everything up.'

'I'm sure that's not true. Look, do you want me to come round? Or do you want to move back home for a while?'

'Thanks, but I need to sort it out myself.'

'But what can you sort out now?'

'I've been suspended from work, Mum.'

'*Suspended?* What for? That's outrageous!'

'I should have kept a better eye on my patients.'

'You can't be everywhere – people must surely take responsibility for themselves? They should man up!'

'They're vulnerable adults, Mum.'

'What do you mean *vulnerable*? You mean *retarded*? I thought you worked in the community?'

'Look, I have to go now. I need to speak to my Kate, my agent.'

'Oh! Talking of which, you were going to put in a good word for me? What did she think of the first fifty pages of *Rose-Marie Gala Touches Love*? Mags says she's going to enter me for a writing competition. Says it's just what the publishers are desperate for – gritty heroines with a backstory looking for twenty-first century romance.'

'I'm sure they are.'

'Do you think it would help if I called Kate myself?'

'I've no idea about anything any more.'

'Don't say that, darling – no need for extra drama.'

'Speak to you later, Mum.'

'Oh! Before I forget … what are we doing for Mother's Day? Did you say you were taking me out for lunch?'

'I don't know … I … er …'

'It's just that everything gets so booked up. Tell you what – surprise me. *Ciao!*'

Helga frittered away the remainder of the morning crafting an email to Kate.

Dear Kate, I am so sorry but a patient-related incident at work has occurred that I am required to manage. As you know, my day job is still very much my priority! The Scot Today interview went fantastically well – I think I answered all their questions in the style of Helga Trumpet. I do believe the photo can be edited – LOL! The Writers' Block was also very well attended and much discussion was generated. I sold several copies of Candy Martini – as expected, the fans that came along already had their copies at the ready! I note a few dissatisfied customers on Twitter but I'm sure there is only a handful.

I will endeavour to submit the subsequent chapters of Candy Martini Goes Viral *as agreed – I think I'm due to submit the next 10,000 words by the end of this week? However, owing to this work crisis, I am unable to interact with my public in my usual way … I'm thinking specifically of my Twitter followers. Perhaps you could post some general tweets along the lines of me focusing on Book Two and my aspiration to deliver a professional product on time?*

*Kate (agent and **friend**), I know you will understand the pressure I am under and that I need to focus 100% on my writing. I would very much appreciate your support at this time. You will hear from me again in one week's time.*

Yours ever, Miss Helga Trumpet

Helga pressed *Send* and fell back on to the settee. She closed her eyes and, when her lids grudgingly prised open, the flat was once again in darkness.

After one week every tin in her cupboard had been opened: chopped tomatoes, oxtail soup, pear halves, artichoke cream. Helga found mayonnaise a reasonable substitute for butter on oatcakes. Finally, it was the milkless coffee that drove her to don a pair of leggings and tackle the late-night corner shop. As though on a supermarket sweep, she grabbed armfuls of supplies: bread, milk, bacon, doughnuts. She took up Donald's recommendation of two Scotch pies for a pound. Filling several plastic carriers, Helga humped her bounty up the stairs, locking the door behind her.

She thought it would be easier to work at night, when the tenement was slumbering. As TVs turned off and music faded, Helga reluctantly reached for her MacBook. Her head pounded as she tried to reread the last paragraph and the words blurred on the screen. Candy Martini had returned home from her whirlwind trip to Geneva to find a bundle of dirty clothes abandoned on her doorstep. On approach, she was shocked to discover it was a young girl with long matted hair and what looked like a broken nose. Candy had offered to pay for a taxi to take the waif to the nearest emergency department, but the girl had refused, saying there was nothing anyone could do for her. The scrawny lass had no inkling whose doorstep she had been sleeping rough in, but couldn't believe her luck at finding the remnants from Candy's recently emptied fridge in the bin. She had never quite experienced the discarded steamed bean and edamame mix before but it had made a tasty snack. There was even a half-eaten tin of caviar and box of water biscuits up for grabs. She had been safe for two nights. Helga paused. This would be a pivotal moment in the novel – what should Candy Martini do? She talks the talk – magnanimous humanitarian, empathetic philanthropist, altruistic benefactor – but can she walk the walk? Should she take this troubled individual and offer her a home, a future – a life? Who knew what hell the girl had come from or lived through? Helga's thoughts drifted to the Scotch pies. She switched on the oven and went back to the page. Maybe it wasn't such a good idea bringing in a character that might derail the storyline? Helga had been advised she needed to introduce a romantic element – a boyfriend, a lover, or fiancé. Apparently it's what her readers wanted – a happy-ever-after story. A few months ago Kate had forwarded a critique from a focus group. Summary: there was little point in Candy Martini achieving immense success and leading the life of an international celebrity without finding happiness herself – it undermined the counsel she doled out if she was unable to deploy it. Helga couldn't think straight. The problem was, she was getting no more sleep during the day than she'd had at night, what with doors banging, Dolly barking, the door entry buzzer giving her a virtual electric shock every five minutes. She took a break, squirting brown sauce liberally over the pies.

Chapter 34

Bobbie struggled through the car park; one hand grasped a V-shaped pillow, a Zimmer frame swung from the other arm and her bag was hooked round her neck. She fought against the wind as dried leaves and dust blew into her face.

'Here, let me give you a hand,' said Vanda, locking the car door.

'I feel like a one-man band, but less musical.'

Vanda took the walking frame, holding the doors open as they entered the health centre. 'How did Mr Cormack get on?'

'I don't know what Sheba was on about. He couldn't have cared less about the bowling – in fact he grumbled the whole afternoon. He was most put out because he'd been watching *Casablanca* and apparently I arrived at a crucial part. I thought I was doing him a favour by telling him how it ended.'

'It's blowing a right hoolie out there,' said Molly.

'You're telling me – Mr Cormack just about ended up in a hedge.'

'So you just missed Chan. She wanted to finalise what we're doing for the Fun Day tomorrow.'

'I hope there's a Plan B,' said Vanda. 'Coffee, anyone?'

'Go on, then,' Bobbie replied. 'That stuff they gave me at the bowling club must have come out a plant pot.'

Molly checked her PC. 'The weather for Friday is meant to be worse. Ninety per cent chance of rain – possibly wintry, and high winds.'

'What about my chocolate fountain?' Bobbie asked. 'I can't do that outside – it'll look like an explosion in a slurry pit.'

'Don't worry, they've made some space in the reception area for the under-fives. The kids get a half-day on Friday so the surgery will close early for the afternoon activities. Chan says the High School along the road is sending their pipe band and some of the pupils are giving a taekwondo demo. Chan mentioned some cookery exhibition too.'

'Oh well, maybe I can put my fountain there?' Bobbie wondered.

'Put your fountain?' Aiden asked. 'What are you lot on about? I hope that's not a euphemism for one of your women's parts.'

'*Women's parts?*' Vanda laughed. 'How Victorian are you? No wonder you can't get a date! I hope you didn't ask Sheba if she wanted you to touch her women's parts?'

Aiden blushed as he made a cup of coffee. 'Who knows what you go on about half the time?'

'I was talking about my *chocolate* fountain for tomorrow,' said Bobbie. 'Although I'd be lying if I said Bob and I hadn't experimented with that body paint. Well, I say body paint – I just melted a bar of Cadbury's and it was all rather messy. Plus I had to wash the sheets afterwards – it just wasn't worth the hassle.'

'What have you been nominated for?' Vanda asked Aiden.

'Cameron and I are doing the photo booth – except he didn't want to pay for the actual booth so he's mocked something up and apparently the podiatrists have been bringing in hats, glasses and clothes all week for the kids to dress up in.'

'That sounds quite a laugh,' said Molly.

'It would be if you liked kids,' Aiden moaned.

'Right, well, I'm off,' said Vanda. 'See you all tomorrow.'

'You're sharp.'

'I know.' She winked. 'I'm going to some salsa festival with Craig.'

'Oh, can you dance?' said Molly.

'No, but I can drink!'

Friday morning broke with grey clouds and a light drizzle of icy rain. Chan wore a high-vis waistcoat over her cagoule as she directed staff to their posts. Ray had coned off an area of the car park for the pipe band and his 'Beat the goalie' but it was too early for him to change into his football top. The surgery reception area had been transformed into a marketplace of stalls, where the kids could do face-painting, pancake-making and even try their hand at pottery.

'Why are you dressed as an astronaut?' asked Bobbie.

Lance swung up the visor on his helmet. 'My job is to direct the families to the range of activities both indoors and outside.'

'I see,' said Bobbie. 'But why are you dressed as an astronaut?'

'I couldn't bear to be touched by all those strange children.' He shuddered. 'And this keeps me safe from germs.' He flipped the visor down and stomped off in his silver platform boots. Bobbie set up her chocolate fountain next to the pancake-making and plugged it in. Molly joined her with a plastic box of fruit. 'I think I'll just leave the fruit in here for the moment or it'll all go brown.'

'Good point,' said Bobbie. 'Here – help me break up the chocolate. It'll melt quicker. Ooh, have you seen Aiden? He's dressed as a pirate – he's brilliant!'

'I knew he'd get into the spirit of it. He wouldn't want to be shown up by Cameron.'

'I know; Quinn's meant to be putting in an appearance today

so Aiden will want to look like he's super keen! He even borrowed a pair of my crutches so he can hop along on a wooden leg.'

A portly Spider-Man was creeping along the corridor, his gloved hands patting the walls. 'Oh – you're good,' Bobbie commented. 'Getting into character, are you?'

'Not really – I can't see a damn thing with this mask on. Anyway, where's your lady friend?'

'What lady friend?' Bobbie said. 'You mean Chan?'

'Who *are* you?' Molly challenged. 'God, this is worse than Halloween!'

Anver pulled up the mask. 'It's me!'

'And *who* are you looking for?' Molly asked.

'The blonde lassie with attitude.'

'Oh, you mean Vanda?' Bobbie answered. 'She's having a wee lie-down behind reception. Turns out she was right – she's better at drinking tequila than salsa dancing.'

'I'd give her till lunchtime,' Molly advised.

'Okey-pokey.' He gave the thumbs up.

The morning passed with a handful of parents, who brought along babies and toddlers to have their share of fun. By twelve thirty the surgery was rammed with school kids on the hunt for free food and drink.

'Bobbie, would you mind fetching another box of fruit from the fridge? Molly asked.

'Sure thing.'

Quinn arrived with his seven-year-old niece and her best pal. He dumped them with Chan, asking her to entertain them while he had a meeting with the GPs. As soon as her back was turned they scarpered, enticed by the smell of freshly made pancakes.

'Would you like to try our chocolate fountain?' said Molly.

'Yes, please!' they chorused.

'Here,' Molly offered. 'You take a skewer and put a piece of fruit on and then you dip it into the chocolate. How cool is that?' she asked, demonstrating with a strawberry. 'Yum!'

One of the girls frowned. 'I don't know if I'm allowed that.'

'Of course you are, love!' Molly smiled. 'It's all free and you can have as many pieces as you like.'

'Did my uncle say it was okay?'

'Who's your uncle?' Molly asked.

'My Uncle Quinn.'

'Oh well, you must tell your Uncle Quinn what fun you had at the chocolate fountain,' said Molly, crouching to their eye level. 'Tell him it was the *best thing* you did all afternoon!'

'Alright,' she giggled. 'Can I have a piece of banana?'

'Course you can, love.' Molly smiled, holding out the box.

The girls had their fill then went on their way, holding hands. Bobbie returned with the fruit, making her apologies. 'Sorry about that – got chatting to Lynn in reception. Did you hear that she just got back from Mexico last week and when she was away she married a twenty-three-year-old fencer?'

'Never!' breathed Molly. 'Twenty-three? Lucky her! He must be fit as well – do you think he's any good at fencing?'

'She says he is.'

'Like Olympic standard?'

'How do you mean?'

'Fencing in the Olympics – because he wouldn't be allowed to enter the Commonwealth Games, would he? Mexico's not in the Commonwealth.'

'No, daftie! He builds fences – to keep animals in.'

Chan came panting up. 'Have you two seen Quinn's niece?'

'Yes, she's just been here,' said Molly.

'Oh, I must have missed her,' Bobbie said, tucking into the blueberries.

'Well, don't worry, Chan – I was extra nice to her and her wee pal and gave them loads of fruit.'

Chan suddenly blanched. 'But you didn't give her any chocolate, did you?'

'Course I did!' Molly laughed. 'What's the point of having a chocolate fountain if you can't dip in the fruit?'

'*Because,*' hissed Chan. 'She has a nut allergy! She isn't supposed to eat anything that might contain nuts!'

'What?" exclaimed Molly. 'Well, why didn't you tell us! She just appeared with her pal – how were *we* supposed to know?'

'Oh my God!' Chan wailed. 'Where did they go?'

'I don't know!'

'I'll help you look for her,' said Bobbie, untying her apron. 'Molly – guard my fountain!'

'They had on identical silver glittery tops and pink leggings, I remember that much. And one girl was wearing glasses.'

Bobbie and Chan pushed their way past uniform-clad teenagers, who seemed more intent on taking the piss than having fun. Bobbie gripped Aiden by the shoulders, almost dislodging his parrot. 'Aiden!'

'Ar-harrr!!'

'I don't have time for that! Have you seen two girls, aged about seven?'

'Sorry, I can't hear a thing!'

Outside, the High School pipe band burst into 'Scotland the Brave', the bagpipes almost drowning out the Fun-Day rabble.

'We're looking for two wee girls – they're both wearing silver glittery tops and leggings. They might have come this way?'

'When was this?' He scanned the crowded room.

'About fifteen minutes ago. One of them is wearing glasses.'

'Oh, I think I might have seen them.'

'Where? Which way did they go?' Chan cried.

He pointed vaguely towards the training room. Bobbie and Chan charged into the room to find several Ikea play tunnels had been tied together to form a maze, which shook violently as children of all shapes and sizes crawled through the multicoloured tubes. Kids dived in one end and popped out the other, their hair sticking up in static clumps.

'What's her name?' Bobbie asked.

'I've no idea. I didn't even get a good look at them.'

'I don't think she's out in the foyer,' said Bobbie doubtfully. 'She must be in there – I'll need to go in.' She got down on to her hands and knees and forced herself into the nearest tunnel. Chan watched the bulbous shape push through as Bobbie edged her way deeper into the maze. 'Can you see her?' Chan called anxiously.

'Not yet. Ooh! Sorry about that – I shouldn't have had all those avocados for breakfast.'

'Is there a monster in the tunnel?' a small, wide-eyed boy asked Chan.

'Help! I think I'm stuck!'

Like a giant snake having a crap, kids were forced out as Bobbie ploughed on. Chan heard a cry from the centre. 'Got her! Oh my God! She's having an allergic reaction!' Bobbie speeded up her crawling as Chan pulled out tangled bodies from one of the exits. Finally Bobbie tumbled out with the girl, whose bloated face was scarlet. 'You ate the chocolate from the fountain, didn't you?' Bobbie demanded, tugging on the girl's hand.

'Yes,' she admitted tearfully. 'Was I not meant to?'

'No!' snapped Chan. 'Your Uncle Quinn told me you weren't to eat anything that might contain nuts! Look at your face – you're all blotchy and swollen!'

'But he—'

'Come on,' Chan urged. 'Your EpiPen is at reception. How are you feeling? Is your throat feeling tight? Can you breathe?'

The girl burst into tears as Bobbie and Chan hurried her towards reception. Chan barked at the receptionist, 'Lynn! Where's the bag that Mr Adamson dropped off?'

'You mean the Dora the Explorer rucksack?'

'Yes! Chuck it here.'

Chan raked around frantically in the bag, eventually retrieving the EpiPen. She pulled the tube open and removed the syringe. By this time Quinn's niece was bawling her eyes out. 'Where's Ashley? I want my friend Ashley.'

'Calm down,' Bobbie soothed. 'You're only making yourself worse. Your face is all puffy and red. Is this what happens when you eat nuts?'

'I don't know,' she sobbed.

'Hang on a mo,' Bobbie said. 'Why has your face gone all streaky?'

'The nice lady,' she blubbed. 'Made me into Po. I'm a Teletubby!'

'Did she paint your face red?'

The girl nodded mutely.

'What's your name?' Bobbie asked.

'Kirsty.'

'And is your friend called Ashley?' Chan said, relieved.

The girl nodded again. '*Ashley!*' she cried as her bespectacled friend appeared in reception. They hugged tightly.

'*EpiPen for Ashley Adamson*,' Chan read from the plastic tube. 'Bobbie! You've got the wrong girl.'

'Well, how was *I* supposed to know? Anyway, why does she have chubby cheeks? I thought her airways were swelling.'

'I think that's just her normal face, Bobbie.'

'But you might have given me a clue!'

'*You're* the healthcare professional – can you not tell the difference between a child in anaphylactic shock and a flipping Teletubby?'

'You were the one about to administer adrenaline!'

'Whoa now, ladies,' Spider-Man intervened. 'You might want to take your dispute outside – this is meant to be a family *fun* day?'

Bobbie and Chan turned round to find a row of horrified parents, gripping the hands of their children and staring open-mouthed as Chan brandished the syringe.

One young child screamed, 'I don't want an injection, Mummy!'

Spider-Man ushered them behind the reception desk. 'Come on, you two – I think you need a coffee.'

'I wish I'd never volunteered to do this,' Chan said bitterly. 'If Mr Adamson gets to hear about this, he'll be furious. Imagine if I'd stuck that needle into the wrong child?'

'Cheer up,' said Bobbie. 'It could be worse. I know you've gone from life-saving heroine to murderous child abuser, but hey-ho – you just need to put it down to one of those days.' At that point a pale and sweaty Vanda sat up from the floor. 'What did I miss?' she croaked.

Chapter 35

Helga's mother opened the card and glanced at the picture of a generic cottage with roses round the door and a tabby cat lounging in the porch. Inside, Helga had scrawled Happy Mother's Day.

'Lovely!' said Eileen, stuffing the card into her bag. 'Really, you shouldn't have.' She gave Helga a brief hug.

'Have a seat, Mum,' Helga offered. 'Would you like a drink?'

'Yes, that would be nice – seeing as how we're not going out for lunch.'

'I just thought it would be better spending time here where we can get peace and quiet. Everywhere will be so busy.'

'Of course.' Eileen nodded, frowning at the dirty mugs and plates abandoned on the floor.

'So I can offer you water, orange juice or milk?'

'*Milk!* I'm not at primary school!'

'Or I can make you a ...' Helga searched her cupboards. 'A dry martini?'

'No wine?'

'Sorry, I haven't had a chance to ...'

'Martini is fine – with ice and lemonade, please? And a slice of lime?'

Helga poured a large slug of Martini into a tumbler and topped it up with flat soda water.

'Lovely!' Eileen repeated, wondering why the aroma of spring lamb and roast potatoes wasn't wafting through from the kitchen. They sat next to each other on the settee, Helga's duvet thrown over the back.

'Happy Mother's Day!' Helga said, knocking back her drink.

'Thank you, darling – so kind. Oh, did I tell you your sister sent a *huge* bouquet of red roses yesterday? They smell absolutely *gorgeous*. I thought at first they were from you, as I know they're your favourite. Here, I took a photo of them.' She produced her mobile and began prodding a finger at it. 'I think they're from Holland. Do stop scratching, dear – is your psoriasis playing up again?'

'Kind of. I've been under so much stress recently.'

'Have you?'

They were interrupted by a clumsy thwack at the door. Helga leapt up to answer it. Donald hovered in the hallway, his hands in a set of oven gloves, gripping a buckled container.

'Hi, Helga! Here you go – shall I bring it in for you?' He made to enter the hall but she stood her ground.

'Don't worry, I'll take it. I'll drop the oven gloves off later, if that's okay. What is it?'

'Erm, I think it's a moussaka. The label said to microwave for six minutes and let it stand but I think we've got a leaky seal. I left it in for ten minutes for good measure but I see it's gone a bit crusty round the edges.'

'I'm sure it'll be fine.' Helga and Donald awkwardly swapped over the oven gloves and foil container. He went to give her a peck on the cheek but she dodged back into the flat. 'Oh – what about dessert?' she asked.

He grinned, pulling a pot of yoghurt from each pocket. 'Mango all right? I'll just leave them here.'

'Thank you so much, Donald – you're a lifesaver!'

'I might see you later, then?' he asked hopefully, as Helga closed the door on his expectant face. She carried the dish through to the kitchen and scooped out the reddish slop on to two plates. 'Lunch is served!' Helga handed her mother a plate, which she balanced on her knees. 'Any cutlery back there?'

They chewed in silence for a few minutes, Helga acutely aware of Dolly's claws scrabbling against next door's laminate flooring.

'Doesn't that drive you mad?' Eileen asked, putting her plate on the floor.

'Oh, I'm kind of used to it by now,' said Helga, her eye twitching. 'Are you ready for pudding?'

'Em … what is it?'

'Mango yoghurt.'

'I don't think I will, thank you. Is there any more Martini?'

Helga topped up her mother's glass with a slosh.

'Look, is everything alright, love?' Eileen asked. 'You seem very distracted and normally you're so … well … on top of things.'

'How can I be alright, Mum? I'm suspended from work!'

'Oh, that – I thought that'd be all sorted by now. That was a couple of weeks ago, wasn't it? Haven't they let you back to work?'

'No, Mum. There's to be an inquiry.'

'Who with?'

Helga shrugged. 'I don't know – my boss. Maybe some senior executive – possibly even the legal team.'

'I don't know why you don't just resign? Put all this NHS nonsense behind you. You're a writer now! You should be focusing on harnessing your talent.'

'I can't afford to give up work.'

'Can't you? Why not? Candy Martini is a bestseller! Get yourself on to that *Loose Women* and it'll sell like hotcakes!'

'It's not that easy.'

'But what about your agent woman?'

'Kate.'

'Tell her to get you some high-profile publicity. Your face should be on the side of every bus! Anyway, what about book number two – surely you got an advance for that?'

'I did, but I'm finding it really hard to make progress and to meet the publisher's deadlines. I'm under so much pressure, it's … well, I'm not sleeping and I can't concentrate.'

'You've definitely lost weight. And is that a cold sore on your lip?'

'Honestly, Mum, I'm falling apart. And to make matters worse, I think I might have lost the plot.'

'Don't say that, darling! I can assure you you're not going mad – it's just you've had so much success so quickly. It's bound to get to you.'

'No – I mean, I have actually lost the plot. I thought I'd saved it in my Candy Martini file but now I can't find it anywhere. I had everything worked out.'

'I don't suppose it's a good time for me to ask what Kate thought of *my* manuscript, is it?'

'I can't face talking to Kate.'

'Oh, but you mustn't bite the hand that feeds you, dear. Shall I give her a call while we're both here?'

'No. In fact, I think I must really be getting back to my writing.'

'Oh. Well, then.'

'Sorry, Mum.'

'Fine – I'll go and find a bus. I'm sure there must be one running a Sunday service somewhere. Perhaps I'll start walking – work off that massive lunch!'

Chapter 36

He sat in his beige bedroom, perplexed. There was little point staking out the health centre each morning when Helga was clearly not at her work. Perhaps she was on holiday? It seemed pretty unlikely, judging by the way she fled on her last day. It wasn't an affable figure he witnessed skipping up the street, rejoicing in the prospect of two weeks' leave, but a woman tortured by some inner demon. He needed to reach out to her. But how? Something told him that Helga Trumpet needed saving!

Chapter 37

Helga stared at the void. The plain white page with grey borders generated zero inspiration – nothing except a needling headache.

> Candy Martini had opened the door to the stray and now they remained rooted in the spacious reception area of her London mansion. Candy's burgundy designer luggage – a wheeled suitcase and matching on-board flight bag – had been discarded behind the front door. The stranger, dressed in filthy rags, stank as though she had just been fished from the Thames and baked dry in a fertiliser spreader. They scowled at each other, neither trusting the other's motive.
>
> 'What's your name?' Candy asked.
>
> 'What do *you* care, missy?'
>
> 'Well, I have to call you something.'
>
> 'It's George,' the girl mumbled. She flicked something brown off her face on to the floor.

Helga *could not* decide on Candy's next move. Okay, so she'd relented and let this lass into her home but should she offer a bed for the night? Candy knew nothing about this stranger – how could she sleep with a delinquent under the same roof? And, boy, did she need some sleep! The conference had been draining enough but the obligatory dinners and committee socialising made her want to throw herself into the very beautiful Lake Geneva.

Candy and George stared each other out – at stalemate. Eventually Candy asked, 'What happened to your nose?'

The girl shrugged. 'Can't remember.'

'Look, you're shivering. Would you like a bath?'

'Really? I'd kill for a hot bath.'

Candy recoiled. 'I don't think that will be necessary.'

'Oh, I didn't mean …'

'I expect you'll need a change of clothes too?'

'I'm not here to put you out, lady. I thought the house was empty – all the shutters were closed. I'll be on my way.'

Candy sighed. 'I'm going to pour myself a gin and tonic while I run your bath. Do you want anything?'

'Cup of tea?'

'Fine. I'm sure I'll have some clothes that'll fit you. There's no point having a bath then putting those tatters back on. Wait here while I get your tea.'

George selected one of the nearby high-backed chairs, not understanding why anyone would want to sit in their hallway. Candy returned with a mug of tea and a plate of chocolate biscuits. The girl snatched a handful, wolfing them down.

'Look, I really need to get to bed. The spare bedroom and bathroom are the first on the left along that corridor. You might as well stay the night – then you can head off tomorrow.'

'I can sleep on the floor here.'

'No need – the bed's already made up. But please, don't go anywhere else. Is that clear?'

The girl nodded defiantly.

Helga paused. She felt bad about the appalling Mother's Day offering. The moussaka had left worryingly stubborn stains on the plates. And how old was that bottle of soda water? It's not that she had let herself down in the culinary department – having barely progressed from Toast Toppers – but she would normally treat her mother to a decent champagne lunch at one of the city centre restaurants. She scratched the back of her neck absently. It didn't feel right that it was a Sunday evening and she wasn't getting ready for work and preparing for the week ahead. Despite leaving Kate to manage her Twitter account, she couldn't help but glance at her feed – 6,994 followers. How hard could it be to get that up to 7,000? She only needed six more followers! She scrolled through the tweets, liking photos and adding comments as she went, making an effort to acknowledge other writers and bloggers. Another book release – *like*! A great review – *retweet*! She scanned the notifications, fearful of anything vitriolic, and followed anyone who had liked the latest post that Kate had put up for her: *Spending Mother's Day with my gorgeous mother – have a great day, everyone!* It had already received one hundred and forty-three likes. An email alert popped up in the corner of her screen.

Hi, Helga! Just wondering how you're getting on with the next 10,000 words? Got a meeting with Phil this week and I just know that he'll be dying to read it!
Love, as ever, Kate XX

Maybe it was just as well she wasn't going to work tomorrow. She sighed, changing into her pyjamas and pulling the duvet round her. 'Go to … Page 180.' The blank screen reappeared like an unwanted rash.

Chapter 38

'I wonder how old Dennis is doing?' Jimmy mused out loud.

'My mum says he's died,' Peter said. 'Do you think we'll have to go to the funeral?'

'Who's having a funeral?' Harry asked, hanging up her coat. 'Anyone I know?'

'Dennis,' said Peter, nodding his head.

'Don't be daft!' Jimmy admonished. 'We don't know anything. I'm sure Helga will tell us he's doing just fine.'

'Where is Helga?' Peter asked. 'Even when I get here first she's normally already setting up.'

'Right enough – there's no tea or coffee.'

'I've got my cola.'

'I'm alright Jack!' Lex said, skulking into the room. Kamal followed and took the seat next to her.

'I thought your name was Lex?' Peter said. 'Have I been calling you the wrong name?' Lex rolled her eyes.

'Here, I hope Helga didn't get into any trouble,' said Jimmy. 'Do you think that's why the group was cancelled last week?'

Peter leant forward. 'My mum said it was cancelled out of respect for the dead.'

'No one's chuffing dead, you moron!' Lex snapped.

'Ooh, did Dennis die?' Princess asked, bounding into the room.

'No!' came a chorus.

'What in heaven's name are you wearing today, girl?' said Harry.

'Oh, this is my Evil Queen outfit from Snow White – do you like it?' Princess pulled the black hood up over her blonde curls. 'I wore it out of respect for poor old Dennis.'

They heard a crash at the entrance to the community room and Dennis cruised in on his mobility scooter. 'I swear they narrow that doorway each week,' he grumbled.

'Oh, Dennis – you're alive!' Princess squealed. She leapt up and hugged him.

'Of course I'm alive – why wouldn't I be?'

'Because of you falling over and whacking your head,' said Peter. 'There was blood everywhere and then the ambulance had to take you to hospital. Don't you remember?'

'Of course I sodding remember – I was there, wasn't I?'

'So you're alright, then?' Jimmy smiled. 'It's good to see you.'

'It was only a knock on the head. If my family thought they needed to arrange a wake every time I fell over after a whisky, they'd have a garage full of sausage rolls!'

'I'm with you there,' Harry agreed. 'I don't know how many days I've lost through the brandy.'

'See this?' Dennis held up his left hand. 'I once got pissed while I was cutting the grass and chopped these three fingers clean off – had to get them sewn back on.'

'Chuffing hell!'

'And another time,' he said, tugging up his trouser legs to show the scars. 'I had been at a pal's leaving do and, as we staggered home, we both got run over by a reversing ice-cream van. Why do you think my legs don't hold me up?'

'I'm glad you're not having a funeral,' said Peter. 'I don't like funerals. My granny died and I didn't like the church. Everyone was sad except me cos the cakes were brilliant. It's the first time I'd ever tasted lemon drizzle.'

The group sat in silence waiting for Helga. 'What do we do now?' Lex muttered.

'Shall I go and look for her?' Peter offered. 'Sometimes she lets me help with the coffee and stuff, but not usually. Not since I spilt the milk all down the stairs.'

'I could come with you?' Princess suggested.

'Right, off you pop,' said Harry, shooing them with her hand.

Peter closely examined the names on the buzzer. 'That's it!' He pressed hard on *Harrison Intervention Team*. The intercom crackled then a voice asked, 'Yes?'

'We're looking for Helga. Can we come in?'

'Helga?' The door buzzed open.

Peter and Princess made their way to the office, by which time Bobbie was holding the door open. 'Crikey!' she exclaimed. 'I don't suppose you've come as Hansel and Gretel, have you?'

'Who?' Peter asked, stepping into the office.

'No – silly! I'm the Evil Witch from Snow White.'

'And I'm Peter.'

'From Peter and the Wolf?'

'No, I'm Peter Gibson.'

'We're looking for Helga,' Princess repeated. 'We're from the Tuesday Chatters.'

'Oh, hello!' Molly said, swivelling her chair round. Peter blushed. 'You're the nice lady!'

'I am indeed,' Molly smiled.

Bobbie puffed her cheeks out. 'Hate to tell you guys but Helga's not here.'

'Is she in trouble?' Princess asked anxiously.

'Kind of,' Bobbie replied. 'She's got to meet with the general manager on Friday morning at Westside to sort it out.'

Molly glared at her. 'Bobbie! That's not public information.'

'Oops! Just keeping them in the loop.'

'Because Dennis isn't dead – he's fine.'

'Well, I'm relieved to hear that,' said Bobbie. 'And I'm sure Helga will be too.'

Molly frowned. 'But didn't you get a call to say the group was cancelled?'

'Only for one week.'

'That's strange. Bobbie, you cancelled the group, didn't you?'

'Erm … only for one week – that's all I was told!'

'Well, they're here now,' said Molly. 'Can't *you* take the group this week?'

'Me!' Bobbie exclaimed. 'I'm a physio – I don't know all about Helga's touchy-feely stuff.'

'Oh, we're not allowed to touch each other,' said Peter.

'Look, I'll help bring down the tea and coffee.' Molly lowered her voice. 'It's only for an hour – surely it can't be that hard to entertain her wee group?'

Bobbie grunted. 'S'pose. But you'll have to call Mr What's-his-face and put him off till tomorrow.'

'Fine.'

'So what sort of things do you get up to in your group?' Bobbie asked.

'Sometimes we play games,' Princess offered.

'And sometimes people like you drop in to talk to us.'

'Right, come on, then.' Bobbie picked up Mr Happy. 'Let's see what your core stability is like.'

'I'll even throw in some biscuits,' Molly offered.

'Helga hardly ever brings biscuits,' said Peter. 'This is much better!'

Bobbie dunked a fig roll into her coffee. 'So my name's Bobbie – I'm the physiotherapist in the team.'

'Does that mean we get a massage?' Dennis joked.

'Only if you want to end up back in A and E. By the way, I'll never remember your names so don't be offended if I get it wrong. Now you all have your tea or coffee—'

'Or cola.'

'Fine. So what next?'

'Helga likes to mix it up a bit,' Harry reported. 'Some weeks we play cards – other times she tries to do a bit of soul-searching. You know – tries to get us to open up as to why we're such a bunch of losers.'

'That's right,' Peter agreed. 'Like Lex is always swearing because her brother got knocked off his motorbike.'

'I swear because you all get on my chuffing tits!'

'In all honesty I don't know which came first,' Harry confessed. 'Do I drink because I'm a loser or am I loser because I drink?'

'I hope you're not expecting me to answer that?' Bobbie asked, finishing her coffee. 'Well, I thought maybe we could do some fun physical activity? Let's all stand up and we'll do some warm-ups before I let you loose on Mr Happy.'

'What am I meant to do?' Dennis complained. 'I can't stand up.'

'Just follow me,' said Bobbie. 'Do the best you can. So we'll start with some gentle rolling of our head from side to side …'

After ten minutes of gentle warm-ups she produced a handful of Therabands – passing one to each member. 'Again, we'll just start off quite slowly. Take an end in each hand and slip the band under your foot; that's right, Jimmy – get it under the arch. Now hold your leg in extension and gently, gently stretch it towards you.'

'Like this?' Princess asked.

'Very good.'

Peter leant back and pulled with all his might. His sweaty hands slipped and the band flew off, whacking Harry in the face. '*Peter!* You klutz. *Gently* she said!'

'Sorry! It slipped!'

'What's *your* name?' Bobbie asked Kamal.

'He's Kamal,' Jimmy said.

'Right, Kamal, would you like a turn on my Swiss ball?' Bobbie asked, patting the pink rubber. Kamal looked horrified, shaking his head.

'The lad never says a word,' Dennis offered.

'Oh, well – what about you?' Bobbie turned to Princess.

'Hmm, I suppose I could try. I've never sat on anything so wobbly before.'

'You might like to get rid of the cloak – think you'll get on better without it.'

Princess removed the full-length cloak to reveal a white tutu dress; the bodice rucked over her stomach. She lowered herself on to the ball, sending the gauze skirt up over her face. Bobbie attempted to smooth it down. 'Blimey – probably not the most practical outfit to wear.'

'I can see your knickers!' Peter laughed.

Princess burst into tears. 'Peter, you're horrid!' She flounced off the ball and returned to her seat.

'We're not getting very far here,' Bobbie frowned. 'How about you – Lex, did you say your name was?'

'No, thanks,' Lex scowled, folding her arms in protest.

'Go on!' Jimmy urged. 'If I try I'll fall off. Give it a shot.'

'Come on, Lex, I want to see how it works,' Harry said.

'It's just a chuffing bouncy ball!' Lex objected. 'I'm not going to balance like a chuffing seal for your entertainment. Forget it!'

'Don't look at *me*,' Harry sniffed. 'I can't with my bad back.'

'Oh, for chuff's sake!' Lex exclaimed. She pushed her chair out of the way and threw herself down on the ball with a furious thump. Like a gunshot the ball burst with a loud *bang*!

'*Fuck!*' Lex screamed as she collapsed on to the floor, arms and legs splayed.

'Help!' Princess howled.

Kamal dived under the table where he shook like a startled deer.

Dennis, Jimmy and Peter nearly fell off their chairs with laughter.

'Mr Happy!' Bobbie cried. 'You killed Mr Happy!'

Lance came charging into the room. 'What on earth is going on? Is this *the incident* Norman mentioned? I heard an explosion! Has someone been shot?' He glared at Kamal under the table. 'Has he got a gun?'

'Calm down, Lance – it wasn't gunfire or an explosion,' said Bobbie in shock.

'I heard someone shout, "You killed Mr Happy!" – what's going on?'

Lex rolled over and held up the flabby pink remains of the Swiss ball. 'Sorry about that.' Standing up she revealed her spiked belt. 'I told you I didn't want to sit on your stupid chuffing ball.'

'Well, keep the noise down, *please*,' Lance complained. 'I've never seen the like! Some of us are trying to do some proper work!'

'Well, I guess that's the end of my exercise class?' Bobbie sighed.

'I don't know about anyone else but *I* feel a whole lot better,' Jimmy chortled. 'We just never seem to have an afternoon passing without some commotion.'

'It never used to be like this,' Harry objected. 'Most Tuesday Chatters we would have a cup of coffee, talk about the weekly news and then go home.'

'I'm not up to running a blooming social – I think I've done my bit,' Bobbie said grumpily. 'I'm going back upstairs.'

'But please say our group will be on next Tuesday?' Princess implored. 'It's the highlight of my week!'

'I think that depends on the outcome of Friday's panel,' said Bobbie, exiting the room.

'What does she mean by that?' Jimmy asked.

'Apparently Helga has to face the general manager on Friday morning,' Princess revealed. 'At Westside.'

'That's where my doctor is,' said Jimmy.

'But if Helga is in big trouble, she doesn't know that Dennis is fine,' said Princess with concern in her voice.

'There's nowt wrong with me,' Dennis agreed.

'So should we let her know?' Harry suggested.

'I don't think it's fair if Helga gets a row because of *us*,' said Princess.

'Or because of *you*,' Peter accused Dennis.

'Eh! What did I do?'

'It was your idea to go to the pub,' Peter stated.

'Er … it didn't exactly require a whole lot of persuasion for you to join me.'

'Dennis is right, we're all in this together.'

'Should we perhaps write a letter?' Harry proposed. 'We could all sign it?'

'I think we're too late for that.'

'How about we just rock up?' Lex muttered. 'Put this arsehole right?'

'My mum says you should always tell the truth,' Peter nodded. 'I can get my dad to take me there.'

'I do feel a sense of duty to Helga,' Jimmy admitted. 'She tried to treat us to a nice evening out and we repaid her by going AWOL then getting her into a world of trouble.'

'But we signed a waiver,' Harry threw in.

'What do you mean?'

'We all signed a waiver saying we accepted responsibility for our own conduct while away from the health centre. That should absolve her from any untoward outcome.' Harry raked around in her handbag. 'Here it is, see! This is my one.'

'Of course!' Jimmy agreed. 'I remember now. What about you, Dennis? Think, man, have you still got yours?'

Dennis coughed into a dirty hankie. 'Oh, probably – it'll still be in my other pair of trousers no doubt.'

'So who's up for it?' Jimmy searched their faces. 'Shall we put the management right?'

Lex shrugged. 'If I don't have this, I'm not chuffing allowed out at all.'

'Sounds fun!' Princess clapped her hands. 'Let's do something nice for Helga!'

'Kamal?'

He nodded his head.

'Right,' Jimmy said. 'Let's make a plan.'

Chapter 39

Helga must have dozed off on the settee. She woke with a start when her neighbour slammed the front door shut. Everyone would be heading off to work as the dark sky began to lighten at the edges. The flat felt cold and damp. She shuffled through to the kitchen and filled the kettle. Her MacBook had been left to charge, the green light glowing cheerfully. She opened it up to find an email from Kate:

Who the hell is George? Why on earth have you introduced a bloody hobo into the story? Phil is furious! He said he specifically asked you to bring some romance into Candy's life – not some stinking down-and-out. Way too political! And depressing! Come on, Helga – let's see some of your magical guru writing that we love.

He needs to see some progress by the weekend.

Yours anxiously, Kate XX

Shit! She'd have to undo all yesterday's work. She began to highlight the offensive text but something stopped her pressing *Delete*. Helga couldn't let it go. Candy had taken over and she was *not* going to allow George to be wiped out. There was a story here and she needed to find out more about this stray who had appeared from nowhere.

Helga made a coffee but found drinking it difficult – the cold sore had spread painfully round her mouth. However miserable the weather was outside, she had to get some fresh air. The slightly whiffy pyjamas were replaced with a heavy jumper and baggy cottons. When the psoriasis was bad, she avoided washing her hair, which stood up in greasy clumps. She pulled on a raincoat and trudged down the stairs. The first bus that arrived took her into town, where she alighted at Princes Street Gardens. A steady drizzle left the civic gardens largely deserted. A young lad flipped open the shutter on his kiosk just as Helga was passing. 'Do you do hot chocolate?' she asked.

'Sure.' He stirred the sugary powder into the hot, frothy milk, sprinkling chocolate over the top. 'Two pounds, please.'

Helga carried her drink and sat on one of the many varnished benches lined up along the park footpath. Beyond the grassy lawns carriages of trains crisscrossed in front of her, transporting passengers in and out of Waverley station. Pigeons pecked hopefully around her boots as Helga finished the remains of her sweet treat. She stood the empty cup on the bench, shoving her frozen hands deep into her pockets. The drink had warmed her temporarily and she allowed her eyes to close. The smell of freshly brewed coffee drifted from the kiosk. Helga was woken by a clang as a passing businessman tossed a twenty pence piece into her empty cup. Oh, how the mighty had fallen! She fished out the coin and dropped the cup into a nearby rubbish bin. Something sparkling caught her eye at the bottom – it looked like a jewelled ribbon. Moving the discarded cups, newspapers and empty chip wrappers to one side she stretched down. Her fingertips brushed the object – so close! She went in for a final dive, retrieving a buckled hair band decorated with plastic gemstones.

'Helga, what are you *doing*?' Donald asked, suddenly appearing at her side.

'I could ask you the same thing,' Helga replied indignantly, convinced it was no coincidence that he had found her raking through the rubbish.

'You look … you look,' he stammered.

'Like a million dollars?'

'I was going to say unwell. What happened to your face?'

Helga sighed. 'Life – that's what happened to my face.'

'I think we should get you home. It's perishing out here and you're not even wearing gloves. Here, have mine.' Donald pulled off his knitted mittens and shoved them on Helga's hands, keeping hold of them as he led her towards the bus stop. 'Why aren't you at work? Are you having a day off? Can't be much fun on your own; you should have given me a call and we could have done something together?'

The bus arrived and Donald jostled Helga from behind. The vehicle stopped and started until they had wound their way along the bridges, down to Cameron Toll and meandered to the left. The dreich streets passed in a blur. As the bus neared their corner shop Donald stood, pressing the bell. 'Do you need anything?' he asked as they passed the garish orange stars offering TWO DO-NUTS FOR FIFTY PENCE and ANY LITER FIZZY DRINK – ONE POUND.

Helga shook her head, reaching into a pocket for the flat keys. They mounted the stairs with heavy feet, halting at her front door. 'Now are you *sure* you're okay? I can come in and make you some Bovril or something to warm you up?'

'I'll be fine,' she answered, fairly positive she wouldn't be. *Where were her keys?*

'What's up?' Donald enquired.

'Can't appear to find my keys.'

'Are you locked out?'

'Seems like it,' Helga replied, tears welling.

Donald looked rather too pleased. 'Right, come and have a seat in our flat and we'll work out what to do. Has anyone else got a spare set?'

'My mum.'

'Right, well, let's get you inside and you can wait for her there.'

Chapter 40

Bobbie had taken the remnant of Mr Happy and pinned it on to Aiden's OT OF THE YEAR poster so that it hung limply from the unzipped jeans.

'Nice one!' Vanda laughed. 'So you got landed with Helga's group, did you?'

'Humph!'

'Had they recovered from their safari into Musselburgh? Tell you what, if they can survive that, they're not doing bad in my books.'

'Helga's got her panel interview on Friday,' Molly said. 'Sheba was on the phone, making sure Helga knows to turn up for it.'

'Did you speak to her?' Vanda asked. 'Did she sound alright?'

'I rang several times and left two messages but she didn't answer. But I see she sent a text this morning just saying "thanx".'

'I hope Cameron is going with her?' Bobbie said.

'Why?'

'He's her union rep – he knows his stuff and won't let Sheba get away with anything.'

'What's Sheba been up to now?' Aiden muttered, removing his cycle helmet. 'Right! Who did that? You bloody perverts!' He yanked the pink rubber off his poster, chucking it in the bin.

'It's Helga's disciplinary on Friday,' said Bobbie.

'Bobbie! It's not a *disciplinary*,' Vanda tutted. 'It's just an informal chat with Sheba and Quinn. I'm sure they'll get it all sorted out and she'll be back at work on Monday.'

'Fingers crossed,' Molly said. 'She must be worried sick.'

'What does "brownies for brownies" mean?' Bobbie asked, clutching a Post-it note.

'Oh, that's mine!' Molly laughed. 'I need to remember to pick up a tray of brownies on the way home. Mandy has her home-baking badge tonight so she needs to take in something she's made.'

'Not that I'm a shining example of cheffing expertise, but isn't that cheating?' Vanda frowned.

'Trust me, Barn Owl does not want to sample anything Mandy has made. Last week Caz helped her make cupcakes … and she thought she was adding vanilla.'

'Wasn't she?'

'No, she tipped vinegar into the mixture. I didn't know whether to throw them out or crumble them on to my chips!'

'So is Helga coming in here first?' Bobbie said. 'Then we can wish her luck.'

'Nah, I think she's been told to go straight there.'

'Pity. She still owes me a tenner for that candle set she ordered.'

Chapter 41

As soon as they opened the front door a frantic Dolly besieged them. '*Sit!*' Donald commanded. 'Now go to your bed.' Dolly scampered off, tail between her legs. The flat was cosily warm, the living room cluttered with framed pictures and ceramic ornaments. Donald strode across to a grey-haired lady cocooned in a crocheted blanket who was wedged into an armchair beside an electric fire. 'Mum!' he shouted into her ear. 'This is Helga from next door.'

'Who?'

'Helga Trumpet – our neighbour.'

'Nice to meet you, Mrs Grimm.'

The woman's pale eyes scrutinised Helga's greasy hair, blistered mouth, shapeless coat and sagging cottons.

'Helga Trumpet?' she asked with incredulity. 'The famous writer?'

'Oh, er, I don't know about being *famous*.'

'Well, you are in *this* house. Donald can barely string a sentence together without it being "Helga this" and "Helga that". Anyone would think you were an international superstar!'

'But she is, Mum,' Donald replied, filling the kettle. 'You should have seen the crowd she drew at Musselburgh the other week.'

'How could I? I wasn't invited, was I? All very well for you to go out gallivanting and leaving me here. I might have been robbed and murdered in my sleep.'

'Mum, I was home by eleven. You don't even go to bed till after midnight.'

The woman snorted, gripping the blanket tighter. 'Anyway, what's she doing here?' She scowled in Helga's direction. 'Visiting the old and lonely, are you? Community service, is it? What did you do? *Accidentally* shoplift a crate of champagne?'

'Mum, don't be rude.'

'Actually, I've been locked out.'

'Ha! You don't even *want* to bloody be here. Mind you, I don't blame you – it's a miserable existence I lead. See out that window?' She poked a bony finger towards the grimy pane.

'I can't see anything,' Helga said. 'What am I meant to be looking at?'

'That's my point – there *is* nothing to look at. Grey skies and rain. If I'm lucky an occasional bird craps against the window. And that stays there until it rains again.'

'Tea or coffee?' Donald asked Helga.

'Tea would be lovely.'

'Don't bother asking me, then!'

'I know what you have, Mum – you always have the same thing.'

Donald handed Helga her tea in a cracked *Eastenders* mug.

'Biscuit?'

'No, I'm fine, thanks.'

'You don't *look* fine,' Mrs Grimm pronounced. 'What happened to your face?'

'*Mum!*'

Helga texted her mother:

So sorry to bother you – locked out! – Any chance you can bring spare key round?

Ping!

```
Mags and I off to writing class - drop it off on way. Half
hour - tops
```

Helga cradled the mug. 'That was lucky – my mum's heading out but will drop off the spare key.'

'You still look frozen,' Donald commented. 'Would you like a hot bath?'

'You know,' Helga replied with a wry smile. 'I would *love* a bath.'

'Don't go using up all the hot water!' Mrs Grimm said. 'It doesn't grow on trees.'

Chapter 42

Sheba dragged her chair round so she, too, was shielded behind Mr Adamson's imposing desk. She handed him a sheaf of papers. He checked his watch impatiently. 'How long will this take? I really ought to be at Waverley Gate this morning for a resilience workshop.'

Sheba shrugged her shoulders. 'I suppose it depends how much they argue the case.'

'Surely there's nothing *to* argue? This link worker bussed a group of helpless patients on an inappropriate excursion during which they were left unsupervised, leading to one poor man being admitted to hospital. Is that the type of behaviour you're condoning?'

'No, but …'

'So aren't we here to negotiate the best way to get rid of her? I thought you'd be delighted – it's one less flunkey for you to accommodate. She's lucky the family have decided not to pursue a formal complaint – she might have brought us all down with her!'

'But we're obliged to hear her side of the story.'

Quinn snorted. 'I'm giving her fifteen minutes then I have to be out of here.'

They heard a knock at the door. 'Come in!'

Cameron paced into the room, sitting directly opposite Quinn. Helga followed, taking the empty seat at his side. Following yesterday's bath, she had gone to get her hair cut, unzipped her only suit from its carrier and polished her black court shoes. She gripped a plastic bottle of water.

'Right,' Quinn began. 'Miss Mount has apprised me of the background to the scenario we find ourselves in and I hope we can all resolve it efficiently and satisfactorily—'

'Excuse me,' Cameron interrupted. 'But "we" do not find ourselves in a scenario. *Helga* is the one who has been subjected to an impetuous and overly punitive response to an unplanned and unfortunate incident. Had you made time for her the following day to take cognisance of the actual events, my client would not have been subjected to two weeks of anxiety, humiliation and emotional strain. The impact on her health has been both physical and psychological.'

'This isn't an episode of *Law and Order*, Cameron,' Quinn snapped. 'I'm not suggesting that the events which took place on the fifteenth of March were in any way intentional but I cannot have my staff behaving in a manner that disregards the rules and puts people's lives at risk.'

'Ask Helga what her role is,' said Cameron. Helga went to open her mouth.

'I know what her role is,' Quinn replied, through gritted teeth. 'She's a link worker in the Harrison Intervention Team.'

'But ask her what her role *involves*.' Again Helga made to respond.

'Her job,' continued Cameron,' is to integrate patients into the community. To include them in normal, everyday activities – to take them out and about and encourage them to try new activities. Correct?'

'We know that,' Sheba replied, desperate to participate.

'So, on the evening of the fifteenth of March, Helga arranged for her social group to have a local outing – which is entirely appropriate for her role and for their assimilation. Are we all in agreement so far?'

Quinn stabbed his pen on the papers. 'But they should have been supervised! Miss Trumpet has to accept responsibility for her actions!'

'I-I ...' Helga stammered.

They heard an insistent knock at the door. 'I thought I told Brenda not to let anyone in here?' Quinn barked. 'I'm busy!' he bawled.

The knock became a thumping. 'Oh, for goodness' sake!' Quinn exploded. 'Sheba – get rid of whoever that is.' Before she could rise the door burst open as though rammed by a cannon. Dennis steered his mobility scooter into the office until it crashed into Quinn's desk. 'What the hell are you doing, man?' Quinn asked. Now that the drawbridge was down, Jimmy, Harry, Lex, Peter, Kamal and Princess trotted in – Princess having chosen the special occasion to come as Jasmine in full-flowing cobalt ballgown, headband and large gold hoop earrings.

Quinn stared open-mouthed. 'What on earth? Look, wherever you lot are supposed to be, it's not here.'

'This is Mr Adamson's office,' Sheba declared. 'Who let you in here?'

'Dennis!' Helga cried. 'How are you?' Her head spun around and she beamed at the Tuesday Chatters. 'Oh, my goodness – you're all here!'

'Do you know these halfwits?' Quinn blustered. 'What are they doing in my office?' He stood up, his knuckles leaning on his desk. 'We're in the middle of a staff review,' he announced furiously. 'You can't just come barging in. Get this circus out of here!'

'Keep your hair on, son,' Dennis said. 'Let's just calm down.' The social group shuffled to one side to allow Dennis some space. 'Sit,' he instructed Quinn. 'Now I do believe that this young lass,' he pointed to Helga, 'has got into a spot of trouble on our account?'

'It's more than a *spot* of bother,' Sheba piped up.

Dennis ignored her, remaining focused on Quinn. 'Are you her boss?'

Quinn fumed. 'I'm Mr Adamson, the general manager.'

'Good,' Dennis nodded. 'Now, whatever you think did or did not happen the other evening – it was of no blame to Helga here. She offered to take us out on a wee social trip and everything was just grand. So, we took it upon ourselves to go off on our own little adventure, didn't we, folks?' Vehement nodding of heads. 'And what happened next, as a result of my fondness for single malt, again had nowt to do with this lassie.'

'But Miss Trumpet was responsible for your welfare,' Quinn asserted. 'She should have been supervising you at *all times* and there never should have been any drinking of alcohol.'

Dennis nodded. 'But you see, that's where she's smart. She asked us, very sensibly, to sign this form here.' He waved it for all to see before flicking it forward.

'What's that?' asked Quinn as though a turd had been dropped on his desk.

'It's the form that Helga asked us to sign, saying that she would only accept responsibility for us as long as we complied with instructions given – which we didn't. She would not be held liable for any unwarrantable behaviour. And *we* broke the rules – not her!'

Dennis leant back on his scooter and grinned. 'It's her *Get Out of Jail Free* card! And we've all got one, haven't we, pals?' The Chatters waved the forms above their heads with a flourish.

'Well,' said Cameron. 'I think that wraps up the hearing, don't you, Mr Adamson?'

'But ...'

'But, what? Helga arranged for her community integration group to integrate with the community,' said Cameron. 'Job done, I'd say.'

'But ...'

'What's your beef, fella?' Dennis growled. 'Why don't you do some proper manager work rather than picking on some wee lassie trying to do her best for a bunch of old bastards? Sorry Lex and Kamal – no offence.' They both shrugged.

'I really do think that's the end of the matter,' Cameron proclaimed. 'Come on, Helga, let's get these people a well-deserved cup of coffee.'

Helga glanced from Quinn's seething face to Sheba's sullen glare. 'Fine,' Quinn muttered. 'I'm more than happy to get back to some actual business. Sheba – do something so this kind of nonsense doesn't happen again. I want a *Lessons Learnt* report on my desk by tomorrow.' He snatched up his briefcase and marched out of the office to a chorus of whoops and clapping. Peter booed Quinn's back as he scuttled off down the corridor. Sheba hurriedly gathered up her papers and swept out in his wake, her head held high.

Helga gave Dennis a hug. 'You were fab! A knight in shining armour!'

'Ach, it was worth it to see the boy's face!' He reversed the scooter, taking a decent chunk out of Quinn's doorframe. Helga directed him out. 'This way to the lift – are you coming too, Jimmy?'

'Right-oh!'

'I'll meet you down at the café,' Cameron offered. 'Follow me, folks!'

Waiting for the lift Helga rubbed Dennis's arm. 'It's so good to see you're alright.'

'It was a lot of fuss over nothing. Honestly, hen, I've fallen over more times than you've had fish suppers.'

'But your daughter was so angry – I thought she was going to sue us!'

'Listen, you've met my daughter – we're about as close as Celtic is to Rangers. I made it clear that she was not making another penny out of me.'

The lift doors opened and he manoeuvred the scooter in. 'I'll tell you a story. A couple of years ago five of my numbers and the bonus ball came up on the lottery. I was cock-a-hoop – was due to get over two grand! Then she tells me she had forgotten to get my ticket. I was gutted.'

The lift doors opened again and Helga led the way to the café. Dennis continued, 'About a month later, she and her boyfriend at the time went off to Benidorm for a fortnight, even though she never had two coins to rub together.'

'That's terrible!' Helga exclaimed.

'Families …' tutted Jimmy.

'That house we're in is mine,' said Dennis. 'She has to keep in with me or she knows I'd sign it over to Pepper in a heartbeat.'

They arrived to find Cameron had pulled two tables together. Helga remained standing. 'Before I get your coffee, I just want to say thank you all so much for coming to my rescue – it means so much to me,' she said tearily. 'I know it can't have been easy for you to get here and Cameron and I will make sure you get home safely.'

'Three cheers for Helga!' Princess squealed. 'Hip, hip, hooray!'

'You're too kind. Now who's having what?'

'Can I get cola?' Peter requested in an urgent voice. 'And can I get one of those pink buns as I've missed my elevenses.'

'Of course you can.' She turned to Cameron. 'And thank you, Cameron – you were brilliant. If I ever commit a murder I'll be sure to get in touch.'

Cameron saluted. 'At your service.'

Chapter 43

Helga decided to ignore Kate's irate emails and Phil's direct order to remove George's character. Despite the advance provided by the publisher, she was backing Candy Martini's decision to allow the runaway teenager into her home. It absolutely was the right thing to do. Yes, Candy acknowledged that she'd never given much thought to the homeless epidemic creeping across London, and no – other than chuck a few coins into Shelter's collection tins – she did not know how to help. But now that a predicament had presented itself, literally on her doorstep, she could not turn her back on George. Here was a genuine and practical way she could make a contribution. Candy had built her fortune and, apart from a handful of charitable monthly donations, she hadn't fully explored the philanthropic side to her character.

> Candy stuck her head round the bedroom door, noting that George had pulled the duvet off the bed and was curled up on the floor. The girl's rucksack, leaning against the wardrobe, stank like a fetid compost heap. She returned to the spacious, bespoke kitchen. Having been away for a long weekend, Candy had back-to-back engagements lined up. She switched on the coffee machine and selected a ristretto capsule. Mid-morning George appeared, wearing the same designer clothes

that Candy had supplied.

'Coffee?' Candy offered.

George shook her head.

'Tea?'

'Okay.'

'How did you sleep?'

'On the floor – why?'

Candy made the tea and pushed it across the table. 'Are you hungry?'

'I'm always hungry.'

'I don't keep much food as I'm often in and out of the country …'

George stared at her.

'I've got some brioches in the freezer?'

'Some what?'

'Toast?'

'Yeah.'

Candy waited until George had lathered chocolate spread on to a mound of toast before she tried again. 'So what's the plan for today?'

'I'm not on a fucking city break,' George muttered. 'I'll get going once I've finished.'

'You don't have to.' Candy had no idea where this was going. 'I want to know how I can help.'

'Help? Why?'

Candy didn't know why. Even she sensed how naff it would sound.

Helga paused to gaze out of the window. It was a chilly, grey Saturday but suddenly her heart was filled with optimism. She heard her mobile vibrate and picked it up, noting with satisfaction that she had tipped over 7,000 Twitter followers. She scrolled through the tweets, pleased that Kate had kept the posts regular and in the spirit of Helga Trumpet. Surely they'd indulge in her foray into Candy's benevolent side? Isn't that what had made Candy famous in the first place? Her desire to help other people? Helga just needed to shoehorn some romance into the plot and everyone would be happy.

Chapter 44

He had tried to keep away, he really had. But something kept drawing him back to that familiar stairwell. The cold, bright morning meant it hadn't been unpleasant to skulk in the doorway as commuters scampered to work. Mondays were marked by the dazed and crabby exchanges of those who hadn't quite come to terms with putting their brains into gear. The minutes ticked by. He had got better at limiting himself to an hour – two hours at most. Helga didn't exactly stick to a rigid morning routine, which meant he had to make allowances. Still, it had been two weeks of nothing … and then, from nowhere, he thought he spotted her wee Hyundai inching its way down the hill. Yes! He recognised the registration number. The sun visor was down but he could just about make out her familiar features. Oh joy! Helga was back to work! Now all he needed to do was put his plan into motion.

Chapter 45

'If only *I* had some romance in my life,' Molly sighed.

'I didn't say anything about romance!' Vanda laughed. 'I said I copped it off with Craig and we spent Sunday on the sofa scoffing a Nando's takeaway.'

'Still – at least you have a man.'

'*I* have a man – that doesn't mean he would know romance if it came delivered by Yodel addressed to Mr Bob Crawford!' Bobbie chipped in. 'Muffin, anyone?'

'Oh, what kind are they?' Molly asked.

'Are you really that fussy?' Bobbie said. 'Are you telling me that if I said "bran" you'd go, "oh – no, thanks, I only like chocolate chip"?'

'True.' Molly plucked one from the tin. 'Did you make these yourself?'

'Shut up! Do I look like Mary Berry?'

The door code sounded and Helga entered the office. She walked straight to her desk, sat down and laid her bag on the floor.

'Helga!' Molly cried. 'You're back!'

'How did it go?' Vanda breathed.

'Want a muffin?' asked Bobbie.

'Look, give Helga a chance,' Aiden said. 'Would you like a coffee?'

'I'd love one, thanks.'

The team all swivelled their chairs round so Helga had a

captive audience.

'Well?' Molly prompted. 'Tell us what happened on Friday!'

'So,' Helga began, 'for a start I never uttered a single word.'

'Was it Cameron?' Molly asked. 'I bet he did all the talking. He never knows when to keep quiet. See at the health centre meetings he just goes on and on and—'

'Molly!' Vanda interrupted.

'Cameron was *brilliant*,' said Helga. 'You'd think he was a proper lawyer.'

'He told me he fancies himself as a bit of a Columbo,' Bobbie said. 'I think he even has the dirty mac – although that could be for something else.'

'Anyway … he had everything under control. And then, the most extraordinary thing happened. Everyone from the Tuesday Chatters turned up!'

'No way!' Vanda exclaimed. 'How did they find out about it?'

'I wonder,' mused Bobbie. 'Someone must have let the cat out of the bag.'

'But who?' Helga wondered.

'So … what happened next?'

'Well, Dennis, the chap who fell and ended up in hospital was as right as rain – thank God! But he laid right into Quinn – said that because I'd got them to sign waivers there was no comeback on me. He said that they were all willing to accept responsibility for what happened.'

'Good for you,' Aiden smiled. 'All that bloody risk-assessment training finally paid off, eh?'

'Muffin?' Bobbie repeated, holding out the tin.

'Thanks. And then Cameron said that there was no case to be had, as it was just a community trip that went wrong – but the group admitted they should never have gone to the pub. Which they shouldn't have …'

'Were they not enjoying your talk, then?' Bobbie asked. Molly dug her in the ribs.

'So is that it?' Vanda asked. Everything back to normal?'

'Oh, I hope so! I need to give Sheba something for her *Lessons Learnt* report.'

'Fuck's sake!' Aiden exclaimed. 'Why doesn't *she* learn to mind her own business?'

'Oh aye!' Bobbie grinned. 'Touch a nerve, did we?'

'She's harassing me about this bloody Master's she's doing. Wants some personal coaching.'

'Ha!' Bobbie laughed. 'You are well and truly Sheba's bitch!'

Aiden shook his head. 'You know, I honestly think it might be easier to get punted back into acute.'

'Really?' asked Vanda.

'I'm just not willing to play ball with her.'

'But are you willing to play *hardball*?' Vanda insisted.

'Have you got hard balls?' Bobbie sniggered. 'Is that what the problem is?'

'You guys are sick!' Aiden muttered. 'Glad you're back, Helga – maybe you can keep the rest of them under control?'

Helga smiled. 'It's nice to be back.'

'So let's have a quick run-through. We'll need to let Helga know what's happening with the patients.'

'For a start, your referrals are up by ten per cent,' Molly said.

'Oh, Miss Mount *will* be pleased,' Vanda mocked. 'Do the numbers get Sheba off your back, Aiden – or does she pay extra for that?'

'Now, Helga,' Bobbie began. 'Are you back to normal duties?'

'Of course.'

'Only I've got this young woman I've been working with – Karma. She's been stuck at home for years – it's complicated. Anyway, it would be fab if you could get her out and about again. Maybe she'd like your social group? Although she doesn't drink.' Bobbie winked.

'I'm sure that would be fine.'

'Any chance you could come with me today? I'd like to discharge her and it'd be better if I introduced you both. She's a bit …'

'What?'

'Different.'

Helga shrugged. 'I think I can cope with different. What time are you going?'

'How about we go this morning? I've got my thingy this afternoon.'

'What's a thingy?' Vanda asked.

'I'm getting my mammography over at Breast Screening.'

'Ah.'

'Well, I could have said "I'm getting my tits squeezed by a sandwich toaster," but I thought *thingy* was quicker.'

'Nice. Does the person toasting the sandwiches know you like plenty of mayo—'

'Anyway!' Aiden interrupted. 'We've got two new patients.'

'And before I forget,' Molly said, pointing to a brown-paper rectangle. 'There's a big poster-type of parcel that got delivered to you last week, Helga.'

'Oh?'

'Aren't you going to open it?'

'Maybe later. I need to catch up with all my patients.'

Bobbie rinsed out her mug and left it on the draining board.

'Ready when you are, Helga?'

'I'm ready.'

'Okey-dokes. Will I drive?'

'If you like; where are we heading?'

'Och, it's away out Balerno way. She lives with her husband in a cottage in the middle of nowhere.'

'Is that why she can't get out?'

'Er, not exactly.'

Bobbie whizzed along the A70, leaving cyclists and buses in her wake as Helga gripped the door handle. 'Thought it was a thirty-mile-an-hour limit along here?'

'Is it?' Bobbie replied. 'Could well be. So how was your weekend?'

'After the whole panel incident was over it was such a relief, I slept for twelve hours straight on Friday night. But I had a deadline to meet for writing so that kept me busy all weekend. I needed to get the next instalment to the publisher. They don't particularly like what I've written so far but I sent it in late last night and am hoping they'll read it today and be convinced. What about you?'

'How do you mean?'

'How was *your* weekend?'

Bobbie puffed out her cheeks. 'Saturday started with me not being able to find a clean pair of knickers. Before I knew it the whole day went on clearing out my clothes for charity. Saturday night Bob insisted on picking up a curry from the dodgy carry-out on our corner. I spent most of yesterday on the pan. Still – silver lining and all that – I've got my weigh-in today and I'm sure I must have cleaned out half a stone. *Hey!*'

Bobbie blasted her horn as a truck pulled out from a junction.

She wound down her window and bawled, 'I know you think you're huge, but you don't need that much space!'

'Where is this house?'

'Nearly there. I know – practically Glasgow, eh? So what don't they like about what you've written?'

Helga frowned. 'I suppose my first novel was very much a fairy story – all about faith and healing. Giving people hope and direction. Did you like it?'

'Um. I, er – I can't believe they're doing more roadworks! I'm going to take this wee country lane to get away from the diversion.'

'So in my second novel Candy has made a mint and she's quite the celebrity. She's looking for ways to give back.'

'Give *way*!'

'Well … more focused on those less fortunate.'

'Sorry, I meant that tractor.'

'But the publisher doesn't like the fact that I've introduced a young homeless girl – says it'll bring the readers down. But I'd say it's the opposite – it's meant to be uplifting. *Stop!* Stop the car!'

'Wha …' Bobbie slammed on the brakes. 'Did I hit something? Don't tell me I've run over another sheep?'

'*Photo!*' Helga cried, leaping out of the car. 'Look – that'll make a great photo for Twitter.' She crossed the lane and leant against the sprouting hedge. A scarecrow leant at an angle as a number of cocky birds perched on its outstretched arms. A flapping crow squawked triumphantly from the stuffed hat.

'Jings, Helga, some warning next time, please. Never mind the scarecrow, what about the Scare-Bobbie?'

'Sorry, but it was such a wonderful shot.'

'S'pose. Anyway, here we are.' Bobbie bumped the car along a muddy track that led up to a dilapidated cottage. The tiled roof sagged in the middle, paint peeled from the window frames and the door had bleached almost white.

'They really are in the middle of nowhere, aren't they? But you haven't told me much about her.'

'Best you go in with an open mind.'

Bobbie knocked on the front door and pushed it open. '*Coo-ee! Only us!*' She walked into the gloomy hall, taking a door to the left. In the frugally furnished living room the walls were bare and the windows without curtains. A young man and woman sat facing each other in armchairs positioned in front of an electric fire. They both looked up as the pair entered. 'Morning, Karma – it's me, Bobbie. Hi, John.'

'Oh, hello,' Karma said, smiling.

'Don't get up. I've brought someone else with me today. This is Helga.'

Helga stepped forward her hand held out. 'Nice to meet you.' It was then that Helga noticed the dark mask fixed over the young woman's eyes. Her straight, black hair framed her plain face. Helga let her arm drop. She turned to John, who stared vacantly into the middle of the room with cloudy eyes.

'Would you like some tea?' Karma offered, rising from her seat. She picked up a walking stick that was leaning against her chair.

'Ooh, that'll be just the ticket!' Bobbie replied. They followed as Karma limped out of the room. Leaning on her stick, she ran her other hand along the wall until she reached the kitchen. She felt for the kettle and filled it with water, letting the kettle overflow.

'Sorry, what did you say your name was?'

'Helga.'

'That's quite unusual.'

'I think I was named after my mum's favourite teacher, who was

German. Mind you ... Karma, is it? That's not exactly common.'

Karma smiled to herself. 'I've got no excuse other than having unconventional parents.'

She poured the hot water into a mug, sticking a finger in to check the level. 'Ouch! Milk?'

'Please.'

Karma topped up the tea with milk and handed the mug to Helga. Yellowy lumps floated on the surface.

'And one for you.' She handed a steaming mug to Bobbie.

'Mind if I wash my hands first, Karma?' asked Bobbie.

'Not at all.'

Bobbie ran the tap, pouring her tea down the sink.

'Let's go back for a comfy seat, shall we?'

John smiled as they entered. 'What's the weather like today?'

'Oh, the usual,' Bobbie answered. 'Wind and rain – in no particular order. Now, how's that ankle of yours, Karma?'

Karma wiggled it back and forth. 'It's still pretty achy but it's getting there.'

'And have you been outside at all?'

'Yes, I've been able to get along to the end of the road and back.'

'That's smashing,' Bobbie nodded, taking notes. 'So I think that you're ready for discharge now.'

'Oh no!' Karma's face fell as she wrung her hands. 'It's been so lovely having your visits.' She pulled a tissue from her sleeve and blew her nose.

'Don't get upset,' John announced to the middle of the room.

'Well, I'm glad you've enjoyed my sessions,' Bobbie said. 'But that's what Helga's here for.'

Bobbie leant back in her chair and indicated for Helga to take over.

'I hope I can help you, Karma. I'm a link worker in the Harrison Intervention Team. My role is to help people integrate with the community and I can see that it would be a challenge out here in the country. Especially if you have a visual impairment.'

'Oh, *I* don't have a visual impairment. It's John who's registered blind.'

John stuck his hand in the air, waving it.

'Right, but I … I mean. I just thought with your eye mask and everything.'

Karma raised her hand to her eye mask. 'I wear this to support my husband – it's a mark of solidarity.'

'I'm sorry, I don't understand.' Helga looked with bewilderment at Bobbie, who gave her a cheesy thumbs up.

'John's been blind since birth, haven't you, love?'

'I have.'

'And when we married I pledged that I would live his life to show my eternal devotion to him. I've sacrificed my sight so we can share the same world.'

Helga glanced back at Bobbie, who was screwing her index finger against her forehead.

'Then you *do* have vision?' Helga checked.

'Oh yes! But I determine not to use it. If John can make a happy life for himself then so can I.'

'So you *choose* to be blind?'

'Well, those are your words but – yes. I'm foregoing my visual freedom.'

'I see,' Helga pondered.

'So to speak,' Bobbie chortled.

'And do you feel this is *helping* your husband?' Helga frowned. 'That neither of you can see?'

'It's our world, isn't it, sweetie?'

Again John nodded. 'That's right.'

'The thing is, though,' Karma added, 'that John now has a very active life outside our home. He's well supported by the RNIB – and even does some work for them. He has Jan, who's a fabulous social worker, don't you, John?'

'That's right,' he repeated.

'And he gets to go to their weekly social club and has outings and he has loads of friends now, because he's blind.'

'And you don't?'

'Well, I don't qualify for assistance as I have sight. Twenty-twenty vision, in fact.'

'But you'd like to get out more?'

'I would!' Karma nodded. 'I feel I'm losing out.'

Or you could chuck your eye mask and jump on to a bus to the city, Helga mused.

Bobbie removed an apple from her pocket and took a noisy bite as Helga scribbled down notes.

'Do you think you can help me?' Karma appealed.

'Well, I do have a social group that meets every Tuesday at our health centre – the Tuesday Chatters. It might be a nice way to have some safe contact with other people.'

'Sounds fun.'

'And then we can talk about what other activities you might want to get involved in.'

'I've always fancied painting, haven't I, John?'

'That's right.'

Bobbie tapped her watch.

'Do you think you could get yourself into Gorgie?' Helga suggested.

'I shouldn't think so,' Karma said, shaking her head. 'How would I manage that? I can't get on a bus, never mind two! And I can't afford a taxi. Don't *you* have transport?'

'Yes,' sighed Helga. 'I'll ask the driver to pick you up but you'll need to be ready by about one p.m. I think tomorrow is a bit short notice so why don't you come along next Tuesday?'

'That would be just fine. Will I meet other people like me?'

'Most definitely,' Helga agreed. 'Then I'll see you next week.'

'Thank you so much. Did you hear that, John? I'm going to have some new friends too.'

'That's right.'

'Well, you might have bloody warned me!' Helga cried as Bobbie sped off down the country track.

'Where's the fun in that?' Bobbie laughed.

'Is she known to the mental health services?'

'She's refused a referral – says there's nothing wrong with her mind.'

'Just when you think you've seen it all …'

Chapter 46

'Hello there, Helga. How are you? Are you feeling better?'

Helga more or less rammed Donald out of the way as she charged into her flat with a, 'Not now, Donald!'

She made herself a cup of strong coffee and reached for her MacBook. Five emails; two from Kate. She clicked the first one open and read it through squinting eyes.

Hey there, Helga, Phil loves the latest chapter! Phew! He says he couldn't see where you were going with the "wee scruff" as he likes to call her but thinks it can work. If you can get the next instalment to us ASAP you should catch him while he's still on a high. BTW – hate to be a pest but you're due your fortnightly blog. Thought you could do something about Easter? Just a thought! Anyway – must dash – got a press conference with our other Star Writer (wink!).
Love as ever, Kate XX.

Helga took a relieved glug of coffee and opened the second email.

Soz! Only me again. Phil says have you remembered you promised to introduce some ROMANCE into Candy's life? I said I'm sure you have … Byee XX.

Well, better get to it, Helga thought. She would start the next chapter and work for an hour then think about food. The letterbox rattled open. 'Helga!' Donald called. She ignored him. '*Helga!* I know you're probably busy but I'm just going to the shop. Thought you might like me to pick up something for your tea? They're doing two Tandoori kebabs for two pounds? Or, what my mum and I had yesterday – Kentucky Fried Turkey Burgers, also two for a pound?' The letterbox stayed open hopefully. After five minutes Helga heard the resigned clang, followed by Donald's frustrated footsteps as he descended the stairs.

Candy put a pen through the day's appointments. She found George sitting on the bedroom floor, repacking her reeking rucksack. The jar of chocolate spread was rapidly tucked into a zipped pocket.

'Right,' Candy said. 'When you're ready, my driver will take us down to the nearest Shelter branch at Fulham. We've got an appointment with a housing advisor called Andy.'

'What's it to you?' George muttered. 'Maybe I don't want you interfering.'

Candy sat on the floor and leant against the bed. She fiddled with her long blonde hair. 'Look, George, I realise I mean nothing to you. And I won't pretend to know anything about you or where you're from. But I've made my money – all this – by steering people to find their way in life. Crazy, eh?"

George shrugged, staring at the hand-tufted wool carpet.

'What I do know is that at some point everyone

needs someone's help with something. You might not like it – or agree with it. But you *will* need help. I could give you money but I know that's not the answer.'

George grunted.

'You need someone who can give you the right advice and support and can help you get back on your feet.'

George bumped her holey trainers together. She remained silent.

'And I'm well aware you think I'm this rich cow who wants to throw her money around for what she thinks is a good cause just to make herself feel better. I get it. And so what if it makes me feel good about myself? Aren't you glad it's *you* that's on the receiving end? Because if you like, I can go down to Shelter and pick some other random to endow?' She gave George a nudge with her shoulder.

George made a face and picked at a scab on her hand. 'S'pose, if you're offering …'

'And do you want to have a home?'

'Course.'

'In London? Is that where you're from?'

'No, but I'm here now. I can't go back.'

'Right – well let's go and find Andy.'

Candy led the way to where a sleek black C-Class Mercedes was parked kerbside, its hazards blinking. The driver, in uniform with a peaked cap, bounded out of his seat and rushed to open the back door. Candy indicated for George to hop in.

'Can you put the rucksack in the boot, please?' Candy asked the driver. A look of horror swept across his face as he quickly tried to come up with an excuse. 'Er, does this *need* to come with us?'

'Yes!' George shouted. 'It's mine.'

'Well, I certainly didn't think it belonged to Madame.'

He attempted to lift the luggage between gloved finger and thumb, slinging it into the boot. Heavy traffic made for slow progress and, despite the chilly March air, the driver wound down his window. George scowled for the entire journey. The only time a faint smile flickered was in response to the driver's fury as he caught sight of her in his rear-view mirror pressing her nose against the cold glass.

'Is that *your* driver?' George asked, after they had been dropped off on the pavement.

'He's not really *my* driver – just someone I can call on if I need to. I hate driving in London.'

An elderly lady, bent to one side and barely able to see over the counter, pointed them in the direction of the office, which meant going back outside and pressing an intercom to gain access. The door buzzed and they climbed one flight to reach a grim office area, lined with rows of featureless staff answering phones. A studious-faced young man with tousled sandy hair appeared from a doorway. 'Hi, I'm Andy.' He held out his hand to Candy. 'Hey – aren't you …?'

Candy's cheeks turned pink as she shook his hand. She removed her designer sunglasses. 'Yes, I'm Candy Martini.'

'Who?'

'Candy Martini – lifestyle guru?'

'Oh! I thought you're the girl who takes our spin class – my mistake! Come on through. And you must be George?'

They sat across from him in a tiny booth, his cluttered desk taking up the bulk of the pod. He raked out a pad of paper and a pen, clearing a space. 'Would you like a drink? Tea? Coffee?' he asked George.

'Yeah, okay – tea.'

'With milk?'

'Uh-huh.'

Andy sprang up again. 'Look,' he said to Candy, 'you don't need to stay if you want to shoot. Now that you've made the referral we can take it from here.'

'Oh, well, I … I suppose I thought you might need some extra finance or something.'

'We always need extra finance!' he laughed, his brown eyes twinkling. 'But we can discuss that another time? Our priority today will be to see how we can help George.' He reached into his jeans pocket, retrieving a business card. 'Tell you what – why don't you give me a call later? Maybe we can grab a coffee when I've finished work?'

'Sure.' Candy blushed again, conscious that she never blushed. She stood up, preparing to leave. 'Do you think I'll see you again?' she asked George.

'Shouldn't think so. Why would you?'

'Then take care.' She bent to give George an awkward hug. 'I hope things work out for you.'

Andy nodded goodbye as Candy closed the door

and took the stairs back down to the street. She rang her driver, who sounded like he was hoovering out his car.

'*Helga!* I know you're in there!' Donald bellowed. 'Are you sure you don't want me to get you something to eat? I can go for chips if you want? How about a nice sausage supper?'

Helga paused as her phone pinged.

Hi, darling! Mum here! Just to say Mags and I are away to Writer's Camp this week. Case you're looking for me – as if! Love XX.

She wandered through to the kitchen, thinking that she'd love a sausage supper sprinkled with salt and smothered in brown sauce. She checked the hall but the letterbox was shut. Donald's boots, followed by Dolly's claws, could be heard clumping down the stairs. She sighed, reaching for a tin of macaroni cheese.

Chapter 47

'And then Chan said, "I don't know what *you've* been using them for but I use them for wiping down my microwave!", Molly laughed.

'Classic!' Bobbie agreed. 'Hi, Helga – how are you?'

'Oh, well, a bit of another all-nighter but I'm getting there.'

'And is it a thumbs up or thumbs down from your publishing pals?'

'They liked it – thank goodness!'

'Great! Fancy a slice of malt bread?'

'Of what?'

'You know, this malt loaf – the squidgy stuff. It's only a pound in Iceland.'

'No, thanks.'

'Have you got any butter?' Vanda asked.

Bobbie peered into the fridge. 'Don't think so. Oh, hang on – what about cream cheese?'

'Doesn't matter, I'll eat mine plain.'

'Morning,' Aiden muttered.

'What's up with you?' Vanda asked.

'I just got off my bike and Sheba called. I was standing in the pissing rain while she bent my ear.'

'Oh aye?'

'I've requested a transfer to the North Team.'

'Oh no!' Molly exclaimed. 'Why?'

Aiden shook his head. 'There's no way I can work with Sheba. She's making my life a misery as it is – can you imagine if we had to share an office? She'd have me dressed as a clown and jumping through hoops – and yes, I'm well aware that people pay good money for that.'

'But you can't let her get to you,' Vanda said bitterly. 'She's taking advantage of your history to make you feel uncomfortable.'

'I know, but maybe it is time for a change. I hear they get a lot of neuro referrals from the Western. Might be quite interesting work. Anyway, she thinks I'm being all melodramatic.'

'Are you?'

'I just feel I'd rather jump than be pushed. At least there will be an element of my choice if I move teams.'

'Malt loaf?' Bobbie offered.

'No, thanks – I'm away to get changed.'

'That's a bit of a blow,' Molly said as Aiden left. 'I'll really miss his …'

'Cheery face?' Bobbie asked.

'Something like that.'

Helga's morning flew by and she was soon stacking mugs on to a tray for the Tuesday Chatters group. She had even splashed out on a box of flapjacks to say thank you.

'Need a hand?' Molly volunteered.

'Thanks, Molly. Gosh, that rain is torrential – it's nearly flooding the car park.'

'So it is! By the way, did you hear what happened last week when Bobbie took the group? Lance thought someone was trying to blow up the building!'

'I did hear,' Helga smiled. 'Let's hope there's no such drama this week.'

Helga plugged in the kettle just as Peter arrived. 'Hello, miss!' He gave Helga a bear hug that she eventually wrestled out of. 'Did we stop you getting fired, then?'

'You did – and I'm very grateful for that.'

'My mum says if you'd got fired you should go to the papers.'

'The papers?' Harry asked. 'Is that what we're doing this week?' She hung up her mackintosh. 'The world is full of such depressing news.'

'Welcome to my life,' Lex muttered. 'I don't know anyone who's ever happy.'

'I'm so happy!' Princess beamed as she flounced into the room in a canary yellow trouser suit. 'I'm going on holiday with mummy and daddy to Lesmahagow.'

'Dressed as a banana?' Harry asked.

'No, silly, this is my going-away outfit.'

'Not far enough away.'

'Afternoon all,' greeted Dennis, crashing into the table and juddering the milk jug. 'Blimey, it's fairly chucking it down now.' He shook the rain off his cap and fought his way out of the scooter's waterproof cover.

'I thought I might need to catch an ark to get here,' Jimmy replied. 'The rain's coming down in sheets.'

'Language, Jimmy!' Princess tutted.

'I said "*sheets*".'

'Oh.'

Kamal hovered in the doorway, drenched in a black hoodie

and jeans. Water dripped off his fringe into his eyes.

'Oh, Kamal, we need to get you out of those wet clothes!' Helga cried. 'You'll catch pneumonia.'

'I had *double* pneumonia once,' said Dennis. 'Ended up in hospital for weeks. I was so unwell I got a visit from the priest.'

'A priest?' Peter said. 'How would that make you better?'

'He paves the way.'

'Like a builder?'

'Exactly.' Dennis rolled his eyes.

Helga tried to tug the hoodie over Kamal's head. 'Someone help Kamal – I'm going to see if anyone has any spare clothes.' Jimmy hauled at the soggy cotton as a dirty pool of water leaked from Kamal's trainers. 'Can I suggest taking your shoes and socks off too?'

'This is better than a strip club,' Harry cackled. 'He'll be down to his underpants soon.'

'I bet they're not dry, either,' Princess added. 'Maybe he'll have to take them off as well.'

Kamal began backing out of the room in panic and bumped into Helga, who was carrying Lance's astronaut outfit. 'I know it's not ideal, Kamal, but it's better than what you're wearing. There's a warm-air cupboard in the men's changing room across the corridor. If you're lucky your clothes might dry out a bit by the time you head off.' Kamal accepted the garments doubtfully. When he'd left the room Helga warned, 'Now, don't anyone say anything to Kamal. He's sensitive enough as it is.' The group nodded in agreement. A few minutes later Kamal returned wearing the silver jumpsuit and platform boots. He clomped into the room, collapsing awkwardly on to a plastic chair next to Lex.

'The eagle has landed!' Dennis guffawed as the group broke

out in laughter. Even Kamal gave a wry smile. 'At least you can do this if you've had enough of us,' Lex said, flipping down the visor.

'Right, let's all get a hot drink. I think we need it.' Helga smiled, passing round the flapjacks. 'This is just a wee thank you for the support you've given me. It was so lovely that you all turned up on Friday like that.'

'It was actually quite handy for me,' said Jimmy. 'I got my blood pressure taken while I was there.'

'Now this week I thought we might try something different.'

'Here we go,' Dennis said, shaking his head.

'We didn't really get a chance a follow up on the Writers' evening. What I have planned for today is to take a few minutes to jot down our thoughts about any book you might have read ...'

'I don't read books!' Peter protested. 'They're so boring.'

'Or a magazine.'

'Have you seen the price of magazines these days?' Harry tutted. 'Some cost about five pounds!'

'Or anything you've read that has struck a chord with you.'

'Do you mean our favourite stories?' Princess asked.

'Not so much your favourite, but something you've read or heard that means something to you.' Helga handed out pens and paper. 'Let's all take a few minutes to reflect on this.'

'But it's so hard!' Peter wailed. 'The only thing I ever read is the back of a cereal box.'

'Or the back page of the *Sun*,' Dennis commented.

Princess closed her eyes in concentration. Harry chewed on her pen as though it were a cigarette. Jimmy doodled a hangman ...

Suddenly the door burst open and Molly stood there panting. 'Helga! Come quickly – there's a man on the roof and he ...' She gasped for air.

'What man?' Helga asked.

'Maybe he's fixing the roof?' Jimmy suggested.

'Or could be a chimney sweep?' said Dennis. 'We still have to get our chimney swept once in a while.'

'No,' Molly wheezed. 'He's asking for you.'

'Why me?' Helga said, a little startled.

'Maybe you owe him money?' Peter said. 'Our window cleaner gets very annoyed if my mum doesn't pay him.'

'Why would he climb on to the roof?' Harry asked.

'I'm just thinking of who would have a ladder.' Peter shrugged.

'Come on!' Molly urged.

'I can't just leave my group,' Helga insisted. 'Look what happened last time I went off and left them.'

'She nearly got fired,' Princess announced.

'But you must. It's an emergency!'

Helga stood her ground. 'Just take a message – we'll be finished in an hour or so.'

Molly pulled Helga aside. 'You have to come now – he's making *threats*,' she said in a low voice.

'What sort of threats?'

'Help! Is he a terrorist?' Princess cried. 'I'm too young to die!'

'Is he going to blow us up?' Peter said anxiously. He ran to the window to look.

'Calm down, everyone,' Helga said. 'I will go and find out what this man wants. Molly – you'll have to stay here with the group.'

'What? Who – me? I can't!'

'Sit next to me!' Peter grinned, patting the seat beside him.

'I'm not leaving the room unless there's another member of staff here.' Helga folded her arms. Molly glared back. 'Fine – but *hurry*!'

Chapter 48

Helga took the stairs two at a time, arriving on the first floor to find Bobbie standing outside their office. She held a cup of coffee in one hand and a tuna baguette in the other. 'Ah! There you are!' Bobbie said with her mouth full. 'Anver's up in admin—'

'*Anver?* Molly just said "a man". Why would I care what Anver is up to? He's probably just working on a tiling job.' Helga turned to go back down the stairs.

'Hold your horses,' Bobbie ordered. 'Anver came down to tell us there's a man on the roof. He's asking for you.'

'But *what* man?' Helga exclaimed.

Bobbie marched off towards the next flight of stairs, slopping her coffee with each stride. 'I don't know! But Anver said he went up to admin to ask for a form and found the office empty and the window open. The rain was piling in so he checked it and found someone had climbed out on to the roof. Come on!'

Helga trotted behind as Bobbie climbed the narrow, twisting flight of stairs leading to the office in the attic. 'Where's Brenda?' Helga enquired.

'She's been off sick all week and Jean's still in Magaluf.'

They entered the small ramshackle office with its pitched ceiling. In the centre of the room, standing in an inch of water, Anver wrung his hands in agitation. 'Finally! What took so long?'

'What's going on?' Helga demanded.

'Hey – don't shoot the messenger!' Anver protested, holding up his hands. He was dressed entirely inappropriately in a pink floral shirt, chinos and tan loafers with no socks. He ran a hand through his black, gelled hair. 'I'm just telling you what I told Molly. I came up here to ask for an expenses form – it costs me money, you know, if I have to go through to Glasgow to pick up the special tiles that fussy Podiatry wants. Anyway, there was no one here but the window was wide open. Me being a smart cookie –' he tapped his forehead – 'thought *What's going on here, like?* I stuck my head out the window and there's this geezer straddling the roof – right at the top of the building. It's bloody dangerous up there, especially with all this rain.'

'What's he doing?'

'As far as I can see, he's just sitting there getting very wet. Anyway, I shouted up to him and he just kept saying, "Get Helga".'

'Is it one of your patients, do you think?' Bobbie asked.

'Could be,' Helga frowned.

'Any attention-seeking patients with a suicidal tendency?' Bobbie pressed.

Helga shook her head. 'I can't think of anyone. There was young Thomas, but he ended up being admitted.'

'I rang Norman,' Anver said. 'I didn't know what else to do.'

'*What?* Jesus, Anver. He'll have Police Scotland on red alert.'

'You think?'

Bobbie punched his arm. '*Obvs!* He lives for this kind of drama. It'll make his year! In fact he'll live off it for the rest of his career.'

'Did I do the wrong thing?'

'I guess not. Anyway – is the bloke still up there?'

'Here, let me have a look,' Helga offered. She stuck her head out, withdrawing it instantly. Her face drained of colour.

'Helga?' Bobbie said. 'Who is it? Is it one of your nutters?'

Helga nodded slowly. 'A prize twat of the highest order.'

'Who?'

'It's Morris.'

'Ah!' Bobbie made a face.

'Who's Morris?'

Bobbie bit off a chunk of baguette. 'It's Helga's ex-fiancé.'

'I see,' said Anver. 'Awkward … So did you break off the engagement?'

'No! He abandoned *me* at the church, the *spineless bastard!*'

'Then what's he doing on the roof here?'

Bobbie gulped down her mouthful. 'Would it be anything to do with him being an attention-seeking patient with a suicidal tendency?'

'Probably.'

'Do you think he's going to jump?' Anver asked.

'Not likely. I just told you – he's spineless. The most courageous thing he's ever done is to ask John Lewis to price-match a thermal vest. He's pitiful. He can't even face the flu jab without an anaesthetic. So, no, he won't be throwing himself off any building. Lego or otherwise. I'd better go and talk to him.'

'Eh?' Bobbie spat out her coffee. 'You can't go up there – the roof's like a bobsleigh run.'

Helga poked her head out of the window again. 'I think the rain is easing.'

'Why don't I go first and see if he'll listen to me?' Anver offered. He dragged a chair over to the window and climbed up.

'Wait for me!' said Helga. 'I need to get him back in here before Norman pitches up and shoots him down.'

'You're mad, the pair of you!'

Anver stepped out on to the rusty guttering, which creaked

under his weight.

'Oooh, be careful!' Bobbie warned. 'This building is crumbling faster than a digestive dipped in hot tea.'

'Is there anything we can use to secure me with? I shouldn't have had pie and chips for lunch today.'

'Today?' Bobbie mocked. 'Try the last five years!'

Helga and Bobbie had a quick scout around the office, opening cupboards and drawers. 'Oh! I know!' Bobbie clapped her hands together. She pulled a handful of Therabands out of her pocket. 'Look – if we loop these together we can fasten one end on to the window frame.' She passed the other end out to Anver, who knotted the multicoloured rubber tightly round his wide girth. 'I could bungee jump with this!' Cautiously he crawled along the sloping tiled roof until he reached a stone chimney pot about ten feet away, which he clung on to as though a lifebuoy. Regaining his composure he shouted up, 'Hey, fella! You're Morris, aren't you?'

'How do you know my name?' the man snapped. 'Is Helga there? Tell Helga I want to see her.'

'Mate, she's not going to come scrabbling up on to the roof just to talk to you. You need to come down. Why don't we both go down into the nice warm office and get a cup of coffee? This isn't getting us anywhere.' He noted with irritation the grimy patches on his chinos.

'No,' Morris argued. He attempted to smooth down his wet hair. 'I'm staying put until I can see Helga. I want to show her I'm serious.' He removed a handkerchief from his top pocket and dried his glasses.

'Or mad,' Anver muttered to himself. 'Look, pal, neither of us is exactly dressed for this situation.'

Morris, sporting a dark grey three-piece suit with a thistle corsage and shiny patent shoes, looked like he'd swum across the Firth of Forth. He inspected Anver from a distance, seeming to notice his strange attire too. 'Who *are* you, anyway? What are you doing here?'

'I'm Anver ... I've got a tiling job on.'

'What's this to do with you? It's none of your business – this is personal.'

'Mate, I'm just an extra in this disaster movie; wrong place, wrong time. If I didn't know better I'd say I'll be the first to cop it. And by the way, have you seen the mighty big crack along the roof? I don't think you're safe up there, pal.'

Morris frowned at the crevasse where water was streaming in. A sudden gust of wind swept across the rooftop, rattling the slates and sending a flurry of soggy leaves scuttling along the guttering. 'Hell, it's freezing up here,' Anver protested. 'So are you coming down?'

'Never. *Helga!*' Morris yelled. 'I know you're in there. I need to speak to you.'

Helga sighed, reaching for the chair. 'I better try to sort this out.'

'It's too dangerous!' Bobbie cried. 'One slip and you'll be pavement graffiti.'

'Cheers, Bobbie.'

'Here, take this.' Bobbie pressed a pound coin into Helga's hand.

'I'm not taking the bus!'

'It's for luck. I don't have a rabbit's foot.'

Helga gingerly climbed over the window frame, gripping the rubber band.

'Who's your next of kin again?' Bobbie asked.

'Bobbie!'

'Sorry – would hate your nice wee car to be claimed by some

random professing to be your mother.'

Helga inched her way along the roof, her white fingers clenching the tiles. She glanced down, observing a sizeable group of pedestrians congregated below.

'Helga! My love – you've come!' Morris beamed from his pinnacle. He straightened his damp tie and attempted to dry his hands on his trousers. 'Here.' Extending one hand he nodded encouragement.

'I'm not climbing up there, you gormless idiot!' Helga ranted. Anver shuffled to make space as she hugged the chimney pot. This generated a cheer from the pavement.

'Right, Morris, you better make this bloody quick – I'm not staying here for a minute longer than necessary.'

'Does *he* have to be here?' Morris said in a fluster.

'It's either with Anver or not at all.'

'Only I've kind of rehearsed a speech and it was really only meant for your precious ears.'

'Fuck it, Morris! You've got thirty seconds on the clock!'

'Don't mind me, mate – I'm not listening,' said Anver. 'See, I'm closing my eyes.'

'Firstly, can I just say how stunningly beautiful you look today? Your skin is radiant, your hair is shimmering, your eyes are—'

'*Morris!*' Helga growled.

The sound of heavy footsteps approaching the attic was followed by Norman, who charged into the cramped office. Water ran off his full-length raincoat and wax sou'wester. 'Afternoon, miss,' he puffed. 'What's all this water on the floor? Anyway … I'm here to take control of the situation, if you could please update me on the current state of affairs *vis-à-vis* the terrorist on the roof. I have informed Police Scotland and they will be dispatching troops any minute. In the interim I have been asked to contain the situation as best I can.'

'Helga and Anver are on the roof talking to him!' Bobbie exclaimed. 'It's Helga's ex-fiancé but he won't come down!'

'What? A member of staff engaged to a terrorist? If she's been harbouring a criminal she'll be slammed up for years.'

'He's not a—'

Norman spotted the chair and marched across to the window. He stuck his head out.

'You pair!' he bellowed. 'Get back in here *this instant*. This is *not* protocol. We have very specific guidance we're obliged to follow for incidents like this. If you don't return to base immediately, I will be forced to charge you with conspiracy!'

'We're just coming,' Helga said. 'Morris?'

Norman tugged on the rubber band. 'Help ma boab!' Anver cried. 'You've landed a big 'un.'

'*Morris!*' Helga hissed.

Norman's mobile blasted the theme from *The A-Team*.

'Sir? Yes, sir, I am on location and can apprise you of the situation. We have one suspect on the roof and two potential civilian hostages.

'Yes, I can confirm that the suspect has been asked to give himself up and return to *terra firma*. However, I understand he is not – I repeat *not* – willing to cooperate. Understood. Exactly. And when can I expect backup? I mean, I'm trying to manage the incident as I've been expertly trained but who knows how a live perpetrator may react under pressure? Roger. Understood. Over and out.'

Norman turned to Bobbie, his face flushed. 'We have to vacate this building immediately!'

'Well, I can't do it on my own. No one's going to listen to me.'

'We have to get everyone out, *now*! It's under the direction of the Gold Commander.'

'Ooh, is he the one on the telly? Does he do the quiz show on a Thursday evening?'

Norman bundled Bobbie towards the door. 'Move it, woman, we have to get everyone out before he blows the whole building!'

'Oh, I don't think he has any explosives …'

'We don't *know* that. We can only go on the facts before us.'

They waded out of the office and back down the twisting stairs. From a rucksack Norman produced a megaphone that he put to his lips. He marched along the corridor announcing, 'This is Mr Norman Pike, security manager for West Edinburgh health facilities. Please leave the building *now*. I repeat – this is Mr Norman Pike, asking you to vacate the premises!'

Chan stuck her head out of the door. 'Shh! We've got a carers' group on in here.'

'A what?' Norman blasted through the megaphone.

Bobbie rolled her eyes and with her left elbow pranged the *In An Emergency Break Glass* panel. The fire alarm reverberated. All the doors along the corridor sprang open as the health centre staff trundled towards the stairs.

'Oh my goodness!' Molly exclaimed. 'That's the fire alarm. Everyone follow me. We need to assemble in the car park.'

'I'm scared of fire!' Peter cried. 'I want my mum!' He turned to Princess and hugged her. 'Don't worry, I'll look after you,' she smiled.

Lex took Kamal's hand as he stomped along in the platform boots.

'Oh good, I get a cigarette break,' said Harry.

Jimmy reached for his coat. 'I hope that awful rain has stopped.'

'Make way!' Dennis shouted as he attempted to steer his mobility scooter through the crowd.

Chapter 49

The Tuesday Chatters stood shivering in the car park.

'Hey!' Lance protested. 'What's he doing wearing my astronaut outfit?'

'Leave him alone,' Molly replied. 'He's allowed to wear what he wants.' Kamal slipped the visor down and tottered into a corner.

'Miss! Miss!' Peter tugged at Molly's arm. 'Helga's on the roof – look!'

'Oh my God!' Molly gasped.

'Look at that *eejit* straddling the ridge,' Dennis muttered, pointing upwards. 'He's going to fall off if he's not careful.'

The crowd divided as two fire engines swept into the car park. Firefighters leapt from the cabin and charged into the health centre, Norman saluting each as he passed by.

From the rooftop they could see the swarm of staff spilling out in response to the incessant ringing. 'I need to go back inside,' Helga warned.

'Please, Helga, hear me out.'

'Why should I?'

'Please. I'm begging you. I'm risking my life for you.'

'We're *all* risking our lives here.'

'I know – I'm sorry. I didn't think about the danger to you. I haven't thought this through at all.'

'That much we agree on. Anyway, why the hell have you been stalking me?'

'I wouldn't exactly call it stalking,' he said in a small voice.

'The flyers? Barney? The endless letters? Hiding in the car park? And please tell me that wasn't you that set fire to the building?'

'It wasn't a fire! I'd never do something that stupid.'

Helga raised her eyebrows. Morris rubbed his hands across his damp trouser legs and leant forward, his hands on his knees.

'Clock's ticking.'

'It was the only way I could be part of your life again. I knew you'd moved flats so the only way I could contact you was through work. There's no way your mum would pass on a message. You ignored all my letters … changed your mobile number. You wouldn't speak to me.'

'Hardly surprising!' Helga snorted, adjusting her position against the chimney.

'I know. I understand your reasons.'

'You understand *nothing*,' she hissed. 'Did you even stop for *one minute* to think about how I would feel? To arrive at the church in my wedding dress, in front of all my friends and family … to be told by your best man that you couldn't go through with it? Christ, Morris, I wasn't exactly asking you to take a lethal injection!'

'I couldn't do it to my mother,' Morris explained.

'*Your bloody mother?* Don't blame this on Nancy!'

'I'm sorry, Helga. *So* sorry. When I arrived at the church and David and I walked down the aisle I saw her sitting in the front pew. She was all alone – looked so deflated. Not like on your side where the front pew was packed. She was lost. It felt like I was ending her life.'

'We were getting married, Morris! We weren't even leaving

Edinburgh, for God's sake.'

'I know,' Morris sighed. 'But it's only ever been the two of us against the whole world. I felt like I was abandoning her.'

'So you abandoned *me*?'

Helga watched a flapping bird as it skittered across the tiles.

'I knew you'd be all right. You've got your mum and sister, your work. And now that you're a famous writer ...' He risked a sideways look.

'Hardly!' she grunted.

'But you have lots going on in your life.'

'Morris, you weren't a *hobby*. I loved you!'

'Loved?' he echoed. 'Past tense?'

'It's very difficult to keep loving someone who destroyed me. Who humiliated me in front of everyone who matters.'

'I know. I'm—'

'You're sorry. Yes, I get it.'

'So what do we do now?'

'Well, I have a group of patients waiting for me,' Helga announced, letting go of the chimney. 'Down there, in fact.'

'I meant—'

'I know what you meant.'

'Will I see you again?'

'Oh, I don't doubt. Edinburgh's a small city.'

'But I meant—'

'*Yes!* Morris, I may have been jilted but I'm not stupid.'

'Do you think you still have feelings for me?' he whined.

'What I think and what I feel are two different things. Goodbye, Morris. I hope you and Nancy are very happy together.'

Morris shifted nearer as though he were about to slide down the roof. The crowd below gasped.

Helga held up two hands. 'And don't ever, *ever* come near my team again.'

'Please, Helga?' Morris appealed.

'You heard her, mate,' Anver shouted. 'Fuck off and leave her alone!'

The thunderous thumping of an engine stopped them in their tracks as a helicopter swooped in an arc towards the building. The whump of the rotor was deafening as the blades churned up a tornado. The three clung to the building in terror. Helga's hair whipped against her face and dust blew into her eyes.

'Oh, Morris, what have you done?' she said under her breath.

As the craft drew level the helicopter door slid open and a uniformed officer, wearing full riot gear, stood with a microphone in his hand. The engine hovered a few feet away. 'This is Police Scotland's Gold Commander speaking. Please stay exactly where you are. I repeat – *do not move.* The building is surrounded and there is no escape. We have police snipers trained on you at all times.' A red dot appeared just to the left of Morris's corsage, which the turbulence blew off.

Shiny chrome ladders clanged against the guttering and a firefighter's helmeted head bobbed into view. He grinned. 'Afternoon! You must be Helga? Come on, love – let's get you down from there.' His gloved hand reached for hers and guided her on to the rungs. The crowd below cheered. Anver clung to the pink rubber cord until he too was assisted to safety. He received a roar of approval and punched the air with one hand like a World Cup goalscorer.

'What about me?' Morris wailed, waving his arms.

'Stay where you are!' the Gold Commander instructed. 'Keep your hands in the air.'

Helga shivered in the chair, wrapped in a blanket. 'Here you go – I've put plenty of sugar in it.' Bobbie handed Helga a mug of tea. 'Fudge doughnut? Lucky I went past Greggs at lunchtime.'

'What's happened to my group?' Helga asked.

'Don't you worry about that,' Molly answered. 'We made sure they all got off safely and guaranteed they'll be back next week to hear all about it. One of them – is it Peter? – was interviewed by the telly folk so he was dead chuffed.'

'The telly!' Helga cried. 'How did they hear about it?'

'Someone will have tipped them off,' said Vanda.

'It's big news,' Aiden agreed. 'I can see the headline now: *Trained Terrorist Takes Health Centre Hostage!*'

'Hardly,' Helga shook her head. 'More like *Sad Bastard Makes Wretched Gesture.*'

'No, I think I like Aiden's one better,' said Bobbie. 'Which is surprising, what with you being a writer and all.'

'How did you manage to get rid of Norman?' Helga asked, sipping her tea.

'Vanda was brilliant!' Molly laughed. 'She told him that you were not mentally fit to give a statement and he should come back tomorrow after you'd had a chance to recover. He wasn't happy but had no choice.'

'Thanks, Vanda.'

'No worries – even the emergency services had had enough of him. For some reason he kept climbing the ladder up to the roof. I heard one of the firemen ask who let the knob loose with the loudhailer. Eventually Sheba turned up and told him to get lost. In fact, *he's* the one that's under investigation for escalating the whole situation. If he'd called the fire service *before* the police, it would never have got out of control.'

'I can't believe Morris made such a bloody drama out of all this.'

'Well, he'll have plenty of time to dwell on his actions down at the police station. They'll keep him there for hours,' said Vanda.

'He might be charged with wasting police time,' Aiden agreed.

'Ah, but he must still love you!' Molly swooned. 'Aren't you the teeniest bit touched by his grand effort, Helga?'

Helga shook her head. 'It was never about me. It was always just about him. *His* needs, *his* mother, *his* voice. He's just a pathetic selfish twat.'

'My mum used to say to me that the only person you can truly rely on in life is your own mother,' said Bobbie. 'Of course, that was just before she upped sticks and left us all for a randy butcher from Broxburn.'

'Well, on that note, I think we should all go home,' said Vanda, switching off her PC. 'It's been one helluva day and I need a drink. Anyone else?'

'Go on then,' Aiden nodded. 'I could murder a pint.'

'Me too,' Bobbie remarked. 'A pint of gin and tonic! Helga?'

'Hmm, I think I need an early night. See you all tomorrow. And thanks.'

'For what?'

'For putting up with Morris's idiotic behaviour.'

'He's a man,' said Bobbie. 'They're all idiots.'

Chapter 50

'Good grief!' Molly tutted. 'Quinn's called an urgent health centre meeting this morning at nine.'

'Have we all to go?' Vanda asked, hanging up her jacket. 'Ugh! I should have gone home when Aiden left.'

'Bit of a session, was it?'

'Put it this way, Bobbie genuinely believes that she *Moves Like Jagger*! She was up on a table at one point. God knows we don't need another pub incident.'

The door opened and Bobbie half walked, half crawled into the office. She collapsed on to her chair and laid her head on the desk.

'Hey!' Molly grinned. 'It's Christina Aguilera. Are you going to show us your dance moves?'

'Just milk, please. And a hot sausage roll, if you have one?'

Aiden breezed in. 'Oh dear – who killed Bobbie?'

'That might have been me,' said Vanda. 'We were about to catch the bus when the DJ started up the karaoke. You know I can't see past *It's Raining Men*.'

'Hallelujah,' Bobbie mumbled into the desk.

'What are we celebrating?' Helga asked. 'Good news?'

'Not really,' said Molly. 'You lot better get yourself together. Quinn's called an emergency meeting in the community room at nine.'

'Let's hope Norman won't be there,' Aiden groaned. 'I couldn't bear a lecture after yesterday.'

'*Shit!*' Vanda exclaimed. 'I bet that's what it's about. We'll all need to keep the windows locked so no randoms can get up on to the roof.'

By the time the Harrison Intervention Team squashed into the community room, it was like being in Next on Boxing Day morning. Quinn forced his way to the front, where an area had been cordoned off with Union Jack bunting.

'You'd think we were expecting the Queen,' Vanda muttered.

'It's all I could do!' Chan replied. 'I had to keep a space for Mr Adamson.'

Quinn stepped over the bunting. 'Right, people!' He clapped his hands. 'A bit of quiet, please!'

The noisy chattering died away to a low rumble. 'Thank you for coming at such short notice. I know how busy you all are so I'll keep this brief. Yesterday's incident was a bit of a wake-up call for many reasons. It put our *Major Incident Plan* to the test – and there will be many lessons learnt from what went well and what did not go well at all. Mr Pike is currently reviewing the sequence of events, taking statements from key personnel and will provide a debriefing session in the upcoming weeks.'

Collective groan.

'Sounds like old Norman will be swinging his pants,' Bobbie whispered.

'Anyway, I'm not here to go into the details of yesterday's events. But what *has* come to light is that we have a very serious issue with this building.'

'It's falling down!' someone laughed.

'It may indeed be falling down,' Quinn said, frowning. 'I have been informed there is a significant fissure across the health centre roof and we have no idea how far it extends into the fabric of the stone walls.' All heads turned to inspect the ceiling.

'An initial health and safety assessment of the area was carried out yesterday afternoon and it's too early to evaluate the degree or severity of the damage. However, we have been advised to evacuate the premises as soon as possible.' There was an outcry of protestations. Quinn clapped his hands in irritation. 'I'm no more happy about this than you. In saying that, all this does is escalate the programme we already had in place for team dispersal. I appreciate you will have patients booked into clinics and that will be difficult to rearrange at short notice. *But!* We have been advised the building must be emptied within the month.'

'A *month?*' Chan cried. 'We can't move everything out in a month!'

'We have no choice. The building will not be insured and we *cannot* have staff or patients here after the date given. I suggest you make no further appointments and focus on rebooking them into your new premises.'

'So are we getting early access into Slateford?' Cameron asked hopefully.

'Indeed.'

'Woo hoo! Score!' Cameron cheered. 'We're out of this dump.'

Vanda stuck her hand up. 'What about us?'

Quinn shrugged. 'Your team will be absorbed within the South Team structure as agreed.'

'So, the Harrison Intervention Team ceases to exist after this month?' Aiden confirmed.

'That was always the plan,' Quinn snapped. 'Now is not the time for sentimentality. We have a mammoth task on our hands and I'm asking you to cooperate in a professional manner. I will be posting weekly updates regarding progress and, Chan, can I ask you to set up a mailbox for any queries? Please don't email me directly with any questions – I simply don't have time to address them.'

'But!'

'What about …'

'Who should we ask?'

A clamour of questions was shouted in his direction.

Quinn ducked his head and bulldozed his way out of the door, looking as though he'd survived a grizzly attack. The football crowd dispersed reluctantly – some winners, some losers.

'I suppose we ought to start packing,' Molly groaned. 'Quinn's right – we'd have to do this in a few months anyway.'

'Reckon we just put a skip in the car park and chuck it all out the window,' said Bobbie.

'I bet Sheba can't wait to start bossing us around,' Vanda said grumpily. She opened one of the cupboards and pulled out a box of dressings. 'And the parking's a nightmare over at Woodlands.'

'Coffee, anyone?' Molly suggested.

'We better eat up all the biscuits,' said Bobbie, opening the tin. 'That'll be one less thing to pack. What do you think, Helga?'

'We just need to look for the positives – like Candy Martini. It'll be a new chapter for all of us!'

'I meant the custard creams, actually. But you're right.'

'They have a great social life apparently,' Aiden said, peeling posters off the wall. 'Always having nights out.'

'That's true.'

'And it's much nearer decent shops – we'll be able to nip out at lunchtime.'

'Not like here,' Bobbie agreed. 'The only thing we're good for here is second-hand furniture or tropical fish.'

'Tell you what,' Vanda proposed. 'Why don't we use the Easter fundraiser as a way to say goodbye to the health centre? To celebrate the time we've had here. More people will want to come now we know we're getting split up.'

'We have had some laughs,' Molly nodded. 'Remember that time, Bobbie, when you convinced Chan she'd been nominated to provide guided tours for all the international visitors to the Fringe?'

'Oh yeah – you kept it up for days!' Aiden grinned.

There was a knock at the door.

'Oh, talk of the devil!'

Chan stuck her head in. 'Hi, guys! You okay?' She handed a piece of paper to Vanda.

'What's this?'

'Mr Adamson wants all the teams to write down week by week what actions need to be done to get everything moved out.'

'Tip top.'

'Sorry?'

'Nothing – we'll get it done.'

Chan sidled up to Helga and in a low voice said, 'I'm really sorry about your ordeal yesterday. It must have been *awful*!'

'Thanks, Chan.'

'And is it true you were jilted by that man on the roof?'

'You know what? Really, it's fine.' Helga patted Chan's hand. 'I've put it all behind me. Of course I didn't think it at the time, but he actually did me a favour by leaving me at the altar.'

Chapter 51

'You won't leave me at the altar, will you?' Andy joked as he topped up the champagne glasses.

'Of course not! Why would you say that?'

'Sometimes I just need to pinch myself. I can't believe how lucky I am.' He held Candy's manicured hand, where he had just slipped a solitaire engagement ring on to her finger.

'Andy, you're the best thing that's ever happened to me. *Ever!* I believe in serendipity – it's what I've preached my whole life. The day I came home and found that wee scrap on my doorstep ... I just never believed what it would lead to.'

'Hmm, that *wee scrap* as you call her scrubs up pretty well,' Andy laughed. 'She's attracting quite a bit of love interest herself, I can tell you!'

'Uh-oh! Maybe I'll be doing the wrong thing in asking her to be my bridesmaid?' Candy said. 'I can't cope with competition!'

'Oh, don't worry, there's *no* competition.' Andy took Candy's face in his hands and kissed her until she melted into his arms.

Hey, Helga! Phil loves, loves, loves it! And so do we all! Congratulations – you've done it again! Candy Martini Goes Viral is every bit, if not better, than the original. Will speak soon but wanted to let you know the wonderful news ASAP.
Kate XX

Helga closed her MacBook and shut her eyes, leaning her head back on the sofa. Maybe she would just have forty winks— *Clang!* The letterbox sprang open.

'Helga? Are you there? I saw your light on, Helga …? Do you want anything from the shop, only there's an extra special deal on this week? You know those pies you like? Well, they're practically giving them away. Two for fifty pence or four for a pound! Helga?'

She opened her eyes. Actually, she *could* go a pie … maybe even two. Isn't that what life as one hundred and fourteen on the bestseller list was all about?